C000228427

# HOROLOGICAL HINTS and HELPS

By

## F. W. BRITTEN

Author " WATCH REPAIRERS' INSTRUCTOR ", etc.

Awarded Silver Medal of the Worshipful
Company of Turners, also Bronze Medal
of The B.H.I.

## FOURTH EDITION

Revised and enlarged

BARON PUBLISHING LTD.

*First Published 1929*
*Second Edition 1934*
*Third Edition 1941*
*Fourth Edition Revised and Enlarged 1943*
*Reprinted 1946, 1950*
*Revised 1977*

© Copyright 1977
The Technical Press Ltd
ISBN 0 902028 64 2

All rights reserved. No part of this publication
may be reproduced, stored in a retrieval system,
or transmitted in any form or by any
means electronic, mechanical, photocopying,
recorded or otherwise except for the quotation
of brief passages in criticism.

Printed in Britain by
Baron Publishing, 5 Church Street, Woodbridge, Suffolk.

# PREFACE TO FOURTH EDITION

THIS book having met with so much success it is gratifying to the author that a third and a fourth revised edition have been called for in quick succession and it is satisfactory to record that the book has been translated into Spanish and published.

From the many letters I have received requests have been made to add instructions on " Quarter Chimes " and " Correcting Bad Depths ". This was complied with in the third edition together with other information.

This fourth revised edition includes information on Alarm Clocks and The Pin Wheel Clock Escapement together with further instruction on French Clocks with more illustrations.

I have just completed for the publishers a work entitled ." Watch Repairer's Instructor " which should prove of value to the students and craftsmen in the trade.

The subject of Electrical Horology has not been treated, it being an exhaustive one, and the reader is referred to the excellent publication so called by H. R. Langman published by The Technical Press, Ltd.

F. W. BRITTEN.

1 WEALD AVENUE,
    HOVE.

# CONTENTS

# CONTENTS

# INTRODUCTION

HOROLOGY—the science of constructing mechanism for measuring and indicating time. It is necessary to have some definite basis to work on. The earth is a perfect clock, the period occupied by its successive rotations are consistent. One such rotation from a fixed star is known as a sidereal day.

Solar time is measured by rotations of the earth with regard to the sun, so that the instant the sun is seen at its greatest height above the horizon it is true mid-day. This sometimes takes place 16 min. 18 secs. sooner, and at other 14 min. 28 secs. later than 12 o'clock mean time. The difference between the sun and clock is known as equation. An equation dial is recorded on many old English clocks. The average is taken of the solar days and called Mean Solar time, and for convenience the Greenwich meridian adopted known as Greenwich Mean time.

# HOROLOGICAL HINTS AND HELPS

## LEARNING TO TURN

Turning is essential to a young horologist in these days. The writer has always advocated and still maintains it is more profitable to teach an apprentice to turn as soon as his indentures are signed. It not only gives the lad confidence, it makes the trade appear interesting to him, and tends to develop his mechanical skill when engaged in horological work.

Some years ago The Worshipful Company of Turners offered a prize for the best specimen of steel turning left from the graver. The winner submitted three balance staffs, pivoted in one piece.

Commence on a brass ferrule suitable for a bow drill, and about the size of one found on the average turning arbor. Punch the centre of a piece of brass, strike a circle from the dot with a pinion gauge, drill a hole, and file round flush with the circle. Brooch the hole to fit an arbor, and place it in the turns with a gut bow ready for turning. When driving the brass on the arbor refrain from hitting the centre with a steel hammer ; tools subject to such treatment get out of truth and have a short life. A brass hammer, or a piece of brass placed on the centre of the arbour is the usual procedure.

There is great art in sharpening a graver. A graver should only be ground occasionally. Many shops are without a grindstone, but where its use is employed unnecessarily the graver will become soft. When the point has gone, whet it on a sharp cutting oilstone. Keep the face of the graver flat on the stone, rub it briskly until the point and edges become sharp, apply

1

plenty of oil, then lay the sides of the graver flat ; one rub is all that is required to remove the burr. Many country watchmakers make their own gravers for cutting soft metal, but when required for turning steel mercury hardened will be found preferable. Vautier and Lecoutre gravers are reliable for turning hardened and tempered steel.

The work must be free from shake in the centres, and put oil to the latter. Adjust the rest so that it comes close

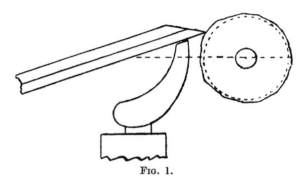

Fig. 1.

to and above the centre of the brass. The point of the graver should touch the brass about half-way between the centre and the top (see Fig. 1). If the point is held too low it will dig in the brass, and off comes the point. Hold the graver firmly on the rest until the point touches the work and begins to cut with the down stroke of the bow. The graver must not follow and touch the brass all round ; it should only cut in *one place at the start*. After several cuts it will be found to touch the brass in a part of a circle, and it must not touch the brass with the up stroke of the bow. This is easily managed by slightly moving the wrist with every alternate stroke. Continue cutting until it touches the whole way round, bringing off fine shavings at each cut. If extra pressure is required, whet the graver on the oilstone. You will probably find the point continually break. Whet it on the oilstone ; satisfy yourself that you are getting off shavings ; if you do not succeed in this you are scraping, and your work will not be true. For ordinary turning the extreme point may have a touch on the oilstone to give it a flat chisel-shape appearance ; the cutting point will be stronger and more liable to retain its cutting edge. The pointed graver is best for turning square shoulders and pivots. Having turned the circumference true, turn the right-hand shoulder, starting with the largest part on the edge. Reverse the arbor in the turns, removing the bow, which must be coiled round the other way, so that the other shoulder to be turned is on the right-hand side of the brass. Shape out the groove, and finish it with a semi-circular pointed home-made cutter.

## THE LATHE

A lathe as a means of turning has practically super-seded the turns for all kinds of watch work. Although the majority of turning is accomplished with a tee rest and hand cutters, the tool can hardly be termed complete for horological work without a slide rest, which will prove a time-saving appliance.

The most useful accessories for watch work are a mandrel head and slide-rest, head, and tailstock, set of step chucks, a set of split chucks not less than 20 (even numbers 2 to 40), a centering plate, centering runner and Jacot pivoting bed, a set of slide-rest cutters, and cement chucks. With such an equipment a watchmaker can turn and fit cylinders, shells, balance staffs, jewel-holes, pivots, keyless wheels and shafts, drill and upright anything appertaining to the ordinary run of watch repairing.

The slide rest is a device for holding and grinding a cutter. The advantage of this tool is the rigidity of the cutter and the accuracy attained in the cut by controlling the two slides, which are operated by handles. If the cutter is fixed too high it will fail to cut, if too low it will dig and break the point. The correct part for

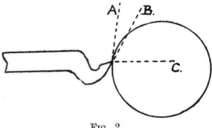

Fig. 2.

the cutter to come in contact with the work is a little above the centre, and the cutting edge should form nearly a tangent. The dotted line A, Fig. 2, shows a tangent from the point of the cutter, B, a line from the cutting edge ; and C, the correct height of contact. We will assume a clock pillar is being turned. The height of the cutter would therefore have to be altered, as the work becomes smaller after two or three cuts, and the cutter will require adjusting different heights for every diameter of metal.

The shape of the tool is governed by the metal to be cut and the angle of cut required. A lathe for a slide-rest is generally furnished with a set of cutters of different angles. To turn a barrel groove, for example, would require a cutter with an acute point, having an undercut which would be quite unsuitable for turning the bottom of a barrel or cover. The writer from experience has found home-made cutters of the required angles more adapted to the general run of horological work.

Tool-making for use in a lathe is not only essential in many instances, but provides instructive practice to a beginner. Experience will teach the variety of cutters and accessories required to save time on various operations. It is important the cutter should be rigid ; it must therefore project from the rest as little as possible and screwed tightly. The cutter in the older pattern tools rested on a ball-socket adjustment which tightened with a screw ; this had the advantage of being quickly adjusted, but the disadvantage is the adjustment is not parallel, and therefore alters the cutting angle.

The more modern slide-rests are made with a slot and screw for holding the cutter, which keeps it parallel for any alteration of height. Lathe cutters for the slide-rest should, if possible, be cranked to bring the cutting edge below the centre of the tool. Downward pressure on the tool then has a tendency to relieve it from the cut, and consequently a smoother cut is obtained. When the cutting edge is above the centre of the body, pressure helps to dig into the metal with a liability to " chatter ", causing a rough cut. The front of the cutter for a little distance below the point should be almost perpendicular, with just a little clearance. When it is ground away with too much angle, it will have a tendency to dig into the work and cut rough.

Most lathes of a larger pattern are made on the screw-cutting or self-acting principle. A leading screw running the whole length of the bed runs through and causes the saddle to traverse the bed with regular movement as the headstock or mandril rotates. The slide-rest is fixed to the saddle. At the back end of the spindle or mandril is fixed a toothed wheel which gears with a series of wheels and pinions known as " change wheels " ; the end wheel is a fixture on the leading screw, thus forming a connection between the latter and the mandril. There is a set of change wheels of different numbers, so that the train may be altered to traverse the saddle slow or fast as desired to suit the style of turning, or to accommodate the pitch of a screw it may be required to cut. For example, if the leading screw has twelve threads to an inch, it is quite obvious that any two wheels having the same number of teeth on the leading screw, and mandril connected by an idle wheel, would cause the slide-rest, which is fixed to the saddle, to traverse one inch for twelve turns of the mandril. A tool, therefore, fixed in the saddle-rest ground to an acute angle would cut twelve threads to an inch.

**Drilling.**—Many lathes are provided with a cone plate, hollow runner, and drill stock for drilling up pinions. This appliance takes unnecessary time in adjusting. The writer from experience, finds the more simple method the quickest and safest—the head stock, split chuck, and tail stock.

A home-made drill will be found most suitable for this class of work. It lasts longer and being especially adaptable in strength for drilling tempered steel. The cutters should be short and stumpy. They can be turned in a split chuck or filed to shape (Fig. 3). The neck is formed to a smaller diameter than the cutting edges for clearance, to about twice the distance of the cutting face shown by the dotted line, which gives the depth of hole capable of drilling. The flats and cutting angle are next filed, and the drill hardened in oil. Being small, it will be found an advantage to hold the oil bath quite close to a small spirit flame, and on attaining a bright red immediately plunge it in. Two cutting angles only are necessary for the motion of a lathe (Fig. 4). When a forward and backward action is used, with the left hand manipulating the fly-wheel, four blades are whetted, two on each side. It will be found quicker to make two or three drills at a time, using small steel to fit the drill-stock.

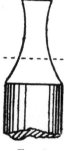

F a. 3.          Fig. 4.

When a new pivot is required to a third or fourth wheel, the pinion can be fixed in a split chuck. If the broken pivot is on the opposite end to the wheel, and the latter is in the way, knock it off with a hollow or brass punch. It is quite a simple matter to drive it on true and tight in exactly the same place. See that the pinion leaf marks on the wheel are in the same relative position.

Screw the pinion tight in a split chuck, catch the centre for drilling with a sharp graver held firmly on the rest close to the work. Then remove the tee rest and place the drill in the centre with the end of the drill-stock running in a centre hole of a runner in the tail-stock. Tighten the latter, but leave the runner loose, so that it can be pressed slightly and advanced with the right hand, while the ferrule of the drill-stock is held steadily between the thumb and finger of the left hand. Use plenty of oil with the drill and apply a very slow, steady motion.

Needles, tempered to a light blue, will be found quite reliable for pivots or any small work. Clean the pinion in petrol and file the plug almost straight until it just fits the hole. Remove the file marks with an arcansas stone, and cut off the end of the plug, square with the nippers until it enters half-way in the hole. The end is easily cut square by twisting the nippers and pin vice in opposite directions. Cut the plug half-way through with a slitting-file for the length of the new pivot, press the plug in and break it off. Rest the pinion on a hollow stake and drive the plug home with a flat-ended punch.

The quickest method is to turn the pivot to size in a split chuck with a sharp pointed graver, and finish it with a Jacot burnisher, or, for safety, burnish it on the bed of a Jacot tool.

**The Shellac Chuck.**—The cement or shellac chuck is one of the most useful accessories. There are usually five or six in a set. The larger variety, or plate chuck, is adapted for turning barrel covers, balance cocks, or any large part that cannot be conveniently fixed in a mandrel plate. The slide-rest is usually employed for this class of work, but a hand cutter could be used when the former is not at disposal. The smaller chucks are intended for turning sinks in ratchets, keyless wheels, the settings of jewel-holes, cylinders and many other parts. The chucks being made of brass, are easily turned to the required shapes. It is usual to drill two large holes at right angles near the end to prevent the heat from being distributed.

Many lathes are now provided with a two-hole screw-plate giving the size and pitch necessary to make extra shellac chucks, or for any special purpose required. The end of a rod of brass is turned and tapped with the plate, then screwed tight in the steel chuck of the head-stock, and turned to shape as required.

Smaller size chucks afford a large variety of turning parts that cannot be conveniently fixed in a split or step chuck. English jewel-holes are shellaced and pegged true to the face of a chuck, with the object of turning the brass setting to fit the hole in the plate. A spirit flame is placed under the chuck until the shellac melts. While the latter is hot a peg is held firmly on the rest with the point touching the centre of the work, and the lathe running, until the shellac is set. The work is thus pegged true ready for turning. The best plan is to shellac the flat or back of the setting to the chuck and turn the largest part to just fit the hole in the plate. The small part of the step can then be turned to a gauge to fit the small hole. An arbor with the position marked, would answer the purpose.

When there is no suitable jewel-hole available, select a loose stone to just fit the pivot and turn a new setting from a piece of rod brass in the lathe. This procedure of setting a new hole takes a very little longer than the usual alteration of shellacing an English hole in the chuck.

Centre and drill up a piece of rod brass in a split chuck, with a hole a shade smaller than the stone. A sink is next turned to just fit the stone (Fig. 5 A), and the face hollowed and at an angle to form an edge to rub over the stone shown at B. Flat hand cutters will be found best for this work, filed to shape on the end of old files, hardened and tempered to a straw colour.

Place the stone in position, holding the rubber firmly on the rest with lathe running at a high speed while the rubber is pressed on the brass rim until the stone is tight. Plenty of oil is required during this operation.

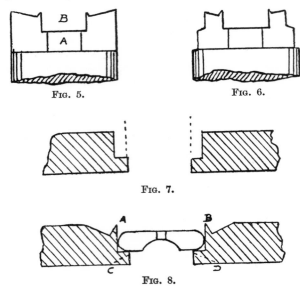

Fig. 5.        Fig. 6.

Fig. 7.

Fig. 8.

A rubber can be made on a piece of flat strip steel filed to a curve at the end, with the point and sides all rounded, so that it is perfectly free of any cutting action. Harden it and polish the rounded end.

The largest part of the rod is next turned to fit the large hole in the plate, and the step turned to fit the small hole (Fig. 6), which can be measured by a gauge as previously described. It is important a sharp-pointed

graver should be used for this purpose, or there will be
a difficulty in attaining a good fit. The length of the
step can be measured from the old setting. If it is lost,
measure the length of the hole in the plate, then take
the measurement of the thickness of the end-stone
setting and subtract the latter from the former.

The rod is next cut off beyond the large step, shown
by a dotted line, the setting reversed, fixed on a shellac
chuck and turned back to the jewel-hole.

A jewel-hole setting is often badly damaged, thus
rendering any turning useless to form a new seat for a
stone. In such cases the best plan is to broach the
whole of the setting and rivet a solid brass stopping.
Catch the centre of the stopping with the point of a
graver, uprighting it from the opposite pivot hole in the
lathe and drill a hole a little smaller than the diameter
of the new stone. Turn a seat for the stone, deep enough
for the top of the brass to project slightly above and
form the setting to be rubbed over. Fig. 7 shows the
section of a brass stopping fitted to the chariot for a
lower cylinder jewel-hole and a hole drilled to the size
of the two dotted lines, which is a little smaller than the
jewel-hole. The large hole shows the sink turned to just
fit the stone, the back of which comes opposite the endstone and nearly to the top of the sink. The edge of the
setting is next turned to bring the top of the sink to a
sharp corner shown in Fig. 8 with the jewel-hole resting
on its bed. With the lathe running, the edge AB is
rubbed over with a " rubber ' and oil as previously
described. Finally the chariot is reversed and the brass
turned away to a sink to free the bottom of the cylinder
at CD.

Small size shellac chucks will also be found useful for
turning the hollow in fusee-barrel arbor ratchets, boring

small keyless wheels, wristlet keyless buttons, and many other small parts. They are pegged true in the usual way, with a spirit flame under the chuck and the lathe running at a high speed.

The " setting up " ratchet in a fusee watch is often left too thick, with insufficient square beyond the ratchet for a key to grip in the act of setting up the mainspring. The ratchet can be sunk to half its thickness, nearly out to the teeth in a lathe with a cement chuck, making a sound job of an unmechanical bungle.

The circular keyless click, which ranks with modern improvements, is quite simple to make. File a piece of steel flat to the required thickness and fix it to a cement chuck. Catch the centre, drill the hole, and turn the edge to size.

A flat-ended sinking cutter, made on the end of an old file, will prove useful to turn the sink for the screw head. Harden and temper it to a straw.

Many horologists prefer to turn cylinders and balance staffs in a shellac chuck. The latter used for this purpose has a cone-shaped end, with the bottom turned to a sharp point or V shape. See Turning Wristlet Balance Staff. The first procedure is to take the height, which is marked on the arbor and brass collet. The hollow of the chuck is then filled with shellac and while the latter is hot and the lathe running, the arbor of the cylinder is pressed in until it reaches the bottom of the cone, with a flat-ended peg held on the tee-rest and pegged true ready for turning. When finished, it is reversed in the chuck and the operation repeated.

**Home-made Accessories.**—The variety of home-made accessories to a lathe for saving time on various operations can hardly be termed complete without a set of rose-cutters. Although these tools are often supplied with a lathe, they are usually unsuitable for the general run of work.

A set of eight or ten will embrace all sizes, from watch bows to small pivots on fusee click steel. They are quite simple to make, and will pay for the time spent on them. Select a piece of rod steel to fit number 28 or 30 split chuck, and turn off pieces of about one inch. A cutter can be made on the end of each piece. Turn the ends perfectly flat, catch the centre and drill a hole in each end different sizes, ranging from the size of the hole in No. 22 split chuck to No. 4. The face of the tool cuts the metal, and so forms the pivot which passes freely into the hole. It is essential, therefore, a true hole should be drilled, or the pivot would be formed eccentric, which is useless.

The teeth, or cutting edges, are filed with a smooth " three square " file, the edge of each tooth being left on the same level (Fig. 9), pass a broach in the hole to remove the burrs. The cutters are then hardened and tempered to a straw (Fig. 10).

To pivot a keyless bow, grip half of it in the vice from one end to the back, and bend over with the pliers for the cutter to free the other end. They are then filed to an obtuse centre as a guide to start the cutter central. Fix the rose-cutter in a split chuck, hold the bow on the tee rest with the pliers and press it central against the cutter. A little oil and a steady motion of the lathe will assist the cutting. When the holes in the cutters are not drilled through to the opposite end, a clearance hole should be drilled from the outside.

Fusee click steel is pivoted in the same manner. File a point on the end at the part to form the pivot. Select a cutter with a suitable size hole and press the steel against the cutter to form the pivot and shoulder.

The burrs should be removed with a graver, or smooth
file.  The action of these clicks greatly depends on the
fit of the pivot and shoulder.  A very little rivet is
required to make them work freely.

Old files are reliable steel, and will be found convenient
for making cutters for the tee rest.  Fig. 11 shows a
general shape for turning sinks, keyless wheels and flat
surfaces.  A smaller size will prove useful for boring holes
in keyless wheels, fusee, barrel, and centre pivot holes.

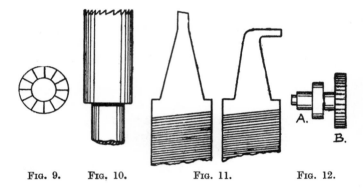

FIG. 9.        FIG. 10.            FIG. 11.            FIG. 12.

A similar cutter, with a thin, flat end, shaped on the
edge instead of the flat for strength, would make a
useful tool for turning the square slot in a " pull out "
keyless shaft.  It is essential this slot should have the
shoulders perfectly square, or the lock piece stud is liable
to ride out.  The cutting edge of this cutter requires to
be ground back at about 60 degrees.  The sides of Fig. 11,
and for boring, are parallel, with the edges cut back less
than a right angle, to cut or bore the sides of the hole.

The advantage of boring a wheel instead of broaching
is, the hole might not be true with the teeth but as the

step chuck grips the wheel true, it is not only making sure of an uncertainty, but the process is quicker. The sides of the cutter for sinking could be either parallel or taper for strength, with the cutting edge ground back and the flat end a little less than a right angle, to ensure a square corner to the sink. The flat end is ground back at about 60 degrees.

The nearest size round shape keyless button is often a little tight to fit over the pendant. The hollow of the button can be turned to fit easily by fixing on a square arbor or a tapped as the case may be, held in a split chuck and turned with a cutter made on the end of an old file. Soften the end, bend it at right angle in the vice and file to shape shown in Fig. 11. File the cutting side to about 70 degrees. These cutters are left nearly dead hard, and should be kept especially for this class of work.

Many repairers fail to realize that a small barrel hook tapped in No. 13 hole of the screw plate is stronger than one of larger diameter, also that it is only necessary to project inside the barrel equal to the thickness of the mainspring. Anything beyond will be to the cost of space used in the barrel, number of turns of the mainspring, and a difficulty in regulating the watch. It is quite common to find a hook projecting inside the barrel equal in length to 3 or 4 thicknesses of spring. When made of a large diameter, they are usually knocked loose, because there are not enough threads in the barrel to hold it. The most simple method to deal with the large hook problem is to reduce it. A very useful tool which saves time can be made from an old barrel arbor, with a very fine cut Geneva ratchet riveted true on the square and hardened, shown in Fig. 12. The arbor A is gripped in a split chuck and the barrel held firmly on the rest,

while the ratchet B cuts the head of the hook to the
required thickness.

**Turning a Balance Staff.**—Split chucks are usually
employed as a means of turning balance staffs.  This
method is a great saving of time on any other form in
the lathe.  It is absolutely necessary the chucks should
run perfectly true.

The best plan is to put the old staff with the balance
in the frame, to see if it is running free of the other
parts.  Any necessary alteration can then be made in
taking the heights, which are then measured on a metric
gauge—or, better still for speed, two gauges, one for the
height of the balance and the other the whole height.

For a full plate " sprung under " balance staff two
split chucks only are necessary to complete the turning.
Select a suitable rough staff block, and fit the lower
arbor into a split chuck.  Turn the largest part of the
staff to fit the spring collet.  The graven marks are then
polished out with oilstone dust.   In the case of a
" Matador " staff the brass collet is left from a smooth
graver, and driven up or down the staff as the case may
be to attain the correct height for the balance.

Sharp gravers are indispensable for quick work.  The
fast rate of cutting, together with a little practice, pro-
produces the ability of a turner, who saves times on
various operations.  Fig. 13 will be found quickest for
roughing down the metal.  The point and side of Fig. 14
is a safe method of finishing the arbor and turning the
shoulders square.  Fig. 15 is a long pointed graver for
turning the hollow to form the rivet for the balance ;
Fig. 16 a half-circular pointed graver for turning conical
pivots.

Next complete the top end of the staff.  Turn the
largest part back to length, and fit the balance tightly

with a square shoulder ; then turn the hollow to form the rivet. The latter should only project very slightly above the balance (see Fig. 17). The dotted line represents the

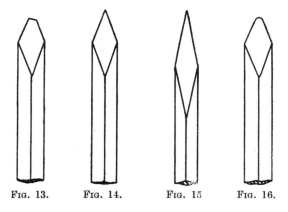

FIG. 13.     FIG. 14.     FIG. 15     FIG. 16.

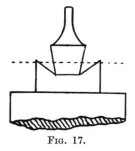

FIG. 17.

top of the balance. When fitted true and tight, the balance will run true, and the greater the hammering from a punch or staking tool, the lesser liability to maintain its truth.

The next step is to take the top height from the seat

of the balance to the end of the top pivot. Remove the cock jewel-hole, and replace the endstone and screws. Turn back the top arbor until the balance is just free of the cock, when the end of the arbor is touching the endstone. The whole of the top part of the staff can be turned without taking it out of the chuck. Leave the balance on the staff and hold the cock, so that the end of the arbor touches the endstone. The arbor is turned away, so that the balance is only just free of the cock. This will give the height of the balance measured from the top pivot.

We are now able to finish the top end without removing the staff from the chuck. When the movement is furnished with a cap it is advisable to try the latter over the frame, and notice if it is below the cock. The cock is sometimes bent up by a repairer ; to leave it in this condition might mean the balance foul of the cap when the staff was finished.

The end of the arbor represents the end of the pivot, which is roughened out and shaped with a half-circular pointer graver until it nearly fits the jewel-hole. Turning pivots in the headstock is a matter that requires a little practice. They have no support. It is therefore easier to snap them off than when running in a centre. The pivot burnisher is usually held against the rest.

It is advisable for beginners to practise conical pivots on pieces of pallet staff wire until they feel confident in obtaining the delicate touch necessary to master the quickest form of staff pivoting.

The staff is then removed from the chuck, and a measurement taken in the frame of the whole height from the outside of the two jewel-holes. Rest the end of the pivot on one jaw of the gauge, and make a scratch on the lower arbor to come flush with the other. The staff is finally reversed and gripped at the body in a large split chuck, to turn the bottom part. See that the lower arbor runs perfectly true. Before screwing the chuck tight, press the thumbnail against the end of the arbor with the lathe running, to get it true. Turn off the arbor at the scratch for the whole height. Fit the roller, polish the arbor, and turn the pivot in the same manner as previously described.

A little practice is required to attain the delicate touch necessary to burnish pivots running in a split chuck. Of course, there is a great saving of time, and it is quite unnecessary to remove the staff from the chuck until the lower end is finished. " Jacot " pivot burnishers are best adapted for this work. The burnisher is rested on the tee rest for support, and moved in the usual way until it just touches the pivot. Many expert pivoters dispense with the rest as a support for the burnisher, but it will be found very useful until feeling confident.

**Wristlet Balance Staff.**—The balance staff of a wristlet watch is on the three-quarter-plate principle. Select a suitable hardened and tempered staff block. The bottom half is turned first. Fit the part intended for the balance in a split chuck with the flange and lower arbor showing.

The first stage is to shorten the lower arbor. It is quite obvious the shorter the staff projecting from the chuck the easier it is to turn and less liable to get out of truth. Turn the arbor off until the top of the flange is just free of the escape cock. This means the bottom of the balance will be just free of the cock.

This measurement can be tried by holding the plate against the staff, with the bottom of the lower arbor resting on the jewel-hole ; a little extra must be allowed for the length of the pivot. Or the jewel-hole could be removed and the end of the arbor allowed to rest on the endstone to give the accurate length, which would represent the end of the pivot.

The largest part of the flange is next turned to size, and the arbor to fit the roller. A graver with the extreme point whetted flat (shown in Fig. 13) will be found quickest for roughing down the metal. When the roller fits three-parts up the staff, grind out the graver marks with mixed oilstone dust and soft steel, and finish with a little diamantine. Steel or bell metal is a matter of fancy, but in any case the polisher must be perfectly clean and filed flat before using diamantine.

Suitable gravers for this class of work are shown in Figs. 13, 14, 15, and 16. Turn the conical pivot and finish it with a half-circular graver, until it nearly enters the jewel-hole. The risk of breaking is greatly reduced by using this shape cutter. The pivot is then burnished in the same manner as previously described, or finished in a " Jacot " tool.

The lower end of the staff having been completed, it is removed from the chuck and the whole height taken, in the same manner as a full plate.

The lower arbor is next fitted in a split chuck and screwed tight enough to hold. If the top arbor is not running dead true, it can be trued by pressing the thumbnail or a piece of wood against it while the lathe is running, and then screw the chuck tight.

The top part of the staff is first turned off square at the scratch, and then the centre turned. It is not absolutely necessary to turn a centre, but essential to shorten the staff square with the scratch if it is to be finished without removing it from the chuck to test the whole length in the gauge. While expert turners adopt this method, it will be found safer for beginners to remove the staff and test the height. It is easily screwed up true in the chuck in the manner described.

The next procedure is to fit the balance tight on its seat. This is one of the most important parts of a staff. On the fit of this greatly depends the running of the balance. The shoulder must be turned square, with the balance pressing tightly against it. A very little rivet is required.

The staff is next turned to fit the spring collet, leaving a shoulder slightly above the balance. When the collet is about half-way down, smooth over with oilstone dust until the collet fits tight. A slight ring with a graver should next mark the staff flush with the top of the collet.

Remove the spring collet and balance, and turn the shoulder of the former hollow to form the rivet for the balance, using a long pointed graver. There is a difficulty in maintaining the cutting edge of a long pointed graver, especially in lathe work. Keep the point as high as possible with the lathe running at a slow motion.

The end of the arbor is turned smaller, leaving a shoulder at the ring flush with the top of the spring collet. The pivot is next turned, using a semicircular graver, and burnished as described.

Many turners prefer to finish the pivots on a " Jacot " tool. They argue it is safer and takes but a very little longer.

The shellac chuck is another method of turning a balance staff. The cement or wax chuck is one of the most useful accessories. There are usually five or six to a set. Fig. 18 shows a shellac chuck with the face turned to a V. These chucks, being made of brass, are easily turned to any required shape. It is usual to

drill two large holes at right angle near the end to prevent
the heat from being distributed.  The bottom of the
cone is turned to a sharp point A.  The hollow of the
chuck is then filled with shellac (shown black), and
while the latter is hot and the lathe running the arbor
of the staff is pressed in with a peg held on the tee-rest
until it reaches the bottom of the cone and pegged true
ready for turning one end.  The staff is then removed,
the heights taken, and the other end pegged true in the
same manner.

Since the " staking tool " has become general there is
a tendency to carelessly fit the balance on any shape seat,
leaving the staking tool to do the rest.  In such cases the

Fig. 18.

metal is forced over on to the balance arm and swells
the rivet end of the seat.  It is quite obvious to drive
such a balance out from the rivet end would stretch the
hole and distort the balance.  This accounts for the
difficulty so many repairers experience in mounting a
balance true when fitting a new staff. The safest plan to
deal with modern work without risk of bending the
balance is to turn away the flange or largest part of the
staff until it is small enough to pass through the balance
hole and drive it out from the bottom end. This method
will be found quite possible without having to re-true
the balance.

**Turning a Keyless Winding Shaft.**—A " pull out "
winding shaft to act properly must be nicely made and
free from side shake.  The idea is right, but the principle

of many altogether wrong. The fit in many high-grade watches is far from perfect, consequently they pull right out, frequently get lost by the owner and give dissatisfaction.

The continual pulling out and in of a shaft has a tendency to loosen any lock piece screw, either a right or left-handed thread, even if it is screwed down tightly. Instead of using a screw thread as the centre of motion for a lock piece, the latter was fitted with thick pivots and a small cock and screw, all trouble would be ended. It would then be necessary to take off the hands and dial before removing the lock piece and shaft, and abolish the ridiculous method of fixing the dial before placing the movement in the case by means of screws on the edge of the plate to hold the dial feet.

There is more strain on this style of shaft than the old form with a push piece. It is therefore necessary they should be perfectly free from shake of any description, or the pivot of the lock piece is liable to work out of the notch. When the sides of the notch are rounded, the shaft can be placed in a split chuck and the notch turned square or slightly undercut with a flat-ended or chisel shaped cutter.

It is by no means difficult to fit a " pull out " shaft to a watch that does not require cleaning, without making it dirty. Remove the hands, dial, the castle and winding wheels and the movement from the case.

The first operation is to fix a piece of rod in a split chuck and turn it down to just fit the hole in the movement without shake. Gramophone needles will be found reliable and convenient size for this purpose, temper them to a light blue. The large size will usually fit the hole in the plate of a wristlet and thus save time in turning to size.

Hold the steel across the plate in a line with the pivot hole and make a scratch to mark the shoulder of the pivot flush with the end of the sink, and another flush with the winding wheel slot to mark the end of the square. Place the steel in a split chuck and turn the pivot to fit the hole, the shoulder forming the first scratch. It is not necessary to remove the steel from the chuck, the plate can be placed against the shaft to try the fit of the pivot. There is a great saving of time by adopting quick methods.

The steel is next turned to the diameter of the square. A good plan is to fit the castle wheel on an old square, then measure across the corners in a gauge to get the diameter required and turn the shaft to the second scratch to fit the gauge.

The next step is to file the square. Remove the shaft and grip it in the slide tongs, or pin vice and rest it on a wood block. The square is one of the most important parts of a shaft. It should not only be filed true, but fit the castle wheel without shake. A badly fitted square might cause the ratchet teeth of the wheel to slip in the winding. A large smooth file will be found best for filing the square, resting the safe edge against the shoulder, and finish with an emery buff.

The shaft is next fitted in the plate and the shoulder of the winding wheel marked with a scratch shown by a dotted line Fig. 19 flush with the slot in the plate. The lock piece is then screwed down for the pivot to bind the shaft and mark the position of the groove while the latter is turned with the tongs. The next stage is to turn a shoulder at the scratch to fit the winding wheel and a square groove to fit the pivot of the lock piece. The groove is best turned with a flat ended or chisel shaped cutter. The sides must be perfectly square, any incline will tend to force the lock piece out when the shaft is pulled. This is a general fault that accounts for so many shafts being pulled right out from the movement.

The end of an old file will prove useful to make a cutter for the groove and the latter should fit the pivot of the lock piece without shake.

The two wheels are then placed in the plate together with the shaft, and the lock piece screwed down. Grip

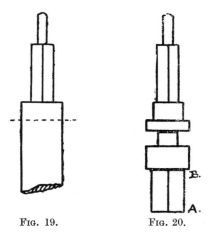

Fig. 19.          Fig. 20.

the shaft with the slide tongs which serves the purpose of the button, and try the action of the winding wheel and the " pull out " device. The groove must be deep enough to free the bottom of the pivot when the lock piece is screwed down.

Fix the movement in the case with the shaft. Hold the button against the pendant in the position it will assume when fitted to the shaft, and make two scratches (Fig. 20), one just to free the pendant A, and the other

to form the end of the square B for the button. Turn
the shaft off at A. Turn and file a square to the other
B to fit the button and drive it on.

**Wristlet Keyless Wheels.**—A badly fitted shaft will
often cause the wheel to slip in the winding. This fault
is generally through the depth being pitched too shallow,
or a wheel too small. In the style of " wristlet " the
wheels at fault gear at right angles.

Assuming the wheel on the plate is screwed down
without shake, the easiest way to overcome the difficulty
is to pitch it deeper. If any teeth are broken, a new
wheel should be fitted, and in either case the lathe would
be necessary to complete the work.

To pitch the wheel deeper, it is necessary to turn away
the sink in the plate which would require fixing the wheel
sink true in the mandrel. This is by no means an easy
operation, because there is no hole or mark on the
bottom plate central with the sink, and to remove the
bar and cement it to a wax chuck central with the sink
would give insufficient surface on the chuck to hold
against the resistance of the cutter.

There are two courses open to us. To " peg the hole "
true, which requires a little practice, or fix the bar on
a cement plate. To adopt the former, screw the barrel
bar on the pillar plate and fix the latter in the mandrel
head, with the screw hole of the sink approximately
true, and the dogs of the mandrel tight enough to hold
the plate.

Splice two pegs together, or cut the ends flat and
shellac them. Many watchmakers use a single peg, but
this is not long enough for a beginner. Cut half the peg
at one end to a flat surface, of about two inches from
the end and cut the end to a long, smooth point. The
latter is used to rest in the hole to be pegged true, while

the flat of the peg is resting for support on the tee rest, which is adjusted as near to the watch plate as possible.

Move the lathe slowly from the gut with the left hand, and notice the peg. The circle the end of the peg describes for one rotation of the mandrel head, indicates the amount the hole is out of truth. This error, of course, is multiplied by the peg, as the distance from the hole to the tee rest is smaller than from the tee rest to the end of the peg. The part of the peg resting on the rest will obviously appear stationary. When the hole with the point of the peg is at its highest, the end of the peg will be at its lowest, and if the circle described by the peg is one-eighth of an inch and the tee rest is one-twelfth, the distance from the point, the error shown by the end of the peg would be eleven times the actual error of the hole out of truth.

Hold a hammer, or file handle, to act as a toucher against the end of the peg, and when the latter is at its lowest point, that is nearest the handle, give the highest part of the edge of the plate a slight tap with a piece of wood, try it for truth and repeat the operation. When the end of the peg is running true, tighten the mandrel dogs.

Many horologists accomplish this work on a cement plate. These are usually home-made. Select a piece of flat brass about $\frac{1}{16}$ to $\frac{1}{8}$ in. thick, drill a hole in the centre about $\frac{1}{8}$ in. diameter, which can be enlarged if desired, and turn it true on a large cement chuck. An inch and a half is a convenient size. The object of a cement plate is to shellac the work to the plate that would fail to have a sufficient grip on a cement chuck. The plate is then held in the mandrel.

The barrel bar could be fixed to a cement plate. Hold the bar on the plate with the sink hole central with the hole in the plate, and mark the steady pin holes. Drill two holes to free the latter and shellac the bar to the plate. Fix the plate in the mandrel head and release the centre to find the sink hole and screw up the dogs.

A sink requires a very little turning in order to lower a wheel sufficiently to attain a correct depth, that previously missed on a few teeth. Slide rest cutters are best adapted for this work. Take a cut across the top of the sink to the centre, then turn the outer diameter or lower sink, which is to free the wheel teeth. If a steel centre is fitted to the sink to come flush with the top of the wheel, a cut across the steel centre will be necessary. When a steel loose centre is fitted held in position by a screw, it will be necessary to place the wheel on the centre piece, reverse it, and see if the latter projects above the wheel. If the projection is much, a little reducing with a file will make it free without " end shake ".

The quickest method of counting the number of teeth in a new wheel is to hold it over the old one and see if all the teeth and spaces are exactly in a line. It will look like one thick wheel.

A new wheel is usually a little thicker than the old. A step chuck is most suitable for holding keyless wheels ; or, failing this, a cement chuck. The thinning and boring can be accomplished in either a slide rest or hand cutter. Use a broad flat-ended for the thinning stage, and a smaller with parallel sides for opening the hole. Gauge the old hole with an arbor and turn out the new hole to fit the arbor in the same place. Finish the wheel with an emery buff, or stone, then harden and temper.

**Cylinder Shells.**—Cylinder shells are easily turned in a split chuck of a lathe, or they can be filled with shellac, cemented to a brass ferrule, and turned in the turns. There is obviously a great saving of time in using shells from the old form with a collet of brass. Less measurement for height, and comparatively little turning, which means about half the time in accomplishing the work.

It will pay to keep a stock of the general sizes in shells separate to cylinders. As a rule, the shell is broken, which means a new one fitted to the old brass would complete the repair in a satisfactory manner.

A cylinder shell, to be the correct size, should have the same amount of shake, between the point of one tooth and the heel of the next, as a tooth has inside the cylinder. To try the size, hold the escape-wheel in the right hand and the shell in the left, and hold the plane of the wheel at right angles to the cylinder. In the case of a new shell, the usual plan is to gauge it by the old one. It will then be the correct size to drive in the brass collet.

The best plan is, first, to punch the old shell out from the top. Place the cylinder on a hollow stake and select a flat-faced punch a trifle smaller in diameter than the cylinder shell. Hold it upright on the cylinder and give the punch a sharp blow ; the shell will then be free to fall through the hole in the stake.

The hole in the brass collet will then act as a guide for the size in selecting a new shell. If the old one is too small, the hole in the collet is broached out to fit the new. When the old shell is too large, with no " outside shake ", the best plan is to fit a new complete cylinder with a brass collet.

Screw down the escape-wheel in the frame and test the shell for height. Hold it upright, with the lower arbor resting on the jewel-hole, and observe the relative

position of the rim of the wheel to the passage of the
cylinder. The shell, when pivoted, will be the length of
the bottom pivot lower than it appears when held against
the jewel-hole. To be the correct length, therefore, the
lower arbor should appear the exact length of the
bottom pivot too high (Fig. 21). The operator will find
this the quickest method of taking the lower height,

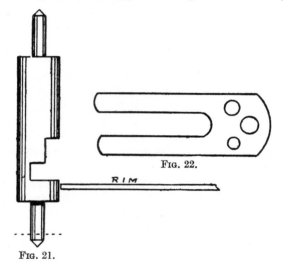

FIG. 22.

RIM

FIG. 21.

and with a little care and practice have no difficulty
in accuracy. Make a scratch on the lower arbor to
represent the end of the pivot and turn the arbor back
to the scratch. The rim should occupy the position
shown before the pivot is turned.

A very simple method of taking the jeight is the
use of a temporary cock. Unscrew the "chariot"
which carries the lower cylinder jewel-hole, and screw
in its place a flat, smooth piece of brass with a groove

for adjustment of the screw and two or three holes at the other end, different sizes, freely to fit the lower shell arbor shown in Fig. 22. No measurement is taken. The thickness of this temporary cock is quite immaterial. A wide piece of mainspring would do, if perfectly flat and made to shape. Its object is simply to form a resting-place for the bottom of the cylinder-shell. Screw the new cock down, with a suitable hole to take the place of the jewel-hole in the " chariot ". Hold the shell upright, with the bottom resting on the new cock (and the arbor through the hole), and notice if the rim of the wheel passes freely in the passage of the cylinder. If the rim is foul of the bottom of the shell, turn away the latter, which rests on the cock until it is free. The measurement for the end of the bottom pivot is then taken. Rest the bottom of the shell flush against the end of the " chariot ", with the endstone removed, and mark the arbor flush with the end of the jewel-hole and turn it off to the scratch.

A lathe is the quickest form of turning a shell. One split chuck will be sufficient to accomplish the whole of the turning. The lower end is turned first to the scratch on the arbor described which forms the end of the pivot. Grip the bottom end in a split chuck so that the shoulder comes flush with the chuck, and there will be no fear of breaking the shell.

The length or whole height is next taken. Unscrew both endstones, screw on the balance-cock, then measure the distance between the two jewel-holes with a suitable gauge. Rest one jaw on each jewel-hole setting and take the reading on the gauge. Remove the shell from the chuck, screw up the gauge to the reading taken. Rest the lower pivot on one jaw, and make a scratch on the top arbor to come flush with the other jaw.

The bottom end of the shell being finished, it now remains to turn the top arbor to the scratch to attain the whole height. The shell is reversed in the chuck for this procedure. It frequently happens the scratch is too close to the shoulder to get sufficient length to form a pivot. In such instances the end of the plug is turned back to the size of the arbor. A sharp graver is necessary, or the shell is subject to crack. The pivot is next turned, nearly to fit the jewel-hole, and burnished.

The shell is then ready to drive into the brass collet. Reverse the balance on a hollow stake and push the top end in the hole ; then adjust it to position so that a line drawn across the lips forms a right angle with the pin in the balance. Drive it in with a flat-ended cylinder punch, the flat resting on the bottom of the top plug. The balance will attain its correct height when the shell is driven home far enough.

**Cylinders with Brass Collets.**—Turning cylinders with brass collets in the lathe obviously takes a little longer than turning shells, because there is more fitting.

Although modern methods have proven quicker in cylinder turning there are many who prefer the orthodox gauge system, which in many instances would be found more consistent to attain accuracy.

The two most general forms of measurement adopted are the cylinder height tool and the brass cock or bar used in place of the chariot. This measurement system can be dispensed with to save time. With a little practice the horologist can take his heights and mark or scratch them by simply placing the cylinder in the frame in the same manner as adopted by turning a shell.

Place the escape wheel in the frame, screw down the cock and hold the cylinder upright with the lower arbor resting on the jewel-hole. The two heights are then taken, the end of the lower pivot and the seat of the balance. The latter represents the bottom of the balance, which must have perfect freedom of the escape cock. These two heights are marked with scratches. With careful observation and a little practice the relative position of the rim of the escape wheel and the passage of the cylinder can be judged and the lower arbor marked. The second scratch is made on the brass collet, which must represent the bottom of the balance. When marking this scratch, allow plus the length of the lower pivot, also the piece on the lower arbor beyond the scratch.

The whole height is then taken, which is equal to the distance between the two endstones.

A small wax chuck of the lathe with a hollow V-shaped end is now employed to hold the cylinder for turning. The cylinder is waxed true, and the top end turned. It only requires reversing once to turn the lower pivot.

A little practice will be necessary to shellac the cylinder true. It is necessary the bottom of the V of the chuck should be dead true. If there is any doubt about it, turn it true with a long pointed graver.

Start the lathe running with a spirit flame under the chuck, apply the shellac to fill the V hole. See " Turning " Wristlet Staff. The lower arbor of the cylinder is next placed at the bottom of the V. There should be enough shellac to cover the cylinder to the brass collet, so that it forms a solid mass. The brass collet is then turned and the balance fitted down flush with the scratch. Next the spring collet is fitted and the rivet turned for the balance. The top arbor is shortened to the scratch and the pivot turned.

The cylinder is then reversed in the V chuck shellaced true, with the knob of shellac covering the whole except the lower arbor. The arbor is turned off at the scratch

and the lower pivot turned.  Finally, boil out the cylinder
in methylated spirit.

Taking the height of a cylinder by means of a
" temporary brass cock " is as accurate as any cylinder
height tool.  This method is recommended to horologists
with little experience in cylinder turning.    See
" Turning " Cylinder Shells.  If, for instance, the jewel-
hole in the chariot is broken and a new one necessary,
we should first punch out the old stone, leaving the open
setting.  At this stage we could use the chariot to rest
the bottom of the cylinder instead of the temporary
cock in taking the height.

**Fitting a Barrel.**—Fitting a watch barrel by means of
the lathe is a good instance of the triumph of time-
saving appliances.

A barrel could be turned in a step chuck, wax chuck,
or face plate.  As most lathe combinations include the
former, which is better adapted to this class of work, we
will follow the various stages in the step chuck.

Carefully examine the difference in height and thickness between the old and new barrel, also the height
between the plates.  It frequently happens the old barrel
is too wide or too narrow for the space attained in the
plates.

We must aim as far as possible to attain sufficient
space inside the barrel to take a mainspring not less
than the height of the old one.  This can be determined
by breaking off a piece of the old spring and placing it
inside the barrel against the edge.  If the top of the
spring is flush or above the groove, the bottom or cover
should be turned away.  Measure the thickness of the
bottom in a gauge and compare it with the old one.
It should be not less than $1\frac{1}{2}$ douziemes.  Where no
stop work is fitted the cover will generally bear sinking.

The sink is turned with the slide rest leaving an outside edge as wide as the groove on which it snaps.

Fig. 23 is a section of a cover sunk out to a thin edge A. The shoulder of the edge shown by dotted lines should come in a line with the inside of the rim of the barrel. If it is left too thick, the outside coil of the spring would jump or bind against it.

Select a step chuck to grip the barrel teeth and run

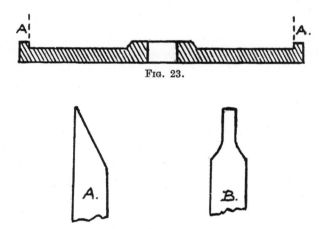

FIG. 23.

FIG. 24.

a slide rest cutter (Fig. 24 A) over the bottom of the barrel to test the flat. The hole is, or should be, true with the barrel teeth. The safest plan is to bore it with a cutter to fit the end of the arbor pivot. The cover is then snapped on and the top hole bored true with a parallel cutter (Fig. 24 B). These cutters require the sides or cutting edges ground back to about 60 degrees. Being small they can be whetted on the oil-stone, the top must be kept perfectly flat.

The barrel and cover holes are next broached slightly from the inside until the pivots enter freely to the shoulders. A little care is required with this operation, or the holes might be out of upright. Give the broach a slight twist, then move it round slowly to see if the bottom of the barrel or cover, as the case may be, is at right angles with the broach.

Snap the cover on the barrel and measure the thickness of the whole. This measurement is equal to the distance between the barrel arbor shoulders plus the thickness of the two bosses (or barrel and cover holes). It is advisable to keep the bosses on the thick side, or the barrel may prove to have too much end shake. Try the arbor in the barrel for freedom. Remember you can always turn away more, but cannot replace it.

In the absence of a slide rest the work can be accomplished with a tee rest and hand cutters made on the ends of old files (shown in Fig. 10). A small cutter with parallel sides would be required for boring the holes, and one with a broad flat end for turning down the bosses.

The next procedure is to fit the hook. The hole is drilled at an incline and the hook screwed in from the inside. The best plan is to form the hook when the steel is in the screw plate. File a piece of steel taper, with about $\frac{1}{4}$ in. to pass freely in No. 12-size hole of the screw plate, and screw in into a full thread. Nip it off close enough on the large scale to form the hook. File the end to an incline and undercut the highest side with a slitting file to form the hook. The small end on the opposite side of the plate without a thread can then be gripped with the pliers to unscrew it from the plate. It is then screwed in from the inside of the barrel in the same manner. A 12-size tapped hole takes a stronger hook than one of larger diameter. The next step is to fit the mainspring and try the number of turns in the slide tongs.

The barrel is finally polished, or snailed. Snailing on the new principle is quicker and gives a finish equal to a snailing tool. Rest it on a piece of cork held in the vice. Drive a pin in the cork through the hole, about half the diameter of the latter, for the barrel to rest against. Place a corner of a new No. 2 emery buff across the centre of the barrel, so that the buff rests against the pin. Give the buff long strokes while the barrel is very slightly moved round with the thumb and finger between each stroke. The width of cork should not exceed the diameter of the barrel so as to enable the thumb and finger to manipulate the barrel. Any particle of emery dust would cause trouble where watch work is concerned. The barrel should therefore be cleaned in petrol and all tools in use, during the emery operation.

**Turning a Fourth Pinion.**—Turning a fourth pinion by means of a true split chuck is undoubtedly a saving of time on the principle of the turns. There are many reasons for fitting a new pinion, and when the old one is available the heights can be attained from it.

We will assume the fourth pinion is lost. The usual course is to send the third wheel and escape pinion to a material dealer, with instructions to sector them for a new fourth wheel and pinion. The first consideration is to find the number of teeth and leaves in the lost wheel and pinion, and being a seconds we know the pinion rotates once in a minute. The pinion will therefore make sixty turns while the centre wheel completes exactly one, and the product of the number of teeth in the centre wheel multiplied by the number in the third wheel will be sixty times the product of the number of leaves in the third pinion multiplied by the number of leaves in the fourth pinion.

We will take an ordinary lever train with a vibration of 18,000 per hour and call the lost pinion $x$. Now we have centre wheel of 64, third wheel 60, third pinion 8, then $\dfrac{64 \times 60}{8 \times x} = 60$, therefore $x = \dfrac{64 \times 60}{60 \times 8} = 8$ the number of leaves in the lost pinion. We next find the number of teeth in the lost fourth wheel, which we will call $x$, and as there are 30 vibrations for one rotation of the escape wheel, multiply the number of teeth by 2, then we have $\dfrac{64 \times 60 \times x \times 15 \times 2}{8 \times 8 \times 7} = 18,000$ vibrations per hour, therefore $x = \dfrac{18,000 \times 8 \times 8 \times 7}{64 \times 60 \times 15 \times 2} = 70$, the number of teeth in the fourth wheel. This train is often used in old English fusee watches only with a fourth wheel of 63, giving a vibration of 16,200 per hour. This can always be ascertained by counting the spring first. All watches are now made with an 18,000 train. To determine the actual size of a wheel without a sector, divide the number of teeth by the number of leaves in the pinion which gears with it, and the product will give the relative sizes. The safest plan is to try the fourth wheel and escape pinion in the depth tool, opening the latter until it corresponds with the fourth and escape wheel holes.

Place the escape wheel and pinion in the frame to judge the space available for the fourth wheel freedom ; this will be a guide. In the case of a three-quarter plate the room is very limited. Rest the polished face of the fourth pinion on the plate level with the lower fourth hole, and mark the pinion slightly above the plate to represent the seat of the fourth wheel. The mark must be made slightly lower to allow for the distance from the bottom of the pinion and the shoulder of the pivot.

Fix the pinion head in a split chuck and turn the pinion to let the wheel fit tightly as far as the mark. It often happens the pinion head is much too long. In this case we may turn a deep nick just beyond the rivet down to the roots of the pinion leaves and break off the leaves on the waste part with a pair of pliers (Fig. 25 A).

A sharp graver is of vital importance when turning the pinion head in the lathe. A graver that would fail

FIG. 25.

to cut in the turns would tear the pinion leaves at the root or bend over the points when extra power was applied running in the lathe.

Many watchmakers of the old school fit and rivet the wheel on first, but it will be found more convenient to rivet the wheel on last when using the split chuck.

Turn the arbor true and polish it, leaving a shoulder free of the rivet for the polisher to rest against (Fig. 26).

Next turn the hollow to form the rivet with a lozenge-shaped graver. It is quite obvious a long pointed graver for cutting hardened and tempered steel should have a more obtuse angle than one for cutting softer metal. Turning these hollows and undercuts, to a beginner, is most disheartening. It's a case of " off comes the point ". It is certainly easier to learn to turn steel hollows in the turns with a very weak hair bow. Having attained the delicate touch, the lathe with a weak tension will then become quite natural. For lathe work the graver must be sharp, with a high incline.

To take the height of the pinion, turn a ring on the arbor close to the pinion face to mark the shoulder of the seconds pivot (Fig. 26 B). A piece of beeswax pressed between the two holes to form an impression of the two shoulders is a good instance of taking the whole height. This will give the distance from the mark or ring to the top shoulder, C. Another good plan is to make a pair of long thin flat-sided callipers with the

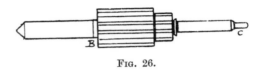

Fig. 26.

ends bent at right angles. Open the callipers until the ends rest on each jewel-hole, then take off the top plate to remove the callipers.

Turn the top pivot and burnish it to fit the jewel-hole. If the holes are brass it will be advisable to leave the pivot rather tight in the hole so as to get a new smooth surface with a round broach. Reverse the pinion in the chuck and turn the seconds pivot forming the shoulder at the ring B. When the seconds pivot is small, the safest method is to employ the lathe with back centre. The Jacot lathe attachment could be used for support, or finish both pivots on the Jacot tool.

We now come to the final stage. Place the pinion in the frame with the dial on and make a scratch on the seconds pivot flush with the top of the dial, turn it off at the scratch and burnish the end. Place the wheel in position on the pinion and rivet it in the same way as a balance staff. The smallest rivet will be necessary if the wheel is fitted tightly on the pinion, and the less hammering the better. A hollow brass stake should be used, which is less liable to damage the face of the pinion.

**Turning an Escape Pinion.**—We will assume the old wheel and pinion are lost. The fourth wheel should be sent to your material dealer with instructions to sector a pinion from the fourth wheel and the pallets enclosed for a new escape wheel. Comparatively few shops keep a sector, and when pinions are kept in stock the depth tool will be found the best test for attaining the correct size.

All modern watches are made with a quick train giving 18,000 vibrations per hour, or 300 per minute. The ratio between the fourth wheel and escape pinion is therefore 10. A fourth wheel of 70 teeth would require an escape pinion of 7, or a wheel of 60, a pinion of 6. In the case of an English lever watch the safest plan is to count the spring. Many of the older movements are made with a 16,200 train, and the ratio between the fourth wheel and escape pinion would be 9.

The first stage is to place the fourth wheel and pinion in the frame with the escape cock screwed on, and notice how much space there is for the escape wheel freedom, a three-quarter plate is usually very limited for room.

Fix the pinion head in a split chuck and turn a nick in the body to form the seat of the escape wheel (see sketch A) leaving the pinion head about the length of its diameter and break off the leaves of the waste piece, B, with a pair of pliers (Fig. 27). A sharp long-pointed graver is necessary for turning the pinion head, or you will find, to your cost, the leaves tear away at the root.

Rest the lower arbor of the pinion on the lower hole, and notice how much of the arbor must be turned away so that the top of the pinion will be slightly above the fourth wheel, allowing a little extra for the length of the pivot. In the case of endstones, remove the jewel-hole and rest the arbor on the former. A piece of beeswax pressed between the two holes to form an impression of the two shoulders is a good instance of taking the whole height.

The next step is to turn the top arbor, remove the

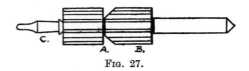

Fig. 27.

graver marks with oilstone-dust, and fit a brass collet about half-way, allowing a little drive to the pinion head. Turn it true with the pinion head in a split chuck, then turn the end hollow to form a rivet for the escape wheel after the style of a balance staff. The lower arbor, C, is next turned with a shoulder free of the pinion head and polished with diamantine and bell-metal or steel polisher. The pivot is then formed to fit the jewel-hole (Fig. 27). Next reverse the pinion in the chuck, turn and fit the pivot to the jewel-hole.

Swiss escape wheels are usually riveted to the pinion. The brass collet with a rubbed-on wheel gives a more finished appearance. It is easier for attaining a shoulder level with the centre of the pallets but as a rule it is left flush with the pinion head.

It occasionally happens there is insufficient room between the escape and fourth wheels to get the former to run in the centre of the pallet stones. In such cases there are two courses to overcome the difficulty : drive the lever and pallets up the arbor, or turn the fourth wheel back on the pinion nearer the plate, and finish the rivet with a facing tool, to correspond with the adjacent parts.

## THE USE OF THE TURNS

**Turning a Balance Staff.**—Many of the old school do all their turnings and pivoting in the turns, and claim that it is the only form to attain the best class work. The lathe is certainly quicker, but the turns are more convenient for many operators at the present day.

We will assume a three-quarter plate watch requires a new balance staff. The best plan is to place the old staff with the balance in the frame, and if the heights are correct measure them on a metric gauge—or better still, two, one for the height of the balance and the other for the whole height. The rivet is first turned away and the old staff removed from the balance.

A full plate balance staff is certainly easier to turn than a three-quarter plate. A turner who can manage the latter will have no difficulty in accomplishing the former.

Select a suitable tempered steel block. These can be obtained at any material dealer, assorted full plates, three-quarter, and wristlets. Screw on the lower arbor of the steel block a small screw ferrule, the smaller the better, about three times the diameter of the flange.

Use a weak horsehair bow and screw the staff in the centres of the turns using an eccentric pivot back centre which will come opposite a circle of centres on the right hand runner and keep the staff parallel. By this method there will be no difficulty in presenting the point of the graver when turning the arbors and pivots.

The staff should have absolutely no shake between the runners. This rule must be strictly adhered to if it is to be turned true. Keep oil to the centres. A graver with the point worn away would fail to cut with a small ferrule. When a large one is employed greater power is obtained and although the point of the graver may have worn away the metal would probably scrape off and the work would soon run out of true.

Turn the flange or the largest part first. Sharp gravers are indispensable to quick turning. Apply plenty of oil, hold the graver perfectly, flat and rub briskly until the point and edge are up. Keep it the same angle on the stone so as to maintain the same shape and cutting angle. Hold it firmly on the rest with the point well above the centre of the steel and cut with the down stroke of the bow. The flange is next polished with a soft steel polisher and oilstone dust mixed with oil. A reverse motion is quicker for polishing. A bow therefore has the advantage of a lathe in this respect.

Fine watches have the flanges finished with diamantine to give a good polish. The staff should be cleaned with pith, or immersed in petrol and brushed to remove all traces of oilstone dust and the polisher filed to attain a clean surface. Mix diamantine with watch oil on a clean stake or piece of glass. Beat well together with a clean knife. Proportions for mixing, about three parts diamantine to one of oil. The amount of oil will appear at first to be insufficient. Beat and mix well together until it assumes a very thick paste. If more oil is added the paste becomes too thin, and all attempts at polishing will prove a failure. One of the greatest mistakes is to apply too much diamantine. A very good plan is to give the polisher one light tap direct on the mixed polish. The polisher is quite a matter of fancy, soft steel or bell metal. Use a quick up and down and reversed motion with the bow until the diamantine becomes

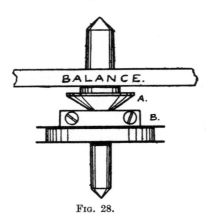

Fig. 28.

almost dry. Always keep polishing material covered when not in use, and on no account use a stake for diamantine that has been used for oilstone dust. It has often been stated that it takes longer to learn to polish brass and steel than it does to turn true. Keep everything perfectly clean and adopt a circular motion. To attain a polish free from scratches is like everything else—practise.

The screw ferrule is next fixed on the lower arbor and the staff turned to fit the balance with the shoulder at the end of the flange. This is one of the most important parts of the staff. On the fit of this greatly depends the running of the balance which must press tightly against a square turned shoulder. It is better to allow a little drive to the latter shown in Fig. 28. The flange A, the screw ferrule B.

To formulate an idea of the relative position of the

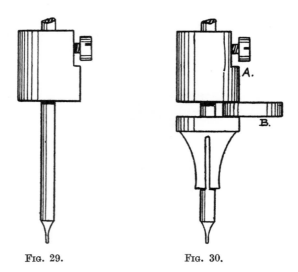

FIG. 29.                    FIG. 30.

balance, a survey in the frame is advisable. Drive the balance on its seat flush with the shoulder, preparatore for taking the height.

Remove the lower endstone and jewel-hole and replace the former. Hold the staff upright with the lower arbor resting on the endstone, and notice the distance from the escape cock to the balance. The arbor is turned away so that the balance is only ust free of the cock. This will be the position it occupies when finished. The screw ferrule is fixed on the spring collet arbor for this operation.

The lower arbor is turned to fit the roller. In a three-quarter plate it is usually fitted flush against the flange, but this depends on the position of the lever notch, which can be measured from the old staff, or in a gauge from the lower staff endstone, with the lever screwed down in the cock. There are many gauges in use for this purpose. The sliding weight is about the most accurate in the home-made class, described by Mr. C. T. Higginbotham in " Precision Time Measures ".

Select a piece of tempered steel wire about the size of a depth tool runner, about two inches long, and polish with oilstone dust. Turn a conical pivot on the end small enough to enter the smallest jewel-hole. A brass sliding weight is turned to fit the arbor shown in Fig. 29. One end of the weight is filed flat on the side and provided with a screw, so that it can be adjusted to any required height and fixed. Fig. 30 shows a spring collet, which is slotted, made to fit the arbor spring tight, thus securing sufficient friction to retain it in any position. The collet could be supplied with a screw, but it is not necessary, as its object is simply to measure the thickness of an endstone to attain the final position of the weight. The large end of the collet and the lower end of the weight must be turned flat and finished on a buff, or the tool will not be accurate.

To take the whole height of a three-quarter plate balance-staff, remove the cock jewel-hole and endstone, and screw on the balance-cock. Hold the tool upright with the arbor through the hole of the jewel setting and the pivot in the jewel-hole resting on the endstone. Release the screw to let the weight down and touch the top of the cock. It is then screwed tight, which records

the whole length of the staff plus the thickness of the
top endstone setting.   Fig. 30 shows how to subtract
the thickness of the endstone setting from the measurement recorded in the gauge.  Hold the setting against
the face of the weight A, and push the spring collet
tight against the setting B.  The space occupied between
the weight and collet is equal to the endstone setting,
and the actual length of the staff will be the distance
from the end of the pivot to the top of the spring
collet.   Slacken the screw in the weight to release the
setting, and let the weight rest gently against the
spring collet.

Tighten the screw, then remove the spring collet.

The height of the roller can be measured in the same
manner by letting the sliding weight down free of the
lever notch, so that it occupies the same position as the
bottom of the roller when fitted to the staff.

The lower arbor is next turned to fit the roller about
half-way, then polish out the graver marks with oilstone dust and soft steel polisher until the roller fits
to the reading of the gauge, allowing a little for drive.
Finish the arbor with diamantine and a steel or bell
metal polisher.  One rub is all that is required to give
it the final polish.

The screw ferrule is next fixed on the lower arbor
and the rivet turned for the balance with a long pointed
graver and a very weak horse hair bow.  The edge of
the rivet should come above the balance about two-
thousandths of an inch.  A higher one with excessive
hammering would tend to throw the balance out of
truth.  The top arbor is next turned to fit the spring
collet, leaving the edge of the rivet as shoulder.  Many
turners turn the top end first, but the method is quite
a matter of fancy.  The top arbor is turned back for the

whole height of the staff as described, and ready for pivoting.

The pivots are roughed to shape, then the backslope, or nick turned with a long pointed graver to prevent the oil from running away from the jewel-hole and up the staff. A weak hair bow should be kept especially for this work, it not only tends to keep the pivots true, but also from breaking. The pivot is finished with a half-circular pointed graver until it sticks on the end of the jewel-hole. Only a little burnishing or polishing is required to let the pivot through the hole.

To be successful at pivoting it is necessary to have

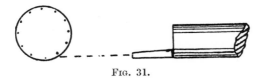

FIG. 31.

fine, small centres near the edge and for this purpose home-made runners are an advantage. File the end perfectly flat, then buff the file marks away and make a circle of fine centres with the point of a sharp graver as near the edge as possible. About twelve or sixteen will be found a convenient number, with each hole ranging a little larger (Fig. 31). Move the graver in a backward and forward motion. Harden the end of the runner and temper it to a straw.

The truth of a balance staff to a great extent depends on the pivots. A well-known advocate used a special small ferrule when starting to turn his pivots, and stated it was the only possible way to keep a staff true. You gain the experience of keeping the point on the graver.

To use the turns successfully instead of a Jacot tool as a means of polishing or burnishing pivots, it will be found more convenient to make your own runner beds. The principle is the same, although perhaps a little more experience is required with pivoting in the turns. In a Jacot tool the runner bed is locked perfectly upright by means of a small locking plate. In the turns the operator has to adjust his own.

To make a bed runner select a pivot back centre that comes as near the outside of the circumference of the runner as possible, and fix it in the turns. A piece of runner steel to fit the right-hand head is next required for making the bed, or the back end of a centre pivoting runner would do. File or turn the end perfectly flat, then screw it tight in the turns and bring the back centre up flush with the face of it. The end of the circumference has ten or twelve flats filed, and each flat has a different size bed. Each bed should be on the same level as the back centre or a pivot is liable to break when pressure from the burnisher is applied. Many watchmakers prefer to abolish the flats and make the beds on the circular rim. Notice exactly how far the end of the runner is above the back centre. The runner is turned in a lathe, leaving a rim on the end. A very little should be turned off the rim to bring it level with the back centre. It is often only necessary to buff it over. Ten or twelve beds are next filed at equal distance, and graduating sizes. A fine slitting file will be found best for this job. Remove the burs with a fine emery buff, and harden and temper the end of the runner to a straw.

It is much easier to maintain the truth of a pivot by turning it to fit the jewel-hole—or until it almost enters than by filing on a " Jacot " bed. The " Jacot " tool is now quite popular as a means of reducing or finishing pivots. The success of this tool greatly depends on the bow and condition of the burnishers. Use a very weak horse-hair bow and keep it especially for pivoting. A burnisher worn smooth is more likely to break a pivot than one that cuts well, because greater force is exerted which is often applied at the root of the pivot. Flat and conical " Jacot " burnishers are sharpened on a strip of lead charged with emery powder, or a new emery buff stick would serve the purpose. Number 2 for a cutting burnisher, and 0 for a glossing or finishing.

Place the burnisher flat on the buff or lead and give it long forward and backward strokes. The edge of the conical burnisher is treated in the same way, moving it with a rounding motion from one edge to the other. Clean the burnishers with tissue paper rubbed with oil before use to avoid any particle of emery cutting the pivot. Apply oil to the burnishers and keep them covered when not in use. If left on the board, the edges are liable to get damaged, and the horologist would find in his experience a " pivot off ".

Keep the steel parts of a " Jacot " tool oiled. Rust is one of the evils a watchmaker has to fight against. Watch hands might be very convenient for distribution neatly fixed on a card in dozens from the maker's point of view, but in time the card absorbs moisture and causes rust. The sooner they are removed from the card and placed in dry boxes with oiled paper, the better for the horologist as a safeguard against rust.

**Turning a Cylinder.**—As a rule the old cylinder is the correct size, and the shell will drive out from the top end, leaving the balance and collet intact. In this case a new shell only is necessary, and the hole in the collet will be a guide in selecting a shell the correct size.

Unscrew the " chariot " or bar in the plate which carries the lower cylinder jewel-hole, and screw the " temporary cock " in its place. (See Turning Cylinder Shells.)

Hold the cylinder upright with the arbor through the hole, and the bottom resting on the cock.  Move the escape wheel round until the rim is in the passage of the cylinder.  You will then see exactly how it is for height.  If the rim is too close, or touching the bottom

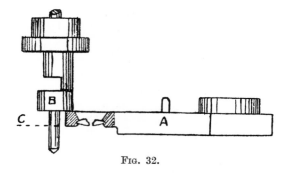

Fig. 32.

of the cylinder, turn away the bottom until the rim of the wheel is in the centre of the passage.

When the rim is in the correct position of the passage, make a scratch on the brass collet free of the escape cock to mark the seat of the balance.  Remove the cylinder, unscrew the endstone, and hold the bottom of the cylinder flush against the end of the chariot near the jewel-hole (Fig. 32).  A is the chariot, B the cylinder, and C a dotted line level with the top of the jewel-hole to mark the arbor for the end of the pivot.  If the cylinder is the correct height for the escape wheel with the bottom resting on the temporary cock, it will be exactly the same if the chariot occupies the same relative position. Therefore make a scratch on the arbor level with the end of the jewel-hole, shown with a dotted line. When an endstone is sunk below the surface of the brass, this extra distance must be allowed in length.

Fill the cylinder with shellac, warm in a spirit flame with a small brass ferrule to pass freely over the shell, so that both forms a solid.

Turn the bottom arbor off at the scratch, which represents the end of the pivot. A very weak horse-hair bow and a sharp graver is necessary for this operation to prove successful. Keep the centres well oiled and the cylinder free from shake in the runners. Fit the balance down to the scratch, which is to form the seat, and turn the shoulder hollow to form the rivet. It will be found necessary to keep a very long pointed graver especially for turning hollows. The spring collet is next fitted to come flush with the rivet.

The whole height of the cylinder is measured. (See Turning Cylinder Shells.)

Turn both pivots down to nearly fit the jewel-holes with square shoulders turned back, and burnish them on a Jacot tool or a runner bed. Boil the cylinder in methylated spirit to dissolve the shellac.

**Drilling Arbors.**—The quickest and most simple home-made tool for drilling pinions is a cone plate fixed to the tee rest of the turns. This device is quick in its action, because the drill rotates, and the arbor mounted with a screw ferrule and another bow moves in the reverse direction. The hole is therefore more likely to keep true.

To make the plate, remove the tee-piece from the rest, select a piece of rod brass or steel, which will fit the hole of the rest, and saw or file a slot in the top to take the steel plate, which is fixed at right angle to the rod (Fig. 33).

The plate is made of soft black steel about 2 inches long, $\frac{3}{8}$ in. wide, and 5 douziemes thick. File the steel taper for strength, leaving the thick end to fit the slot in the rod. Buff out the file marks on both sides. Mark a line down the centre of the plate and drill three or four holes of different sizes, which will represent from

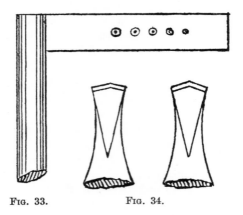

FIG. 33.          FIG. 34.

the smallest to the largest required in drilling up for a pivot. Chamfer the holes on one side, so that the ends of the arbors to be drilled shall run true with the hole, shown in Fig. 33.

The cone plate is next hardened and tempered to a red, then soldered or riveted to the stalk. The latter fixture makes the neatest job, and two holes for rivets will be sufficient if the plate fits the slot. Adjust the latter at right angle to the rod before drilling. The cone holes will then run level when the rest is pulled.

Home-made drills are the best for this work. A great

deal depends on the style of drill. It might fail to cut for many reasons. Too large or too taper in the neck is a common fault, and the reason why so many break in the drilling process ; the neck for want of clearance in the hole snaps off. When running out of true it will often foul the corner of the hole as the drill deepens and break.

Slower motion is necessary for drilling steel than brass, and for tempered steel the work is accomplished even at a slower rate. If a drill is cutting, the same pressure and rate of motion should be continued. To use extra force or greater speed is courting disaster. The process is slow, and extra speed applied with the object of quicker results will result in a broken drill.

Fig. 34 shows the usual forms of home-made drills for pivots. Two cutting edges are required each side for use in the turns. To make them see " Lathe " Drilling.

The pointed end drill in Fig. 34 is for centering and starting. A hole in the cone plate being selected to fit the drill without side shake. The flatted end is then used to drill the hole the required depth.

To adjust the cone plate, screw it in the rest in place of the T-piece. A hole is selected that fits the drill without shake. The back and front runners are pushed flush with the plate, to see that the two holes in the runners are parallel with the hole in the plate. Screw a ferrule on the pinion arbor and pass the hair of a bow round the ferrule, the reverse way to turning, so that the arbor moves in the correct way for turning with the up-stroke of the bow. Screw the pinion up in the turns with the pivot running in a centre of the runner and the shoulder of the broken pivot running in a chamfer in the cone plate. The centre of the drill should run in a centre of the other runner, and the blade in the hole of the cone plate. Place a hair bow on the ferrule of the drill in the opposite direction of the other bow. The runner which carries the drill centre is loose and pressed forward by the first finger.

Hold the two bows together with the thumb and finger, and when started the two ferrules will rotate in opposite directions, while you press the runner which advances the drill. Short and slow strokes are essential to attain success. Apply oil. The two moving in opposite directions tends to cut better and keep the drill true.

## PIN WHEEL ESCAPEMENT

The pin wheel escapement was invented by Amant of Paris about 1749. It is to be seen mostly in French bracket clocks of high quality which give a close rate in timekeeping. When properly constructed it is a dead beat, Jean André Lepaute improved the escapement by placing the pins on both sides of the wheel, and claimed the pallets were both the same length and the pull would be nearly equal.

Fig. 34 A shows the pin wheel escapement of Lieut. W. D. Stott's famous clock by Amant. The escape wheel A is a plain disc fitted with 22 pins all on one side, and fixed near the outer rim of the wheel as seen from the dial, together with the escape pinion of eight leaves.

The impulse is given to the pallet B and C equal to the distance between two pins minus drop, which is very slight, about 1 degree on each pallet. The impulse on the entering pallet is shown by the two dotted lines at D, and on the exit pallet at E, and from the lower line to the pin outside the exit pallet F is the amount of drop.

Fig. 34 A shows the pin F just dropped off the exit pallet with the preceding pin locked on the entering pallet. The wheel pins are of brass which give a smooth acting contact, and assuming the pallet faces are well oiled, such a clock should run a large number of years without showing any signs of wear.

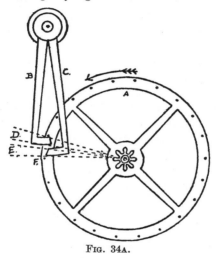

Fig. 34A.

There is no difficulty in polishing the acting surfaces of the pallets, and removing the wheel pins when signs of wear occur. A little care is required to see any new pins are exactly the same size as the old ones.

Antoine Thiout refers to Amant as a clever horologist of Paris in his *Traité d' Horlogerie*, Paris, 1741.

When properly constructed it is a dead beat escapement; it is simplicity itself. The impulse is given to the pallets B and C equal to the distance between two pins minus drop, which is very slight, about 1 degree on each pallet.

The fusee and great wheel are placed in the centre of the movement with the barrel below. The clock has a sheleton frame, with a silvered dial above the fusee arbor, giving it a very artistic appearance. The great wheel has 192 teeth, diameter $4\frac{1}{2}$ inches. The centre pinion 14 and the third 12 leaves. The fusee makes about 13 turns. The wheels are screwed on brass collets driven on the arbors.

A fine example of ormolu work encircles the dial in a design of acorns and oak leaves, the hands being nicely pierced in floral design. The pallet cock, which is a work of art, carrying the silk cord suspension, has a screw which holds the frame at the top pillar.

The pin wheel is generally understood to refer to the escapement used in turret clocks. It is a dead-beat and when properly constructed gives excellent results. This escapement was invented by Jean André Lepaute about 1755. He designed half-circular pins and placed them alternately on each side of the wheel, this method enabled the pallets to be the same length ; but there is no disadvantage in having one pallet a little longer than the other, provided the short one is put outside as shown in illustration. Later they were all fitted on one side, and flattened at the bottom.

It has an advantage over the Graham from the fact that the pressure on the pallets is always downward and therefore any wear on the pallet holes would not effect the impulse. The impulse is divided between the pallets and the pins with a very small drop. The locking faces are left slightly rounded to reduce friction. This escapement is to be found mostly in turret clocks of an older pattern.

# WATCHES

## METHOD OF CLEANING

Before starting to clean a watch it is usual to examine the parts and note any faults likely to cause trouble, and repair them before the cleaning operation.

There are several methods of cleaning, and each a different formula. The main feature is to remove all dirt and thick oil, and for this reason the general plan is to immerse the parts in petrol, they are then held in tissue paper and brushed with a circular and cross motion. The brushes are cleaned by rubbing them on chalk and a dry crust. The leaves of the pinions should be cleaned with pointed pegwood. Polished wheels may be brushed with metal polish, and jewel-holes with endstones removed and allowed to remain in petrol a few minutes, the latter brushed flat on the board, holding them with broad pointed tweezers. The balance-spring should be removed, and placed in the petrol bath (see Faults in the Balance Spring. Wristlet Watches).

Many beginners pay too much attention to the brightness of the gilding, and insufficient to the pivots and holes. Clean the latter by twisting in them a pointed piece of pegwood. Cut away the dirt from the pegwood and repeat the operation on each hole until the peg is removed perfectly stainless. Some repairers prefer to immerse polished brass parts in cyanide of potassium, but this requires the steel screws removed, holding the pieces under running water, and another bath of methylated spirit.

The old style of Clerkenwell bench, mahogany, with a chest of drawers fixed, is the most convenient;

height about 3 ft. 4 in.  The bench should be kept
covered when not in use.  For this purpose make a
wooden cover to fit over, like the lid of a box, with
sides high enough to clear contents of the bench.  A
roll top bench is the latest improvement.

## OIL

The selection of oil is an  important feature.  The
smaller timekeepers require oil of thinner properties,
and for this reason it will save considerable trouble to
use oil by makers of repute, labelled for the purpose it
is intended.

Many of the old school make their own oil for watches
and clocks, by a process of filtering pure olive oil.  It is
exposed to a low temperature for a short time to allow
any unsuitable matter to separate.  A slow process then
follows of alternately standing and filtering.  These
old horologists gained their experience in the days
when good oil was uncertain.  The writer does not
advise such experiments at the present time, which is
not only a waste of time, but might prove costly in
the end.

Oiling a watch or clock may seem a trifling matter,
yet there are many timekeepers repaired and cleaned
in a satisfactory manner and for lack of knowledge in
oiling rendered useless for consistent time-keeping
purposes.

The fault is not only through using unsuitable oil,
but in the application.  There are more watches brought
into the average shop with the complaint of bad timekeeping, through too much oil than insufficient.  The
writer often has to dissemble a watch and clean it
because the oil is not confined to the acting surfaces and

oil sinks. The capillary attraction not only acts as a brake to the escapement, but it is inconsistent.

Capillarity is the attraction which exists between some fluids and solid bodies. Oil sinks are formed in watch and clock plates so that by capillary attraction the oil is kept close to the pivot instead of spreading over the plate. Back slopes are formed on arbors having conical pivots, so that the oil may not be drawn up the body of the arbor. When there is no back slope or under-cut, the amount of oil should be considerably less. When the oil spreads over the sink or back-slope, capillary attraction will obviously draw it away.

Any particle of substance left in a hole would cause the oil to corrode in a very short time and end in trouble, which is often attributed to the quality of oil—bad.

Working to a system will prove a great saving of time. A steel oiler should be kept especially for watch work, and one a little smaller for small wristlets. A piece of clock pegwood will be found convenient for a holder. Such tools kept on the bench are always ready, but must be wiped before being used. Oil cups are all provided with a cover, and to keep the oil clean close the lid immediately after the oiling operation.

The back centre pivot as a rule has no oil sink, and it is usually found to be worn the worst because too much oil has been applied, which is obviously drawn away by the cannon pinion. In such instances it will be safer to oil the pivot and shoulder before placing it in the plate. Fusee pivots are best oiled in the same manner.

Club tooth escape wheels are fitted to modern escape-ments, for one reason they easily retain the oil on the acting surfaces. It is only necessary to apply a little oil on the impulse pallet faces, and on a few of the club teeth. The escapement in motion will then spread the

oil on the acting surfaces.  A little care is required not
to let it run down the roots of the teeth.

The pallets of a wristlet watch are very close to the
cock pallet hole.  This suffers the most with too much
lubrication.  An extra small oiler should be employed,
or apply a little at the shoulder of the pivot before
letting on the cock.  Too much oil here would mean a
hopeless case of regulation.

The impulse, or roller pin has, or should have a
rolling action, with a little or no friction and requires
no oil.  Lever platforms of carriage clocks often display
red dust at the lever notch, and for some unknown
reason they are wrongly constructed.  The pins are often
the wrong shape, the notch left rough and too large for
the pin, giving too much drop.  The best plan to overcome this difficulty is to polish the notch and fit a
larger pin to abolish the friction, and increase  the
impulse.

Oil dries up much quicker if movements are stationary
than if they are kept going, and the smaller the amount
of oil, the quicker it dries up.  Therefore, the smaller
the watch, the more often it requires oiling.  The oil
dries up completely in small fine wristlet watches in
six to twelve months.  They should be thoroughly
cleaned and re-oiled once every year.  It is folly to let
such finely poised mechanism run in dry pinions and
pivots, wearing them out rapidly.  Every machine wants
oiling regularly, and so, most certainly, watches.

## THE  CYLINDER  ESCAPEMENT

The cylinder escapement invented by Thos. Tompion
about 1695.  Watches of the old style were furnished
with an adjustable bar or chariot screwed to the plate

carrying the lower cylinder jewel-hole. The object was to adjust the depth of the escapement. The more modern cylinder watches of the rough class have a chariot similar in shape but without the adjustment, and in the majority of cases the depth is too deep or, shallow to attain reasonable timekeeping.

To alter a chariot to give a sliding adjustment, reduce the diameter of the screw head, and draw file the hole to free the screw threads. Broach the steady pin holes and file the end and nose of the bar if either touch the

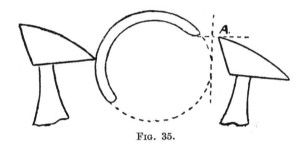

Fig. 35.

plate, so that it is free to move forward or backwards in its sink. All burs should be carefully removed, and by bending the steady pins in the reverse direction, the adjustment of the chariot will be accomplished.

A common fault in cheap class cylinder movement is shown in Fig. 35, the escapement pitched too deep, giving too much "outside drop" with none inside. The drops could be equalized by pitching the escapement shallower. The drop is equal to the distance from the heel of the tooth A to the corner of the exit lip of the cylinder. By pushing the chariot over to bring the cylinder jewel-hole farther from the escape jewel-hole, the drop would be reduced by half.

The escape wheel out of round is another general fault, causing one or two teeth to miss the locking which would result in an inconsistent gaining rate. Pushing the escapement deeper is the general remedy.

A cylinder fitted the wrong size with no " inside " or " outside " shake, is another form of trouble. When the escapement depth is about correct, and the price paid for repair does not permit a new cylinder, the best plan is to stone away the points of all the escape wheel teeth, slanting from the under side of the tooth so as not to alter the angle of impulse.

Comparatively few faults are more perplexing to the average cylinder escapement than the " set ". An escapement that " sets " is unreliable. The watch probably would keep good time for a certain period, then stop, and start off in the pocket, or on the wrist, giving the wearer the impression it requires regulation.

There are many causes for "setting", mostly original, and might be summarized as follows : Escapement too deep ; incline of escape wheel teeth too high, or unequal lengths. No " inside " or " outside " shake, sometimes both. Balance too heavy compared with the force of the mainspring. Loss of motive power in the train usually attributed to bad depths. Rough or worn edges to the cylinder-lips. Cylinder pivots too tight in the holes.

Setting an escapement shallow is accomplished by the chariot. There must be a decided drop both on the inside and out of the cylinder shell. A wheel with the incline of the teeth too high will record itself by " setting " on the plane. Unequal length teeth can be observed by trying the wheel right round. Mark the long teeth with a little red stuff on a peg and stone off the points to equal lengths.

A cylinder watch fitted with a balance too heavy would give many repairers the impression the main-spring was not strong enough. An examination of the interior of the barrel would soon disclose the relative proportion of the spring to the barrel. A worn spring should therefore be replaced by a new one. To fit a spring too strong for the barrel to drive a heavy balance is creating one fault to overcome another. Assuming other depending properties are correct the best plan is to fit a new balance and spring. A light balance when started will almost immediately attain its maximum vibration, while one too heavy will perform the first few vibrations very short, gradually increasing until the full vibration is attained.

A loss of impulse is often attributed to a loss of power in the train through bad depths. (See Correcting Bad Depths.)

No " inside " or " outside " shake is often noticeable when the drops are hardly perceptible, although the cylinder might be the correct size in proportion to the wheel. No inside drop would cause both the point and and heel of a tooth to rub inside the cylinder. With no outside drop the heel of a tooth would rub on the outside of the shell, while the point of the receding tooth would rub on the opposite outside edge. Either would cause the escapement to set. To overcome this difficulty, stone the points of all the teeth from under the point so as not to alter the shape of the incline.

Notice if the balance is true, and free of the stud, index pins, escape cock, and centre wheel—sometimes the latter is out of flat, and when you are examining the escapement the part that is bent down the most is not opposite the balance. If the centre wheel looks too close to the balance to be safe, remove the escape wheel, move the train round ; you will then see if the centre wheel is out of flat and touches the balance. This is a common occurrence : a watch often stops with the balance touching the centre wheel dial up, when the wheel is out of flat.

The balance and escape wheel should be upright. Most cocks will allow a little pushing over to attain this. The escape pinion must have as little end-shake as possible ; when the escape cock is screwed down press a peg slightly in the centre of the cock near the hole, and look at the top pivot with a strong eyeglass ; if you see any slight movement of the pivot through the hole you know it has sufficient shake.

After cleaning the watch and replacing the escapement, get it nicely in beat. Wind the mainspring a few teeth, move the balance round slowly with a peg until the tooth drops on the cylinder, release the peg immediately, then the balance should start. Try the balance each way, and if it fails to start—move the collet round a little in the same direction as you moved the balance when it failed to start.

To regulate a modern watch which has a cylinder escapement is invariably a source of trouble. There are more watches brought in for regulation fitted with this escapement.

The cylinder is a frictional rest escapement, and, therefore, it is important the motive power should be consistent. The vibration of the balance should be two-thirds of a turn ; any increase will cause trouble in regulation. When the vibration is more than two-thirds the usual procedure is to fit a weaker mainspring. The vibration might be lessened by pitching the escapement shallow, or fitting a new escape wheel with a flatter incline to the teeth.

With an escapement of correct dimensions, the cylinder should have the same amount of shake between the point of one tooth and the heel of the next, as a tooth has inside the cylinder. The amount of shake represents the " drop " ; therefore, if the shake outside the cylinder differs from the inside, the drops will be unequal, and this is attributed to a cylinder the wrong size.

" Wheel foul of passage," or bottom of the cylinder is one of the most common faults, and would cause a watch to gain at an inconsistent rate. The cause is often an escape wheel out of true in the flat. Truing the wheel up or down would be a simple remedy. When the escape wheel is running true, hold the movement on its edge to obtain the best light, and move the rim of the balance round slowly with a peg to examine the action of the escapement. It will then be noticed if the rim of the wheel touches the bottom plug, or top of the cylinder passage. In the former case lower the cylinder by shortening the lower pivot and reducing the endshake or raising the escape wheel.

The latter fault requires the alteration in the reversed order, by raising the cylinder or lowering the escape wheel. The former can be raised by filing away the brass setting of the bottom endstone until the stone is flush with the top, or by knocking out the old stone and replacing it by a loose one to rest on the back of the jewel-hole.

To true or alter the height of an escape wheel is accomplished by bending the arms on a lead block with a few light taps from a small round-faced punch. Select a piece of lead about the diameter of a large escape wheel. Shape it out with a hammer to a circular top, and form a bevelled edge to free the escape wheel

teeth. Hammer the bottom part square to form a
shoulder to rest on the vice in the same style as a hollow
stake. Cut a small hole in the top with a graver,
large enough to admit an escape pinion. (See Fig. 36.)
If the escape wheel is foul of the bottom of the cylinder,
mark the arm where the rim touches with a little " red
stuff ". Place the wheel on the lead stake, the pinion
going through the hole, and hold a small round punch
on the arm ; give it a few light taps with a hammer,
moving the punch slightly between each blow. If the
wheel is foul of the top of the passage of the cylinder,
repeat the operation, except, of course, the wheel is
reversed on the stake. The wheel is then placed in
the callipers, and tested for running true.

When any difficulty arises in observing the action
of the escapement, incline the movement in a vertical
position, lead the balance round with a peg, and
immediately a tooth drops move the balance slowly
in the opposite direction. The balance should have a
perceptible movement before a tooth advances. When
there is any doubt about the safety of the locking,
very slowly continue the movement of the balance
when a tooth has dropped, and if the wheel has a slight
recoil the tooth fails to lock, and the chariot requires
pushing nearer the cylinder jewel-hole.

The balance and spring require careful attention.
Try the balance on a poising tool. For a cylinder
wristlet the balance is best left in poise ; in a cylinder
pocket-watch slightly heavier nearest the six o'clock
or farthest away from the pendant. (See Applying
a Flat Balance Spring.)

Many cylinder watches become a source of trouble
to regulate after running about six months. The fault
is usually in the steel, and the continual grinding of the

metal, together with the oil and dust, naturally tells the tale. In such instances clean the escapement.

The cylinder and escape wheel teeth are easily broken by using force when the balance appears to be locked, through the banking-pin getting past the banking. The balance in this instance will only move in one direction. To release it without damage, hold the rim of the balance, and move it back slightly while you move the escape wheel back with a peg to free the corner of the cylinder shell. Then release the balance and escape wheel. The cause of such a lock is either

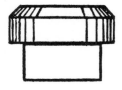 

FIG. 36.

the pin under the cock requires bending nearer the rim of the balance, or the pin in the latter has come out. Sometimes a new cylinder has been fitted with the balance riveted in the wrong place. The quickest plan in this case is to drill a new hole in the rim of the balance for a new pin a little nearer the exit lip of the cylinder. The distance for drilling can be determined by moving the balance round to see the exact place the old pin is to the pin in the cock immediately the wheel locks the cylinder.

**Fitting Cylinder Plugs.**—A tight cylinder plug is a source of trouble at any time. The length of bearing for a top plug affords a tight grip which is often too great for a blow with the cylinder punch to overcome, obviously the punch breaks. In such instances the safest plan is to remove the bottom plug first, reverse the cylinder and use a straight punch, going through the shell of the cylinder with just a little shake.

A very useful cylinder stake can be obtained from any material dealer. The circular top (Fig. 37) has a removable cylinder punch with flat end (Fig. 38 A) to rest the shell in the process of driving in a plug.

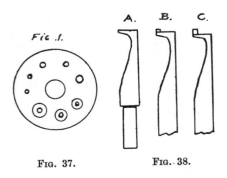

FIG. 37.          FIG. 38.

There are also about five holes and three cone holes, all of various sizes. The latter are intended to start a plug, and the straight holes to rest the projecting part and drive it straight out.

The lower plug is always short and therefore affords little grip for holding the shell. To start a cylinder plug rest the bottom of the shell in a cone hole, hold it upright with a cylinder punch between the thumb and finger of the left hand. A slight tap from a hammer held in the other hand will then start the plug shown in Fig. 39 by a black line. A punch with a short foot, shown at B, will be found best adaptable for starting the plug. One with a longer foot, C, will **drive** it right through a plain hole.

The cylinder is next reversed, and placed in a cone hole. It is now quite clear with the bottom plug removed the tightest will yield to a sharp blow from a straight punch going through the cylinder shell. The old plug will serve as a guide to determine the length beyond the brass spring collet seat.

Cylinder plugs are obtainable from any material dealer, in boxes of assorted sizes, each numbered.

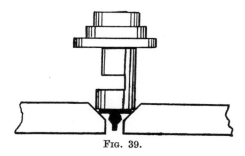

FIG. 39.

Select one to just fit the shell, allowing a little for drive. The back slope and shoulder are usually left a little long. A split chuck will be found best for turning back the slope and shoulder to the gauge of the old plug. Screw the tee rest close to the work and use a sharp pointed graver. To drive in the bottom plug, rest the inside of the lower part of the shell on the end of the flat-ended punch (Fig. 38), place the plug in the shell and drive it home with a small hollow bell shape punch to just fit over the pivot and rest on the cone.

In the case of a broken cylinder the quickest method is the use of a lathe, a split chuck, and a new shell. (See Turning in the Lathe.)

**Fitting a Cylinder Escape Wheel.**—An escape wheel of suitable diameter should be selected.  When the wheel is placed with the centre over the jewel-hole, the heel of a tooth should extend just beyond the centre of the lower cylinder hole.  Try the shake inside and outside the cylinder.  It often happens with the cheap grade watch, a cylinder is too large or too small.  Many watchmakers equalize the drops by altering the depth of the cylinder by means of the chariot.

The centre of the wheel requires softening for opening the hole.  Next mount the wheel on a piece of taper steel wire, held in a very small spirit flame near the wheel until the heat runs up the wire and the centre of the wheel turns blue while you hold your hand round the flame to form a wind shield ; any slight draught will blow the flame on to the wheel and soften it, and a little judgment is required not to let the temper extend beyond the arms of the wheel.  Using oilstone dust on a peg will remove the colour and leave the wheel in its original condition.

A broach, like any cutting tool, requires sharpening, and if the edges are gone extra pressure will be required for the tool to do the same amount of work.

The escape wheel will be found quite easy to broach the hole true by holding it between the thumb and finger.  A four-cornered broach is more adapted for this work.  A wheel is easy to grip and it only requires ordinary ability to judge the amount of force it will stand during the broaching process.  Assuming the broach requires sharpening ; screw it in the pin vice, place it flat on a block and stone one side ; turn the broach over and treat the other sides the same until the edges are sharp.

The old and new wheels should be placed on the

broach ; the former answers the purpose of a guide for the size of the hole. By moving the wheel in the thumb and finger, and the broach in alternate directions, the truth of the wheel is maintained ; let it down as far as the old wheel to be on the safe side. Keep plenty of oil on the broach. Then try the wheel on the pinion ; it should fit on the end by the rivet to allow a little drive.

The wheel should then be mounted on an arbor ; select a weak hair bow and turn back the boss of the wheel until its thickness is slightly less than from the seat to the rivet of the pinion. A very good guide is to measure it from the old wheel. The diameter of the boss will generally require reducing.

The pinion is next placed on a hollow brass stake and drive the wheel home with a hollow punch. The best plan is to try it in the frame with the cylinder before riveting the wheel ; it can then be seen if the height is correct, sometimes a little of the pinion seat requires turning to lower the wheel. Rivet the wheel on the same way as a balance and staff, moving the wheel round with the third finger between each blow of the hammer. Of course it should require a very little riveting and the blows very slight. Give the rivet a few rubs with a small facing tool and a little diamantine to give it a finished appearance.

If the wheel is a little out of flat it may be trued on a piece of lead held in the vice. (See Cylinder Escapement.)

**Pin Pallet Lever Watches.**—The pin pallet escapement is fitted to cheap class watches generally, with brass holes throughout. Although they appear under different names, the principle is the same—the hands being driven from a wheel on the barrel cover instead of a centre wheel turning once in an hour. Anything appertaining to lasting property is entirely ignored.

In many instances the movements are so rough a little discretion is necessary to decide if they are worth repairing. To repair them would necessitate a little time spent on reducing friction at the acting surfaces, which in the majority of cases would account for the watch coming to rest.

Lead the balance round slowly with a peg until a tooth drops on a pallet pin, then try it in the opposite direction to see if the pin falls on the locking corner of the tooth. These wheels are often a little out of round, the safest plan is therefore to try the wheel on every tooth. " Wheel misses locking," is quite a common fault in these escapements, which cause the watch to stop, and is due to worn pallet pins, or an original fault.

Many of these movements have the plate split between the escape wheel and pallet staff holes, with an adjustable screw running through the plate to adjust the depth of the escapement. A slight turn of the screw head is quite a simple matter to make the escapement safe. When there is no adjustment in the plate push the pallet cock over a little. If the pallet pins are worn, replace them. Hold the pallets on a hollow stake in the vice and knock out the pins from the back with a small flat ended punch. File the pins on a piece of needle steel tempered to a light blue, stone and burnish them smooth to just fit the holes almost straight. If left too taper they will appear too large at the acting surfaces, and cause the wheel to have " no inside " or " no outside " shake, and probably stop occasionally, which would give further trouble to locate the fault.

Fig. 40 shows an instance of the escapement too

shallow with the pallet pin A just missed the locking
face of the escape wheel tooth. Part of the rim of the
escape wheel with four teeth is shown black and moving
in the direction of the arrow. The pallet pins are
fixed in two curved arms which form part of the lever.
The safety roller is shown at B. It will be seen by
the crescent in the roller, which has just passed the
line of centres, that the lever has just unlocked the
escape wheel and allowed the tooth at A to drop on
the pallet pin ; but instead of falling on the undercut
or locking face, the impulse face of the tooth has dropped
on the pin, which immediately presses the lever in the

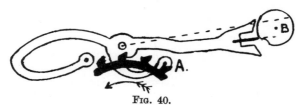

Fig. 40.

opposite direction, and the safety nose of the lever rubs
against the edge of the roller which checks the vibration
of the balance. The vibration of the balance would
fall off in such cases, and probably stop. The dotted
line indicates the centre of the lever when a tooth has
dropped on the other pallet pin. The centre of the
lever must therefore occupy the same angular distance
each side of the line of centres immediately a tooth
has dropped.

The balance staff holes get worn in a very short
time. A worn staff hole will often create a combination of faults which frequently baffles the repairer.
The safety piece foul of the roller edge, the unlocking
piece foul of the wings of the lever, or the lever on the

wrong side of the roller, giving the horologist the impression it has overbanked. This will often happen when the wheel misses locking, and the safety piece is too shallow. With a shallow escapement the safety nose should be pushed in as near to the roller edge as possible, with just a little shake on each side of the lever. If the balance staff holes are wide, it will pay in this class of watch to fit new bouchons.

The escapement in the style of lever shown in the sketch can be made deeper or shallower by bending the curved tail of the lever which holds the entering pallet pin. A little care must be used to determine if the curve is soft enough to permit bending.

The pivots of these watches are usually very rough, and when the vibration of the balance is good, it is a wise policy to leave them.

The motion work of these watches are continually a source of trouble. Customers complain the hands get wrong or drop off. This is particularly noticeable in the larger variety, or " Goliath " pin pallet. The trouble emanates from the cannon pinion being too large in the hole for the stud and the hour wheel too large in the hole for the cannon. With such rough work the wheels obviously get out of gear with each other. A new pipe or bouchon to either wheel and a motion collet is the best way out of the difficulty.

The cause of a minute hand dropping off is because there is insufficient room between the dial and top of the cannon pinion to fit two hands and allow for freedom, although there is three times the space between the top of the cannon and the glass. The most satisfactory method is to fit a new pipe to the cannon pinion to come much higher, also a new pipe to the hour wheel to come well above the dial.

## KEY WINDING WATCHES

**Fusee Watches.**—There is no more troublesome watch to repair than a fusee when the stop-work, fusee chain, barrel holes, and fusee work are badly worn.

Many years ago, manufacturers had a weakness for large escapements with heavy balances. Vibration in these cases was sacrificed for weight of the balance, These badly constructed watches occasionally appear for repair. It would be useless to fit a lighter balance, which would only "set". These movements would have to be reconstructed in order to get a vibration which would be satisfactory for the lever movement of to-day.

In many of the old fusee lever movements, mainsprings have been fitted too strong to overcome the extra friction of worn parts. Such springs fail to give sufficient number of turns for an equable pull from the fusee, there is also a greater strain on the barrel, which might split with the breaking of the spring. The strain on such a chain is excessive and would probably cause a break.

A fusee mainspring, to be correct, should give at least $3\frac{3}{4}$ turns in the barrel. There is no rule regarding the number of teeth for "setting-up". It all depends on the strength of the spring. A four-turn fusee would require three turns of the barrel to drive it, and the amount to set up, assuming the spring to make four turns, would be about half a turn. The safest plan is to test the pull of the mainspring with the adjusting rod. This tool is seldom used by repairers because it is old-fashioned. The statement is quite logical. The fusee watch is probably older than the rod for which it was made, and when the former is accepted for repair the latter is indispensable to attain the best results.

To use an adjusting rod fix the hollow square with adjusting screw on the fusee square, and wind the fusee one turn by means of the rod. The weights are then adjusted until the spring is able to lift the rod from a horizontal position. The rod is then turned for the full number of turns of the fusee, and allowed to run slowly back, each turn being checked by the right hand as it reaches its highest point. The spring should first raise the weight at each turn. A mainspring too strong will show a greater pull at the top turn. The lower turns can be equalled by setting up the spring.

Comparatively few faults cause more trouble than a chain which rides the barrel and ultimately stops. A chain too long will often ride the barrel chain hook. One-sixth of a turn on the barrel when the fusee beak has reached the stop is sufficient, if more, the chain could be shortened. A hole drilled a little higher on the barrel for the chain hook is sometimes necessary when the chain is the correct length.

Worn barrel holes are often the cause of the chain riding the hook, or the balance rim foul of the barrel. This is noticeable in a " spring above " watch with the barrel running out of true. When there is any doubt about it, place the barrel and fusee in the frame with the third wheel removed, and wind the fusee with the slide tongs, letting it run slowly back, to observe the freedom of the balance. A new bottom hole to the barrel will usually put this right.

Worn fusee holes are the cause of many faults. With a fusee running out of upright, the stop work might come into action on the third turn of the fusee, or the great wheel foul the plate or centre wheel. A favourite remedy is to bend the end of the stop work down, but this should only be accomplished assuming other depending properties are correct. The top fusee hole wears in the direction of the barrel and in most instances it is the cause of the trouble. When the great wheel depth is correct with the centre pinion the safest procedure is to fit a new top fusee hole uprighting it from the bottom.

The fusee stop work is a fragile piece of mechanism

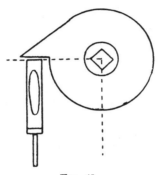

FIG. 41.

and often becomes damaged in cleaning. Many repairers brush the top plate without removing the stop or spring, which is a very risky operation, and often results in the fusee beak catching the stop on the third turn, or missing the contact at the correct place. Remove the spring and examine the stud and stop, the former must be tight in the plate with sufficient freedom in the slot to allow the stop to move freely up and down, without side shake. The face of the latter should form a right angle with the centre of the fusee pivot hole (see Fig. 41). The pin must fit both sides of the stud hole tightly with freedom at the stop hole. It will pay in the end to replace a badly fitted pin.

The back of the fusee beak will sometimes catch on the stop when the watch has run down a turn. This fault is because the stop has got bent and foul of the corner of the sink, or the spring fails to act. The barrel might have too much endshake, bringing the top coil of chain too high and not allowing the chain to release the stop in time.

A new stop piece is occasionally fitted which causes trouble. If left too thick the fusee might catch on the first turn down and would require filing away on the edge nearest the fusee hole. A stop left too long, or short would probably slip off the fusee beak. When there is trouble with the lock, the face of the stop can be filed V shape, so that the beak presses well into the V.

A barrel knocked out of shape at the hook, through the breaking of a mainspring, will often cause the chain to foul the potance or rim cap and stop. The marks from the rubbing of the chain will be seen. Remove the mainspring and a few light taps on the rim will put the barrel in its original shape.

It is a good plan to put the fusee, barrel, centre, third and fourth wheels in the plates by themselves, move them round, try the freedom and endshakes ; a fault will here be detected which may not be noticed when the movement is together.

The centre wheel probably causes more trouble through being foul than any other wheel in the frame, but it is not always the offender in this respect. The centre wheel should be perfectly upright, or there would be trouble with the hands being foul of the dial one side, and too close to the glass the other. Worn pivot holes will also cause the wheel to foul the barrel, fusee, or plate. This will usually show a bright mark at the place of rubbing, and will be a guide for the remedy. When a pivot is worn badly it should be turned and polished, and a new hole uprighted in the mandrel to attain the best results. There are many watchmakers who do not possess a mandrel or lathe, and their only way of uprighting a wheel is to draw over the hole and rebush it. With a little practice this form of procedure will prove fairly accurate.

The faults which cause a chain to " ride " can be traced to a strained or distorted chain through a main-spring being fitted too strong. One badly repaired with the rivets fitted out of upright. Barrel chain hook badly fitted. Chain foul of potance, name bar, or cap, too thick for the fusee threads, or the latter worn and require re-cutting.

The usual procedure is to fix the slide tongs on the fusee square, gripping the former with the palm, centre, third and fourth fingers of the left hand, the thumb and first finger holding the edge of the plate. The motive power is thus arrested while the right hand is free to unscrew the bar and remove the third wheel. The bar is then replaced without risk of damage to the pivots. The mainspring is then wound slowly from the slide tongs, observations being carefully fixed on the working of the chain. Commence with one turn of the fusee, allowing the tongs to run slowly back through the fingers, and increase the number until the spring is fully wound. When the chain is foul of the potance or name bar its traverse will be felt from the slide tongs with a jerky movement and an unequal pull. The cause of any chain trouble will be easily located during its working from the barrel to the fusee, and *vice versa*.

A buckled chain is removed, hammered flat on a stake with a few light taps. Reversing it or changing the hooks will often have the desired effect.

It should run easily into the fusee threads without shake. When the links are faulty or rivets loose, a new piece of the same size is joined in place of that discarded. There are many methods of repairing chains, all correct are on the same principle. On no account soften it or use brass for the rivets. The

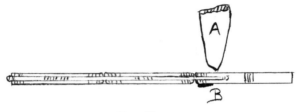

Fig. 42.

chain can be laid on a lead block or hollow stake held in the vice, and the rivet started with a light tap from a sharp pointed punch or a sudden press from a graver (see Fig. 42). When the rivet has started, it forms a projection B to fit into a hole of a hollow stake. A light tap is then required, using a punch which just passes through the hole (see Fig. 43). The stumps of pivot broaches whetted to the required size are useful for this purpose. A tempered needle will be found reliable steel for making the rivet. It is filed slightly taper, and finished with a small oilstone slip. Place the chain on the work board and press the rivet in, the leverage of the pin vice will enable sufficient force to fit the rivet before nipping it off. It is stoned flush with the link each side : two or three light taps with a round-faced hammer will suffice to keep it secure.

It is by no means uncommon to trace the fault to a worn or dirty winding ratchet which fails to grip the clicks. The force exerted by a strong mainspring when the ratchet fails to engage the clicks will find the weakest part in any chain. It is advisable to unpin the fusee. The pin is or should be fitted from the hole nearest the fusee " beak " or stop. Rest the arbor, on a grooved brass or boxwood stake held in the vice,

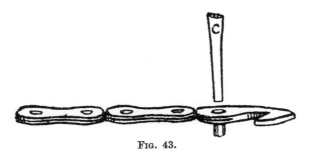

FIG. 43.

and the pin will yield to a blow using a long flat-faced punch the same size as the end of the pin. The condition of the inside of the fusee will then be seen.

A full plate is fitted with a brass ratchet, the latter held to the fusee brass with two small brass pins. Remove the old ratchet by forcing the blade of a penknife under the teeth. The old pins, as a rule, will come out with the ratchet, if not, they can be pulled out or nipped off.

The best plan is to disregard the old ratchet and select a new one to accommodate the clicks. Place the steel maintaining wheel on the board, and select

a wheel with the bottom of the teeth flush with the
point of the clicks.  This can be determined by placing
the ratchet over the central with the maintaining wheel,
shown in Fig. 44, the ratchet marked A.

When either of the clicks are badly worn, the safest
procedure is to replace them.  Rod click steel is made
for this purpose, obtainable at any material dealer.
A click will push out from the rivet hole at the back
of the ratchet wheel.  A pivot is first formed on the
back end of the rod to just fit the hole in the ratchet.

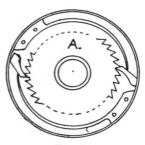

Fig. 44.

A lathe rose-cutter will be found the quickest method
for this work, or it can be filed in a pin-vice or hand-
tongs on the vice.  Hold the steel vertical over the
pivot hole of the wheel to locate the exact place to
form the pivot, allowing sufficient metal beyond to
bank against the steel rim shown in Fig. 44.

The click must move on a perfectly smooth surface,
and any rough marks can be cut away with the side of
a sharp graver.  The click-steel should be filed to an
obtuse point to present to the hole in the rose-cutter.
A perfectly flat shoulder can be obtained by holding
the click-steel firmly on the rest and adjusting the

latter to get it level. Cut the pivot back sufficiently to permit it going through the hole and allow a little rivet.

The pivot is next fitted in the hole of the wheel, a pivot file should be employed to give it a smooth surface, and the back filed away so that it banks against the rim. The point of the click is next shortened to length and cut back to the correct angle, so that a tooth draws the point in and locks. The clicks should

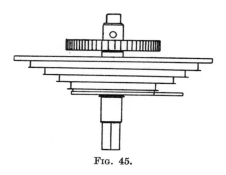

Fig. 45.

alternately come into action, when one is locked on a tooth the other is riding over the incline (see Fig. 44).

Having filed the click to shape, it is next cut from the rod with a nicking file, filed flat on a cork level with the rim, finished with a stone, and a few light taps with a round-faced hammer will suffice for a rivet. Move it forwards and backwards to see if it is perfectly free and remove all burs.

The ratchet is next fitted to the fusee brass. Place it in position on the maintaining wheel to be sure it is the correct size in relation to the clicks (Fig. 44), and make a small dot to denote the side which comes flush with the fusee brass, and thus avoid the chance of mounting it the wrong way. Broach the hole carefully to let the ratchet half-way down the fusee arbor (Fig. 45). Remove it and chamfer the hole at the back to remove the bur, and make two marks with " red-stuff " opposite the old holes on the fusee brass, so that the new holes can be drilled perfectly clear of them.

Place the ratchet in position shown in Fig. 45, with the winding square and pivot in a hole of a hollow stake and the fusee resting flat on the steel stop. Drive the ratchet down tight, flush with the fusee brass, using a hollow punch to fit over the pivot and arbor. Next cut two dots with a sharp graver on the ratchet just clear of the teeth, to mark the position of the pin holes, and drill them through into the fusee brass, the smaller the pins the tighter they will hold. The holes should be about half the distance between the point of one tooth and the next. File pins almost straight on a block, fit them in the holes tight, nip off above surface of ratchet, allowing a little drive.

Place the fusee on a hollow stake as described in driving on the ratchet, and drive the two pins in with a flat-ended punch. It is quite obvious, if the pin holes are drilled small, the pins will have a tighter grip for a small diameter. The top pivot of the fusee is next fitted in a split chuck of the lathe, the surface of the ratchet turned back until it is slightly below the outer edge, and a hollow turned in the centre out to the arbor with a long-pointed graver to free the boss, or centre of the steel wheel. A little care is required not to touch the arbor of the fusee with the graver. When cut to the bottom, the centre will come out in a ring.

**Fitting a Winding Ratchet to Hanging Geneva Barrel.—** To fit a new ratchet is not an uncommon occurrence, but in the case of a solid arbor, or hanging barrel, there is much more fitting and turning, and obviously more time spent on the work. A new ratchet could be fitted to the old arbor, making a sound job and taking a very little longer than a loose ratchet to a three-quarter plate arbor.

The hanging barrel is very simple to remove without the inconvenience of disturbing the other parts. The star wheel stop work is unsuitable as applied to most hanging barrels. Remove the stop work and the problem is solved. Worn barrel holes often cause a star wheel to lock before the required time. The bar hole and ratchet should be examined, a wide hole or loose ratchet generally means great wheel depth, too deep or shallow, barrel foul of centre wheel, bar, plate, or click. These overlooked faults reducing the motive power, frequently account for bad time-keeping in a hanging barrel.

Examine the action of the old wheel and click to ascertain the size of the new one. Place a key on the square, winding the arbor one tooth, and notice if the point of the click drops at the root of the next tooth without shake. If the wheel is the correct size it will serve as a guide for the new one. A ratchet wheel too small is often the cause of a click failing to grip the teeth. The locking face should be set back at a little less than a radial line drawn from the centre of the wheel to the point. Sometimes the face assumes a radial line through wear. The click should be softened, the point filed, undercut, hardened, tempered, and polished.

Screw the cap on to see if the old ratchet is the correct thickness. If the arbor rocks the new ratchet is left thicker. It will be noticed in some movements the

edges of the teeth are so sharp they have cut away
the brass and become loose, and for this reason many
high-class bar movements have the edges bevelled.
The ratchet is then thinned to the required thickness
on a piece of cork or soft wood in the vice, and the hole
opened with a square file until it fits the winding
square.

The barrel arbor is softened, gripped in a split chuck
in the lathe, and the ratchet turned away, leaving a
small shoulder to rest on the barrel bar.   The remainder
of the ratchet is turned to half the thickness down to

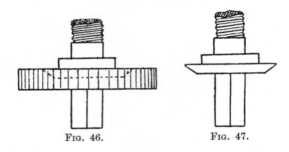

FIG. 46.        FIG. 47.

the extreme diameter of the square. (See Fig. 46,
which shows the arbor.)   The ratchet is turned away
to the dotted line.

The square is filed on the remaining piece of ratchet
the same size as the winding (see Fig. 47). A file with
a fine edge is necessary for this operation so that the
square comes flush up to the shoulder.

The new ratchet is fixed on a step or cement chuck
and a sink turned the same size and thickness as the
shoulder left on the arbor, so that the ratchet fits
down on the square and occupies the same space as
the part of the ratchet turned off the arbor.   The

latter and ratchet are held tight when the cap is screwed down. They are finally hardened, tempered, and polished.

The perplexities of the hanging barrel are not always the cause of a worn ratchet or wide barrel holes. It is remarkable the number of bar movements that stop through worn ratchet sinks, or cap screws overturned. The arbor being supported in only one bearing, requires more attention to keep the barrel vertical and in a rotary motion. This bearing requires freedom without shake, and when allowed to remain loose the error is plus the shake in the barrel holes.

To fit a new hole in the barrel bar is not always an easy performance, the V cut to fit the point of the click being so close to the hole that to rivet a bush in the usual way the hole would burst. It is advisable in such cases to carefully fit the stopping with a short rivet at each end, soften it, and file two or three slight V notches in the hole on the opposite side to the weak place, so that the stopping will have a firm grip with a less amount of hammering, and thus avoid the chance of splitting the hole. A cement chuck will be found the safest to give support when turning away the rivet.

A ratchet with too much shake when the cap is screwed down is usually altered by thinning the cap, unless the latter is flat ; when the top of the bar where the cap rests is turned to reduce the shake. A side click with the point riding above or below the ratchet should be re-steady pinned, or the winding work is liable to fail and the mainspring break.

### CORRECTING BAD DEPTHS

The term depth is the amount of intersection between the teeth of a wheel and pinion gearing together. The depth is measured from the distance between the centres of the two pivot holes of the driver and follower, and an imaginary line from these points is called the line of centres.

The question of the depth of wheels and pinions depend on the condition of the gearing. The object of pitching a depth is, as far as possible, to get the smallest amount of friction. Theoretically there should be no friction, simply a rolling action. The action should take place on or after the line of centres.

As a rule, in horological mechanism, the wheels are drivers and the pinions followers. One of the greatest troubles existing is the inaccurate size of the driver and follower, which means a bad depth and consequently an occasional stop. Engaging friction is the action taking place before the line of centres. With low numbered pinions we attain more engaging friction, but they have the advantage of more shake, and therefore not so sensitive to stop with dirt.

The majority of wheel depths can be examined by observation. When the lead is not visible, press lightly on the top pinion pivot with the point of a pegwood, while the other hand leads the wheel round gently by means of a pegwood cut to a wedge shape. Try the different freedoms in each position of a tooth, and notice if the lead takes place smoothly without scraping or rattling. It is possible where the jewel-holes are large or flat to look through with an eye-glass and observe the action of the teeth, and leaves with the plate resting on the bench or inclined for the light to be reflected on the jewel-hole. Many watches have sight-holes or openings drilled in the plate, to enable the horologist to examine the depth. It is quite obvious a large or worn hole, while not always stopping the watch, will materially effect the motive power by causing unnecessary friction, which means a source of trouble in timing. It is advisable in all cases where there is a doubt about a depth to place the wheel and pinion in the depth tool.

It frequently happens the lead is invisible in the plates. In such cases the depth tool will afford a better idea of the gearing. By verifying a depth in the tool, the workman with a little practice will become quite capable of discerning a depth with the touch of two pieces of pegwood, while the driver and follower are in the plates.

High numbered pinions give a better facility for attaining the lead on the line of centres, therefore a better rolling action, and with high-class watches they are found to give the best results. There should be sufficient freedom in the spaces, the wider the spaces the weaker the tooth. A good proportion for a pinion of twelve, is two-fifths. Many watchmakers have an objection to high numbered pinions, because they are too weak at the root, but the fault is usually the leaves are cut too long. They should be less than half the radius of the pinion.

The lower the number of pinion the more the engaging friction, assuming other depending properties are equal. Unnecessary friction or loss of motive power is frequently in evidence with a pinion too large, or too small, in the form of " catching ", when the point of a tooth retards a leaf of the pinion, or the back of a tooth rubs a pinion leaf. The latter fault is perhaps the most common, and easily overcome by thinning, but *not* shortening the wheel teeth in a " rounding-up tool ". The term " catching " must not be confused with engaging friction, both might signify wasted energy, the former is a fault, the latter contact before the line of centres. Catching not only means a waste of energy, but unnecessary wear on the acting surfaces which is seldom consistent, and hopeless to get good time-keeping with such a fault.

A watch that stops through a bad depth is best located by tracing the loss of power from the escape wheel. A worm hole, or one bushed out of upright is often the cause of the fault. A wheel out of round, or too deep, should be topped. The best plan is to try the escape pinion and fourth wheel separately in the frame. Hold the escape wheel with a peg, lead the fourth wheel round slowly, and try the shake ; a shallow depth will probably make a buzzing noise. Then try the fourth pinion and third wheel in the same way. When there is any doubt about a depth, place the wheel and pinion in the depth tool, and compare the latter with the distance between the holes in the plate. A pinion too large can be corrected by pitching the depth deeper, or one too small by pitching it shallower.

The motion work affords a good example of pinions employed as drivers. The shape of the wheel teeth is not such an important factor as there is practically no resistance. Although many cannon pinions are made with semicircular addenda, a better depth would be obtained under their theoretical principle—the cycloidal addenda with semicircular for the wheel teeth. Many causes of stopping in a keyless watch can be traced to bad depths in the motion work. When the set arbor is out of round, and it is found necessary to tighten it so that the hands will carry on the loose side, the minute wheel will fail with setting hands on the tight side if the depth is shallow. A larger minute wheel or new set arbor is the best way to overcome the difficulty.

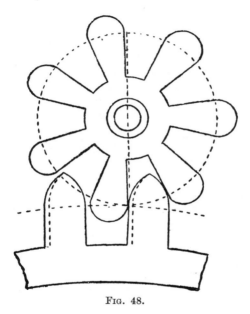

FIG. 48.

The relative sizes between the driver and follower are proportionate to the number of teeth. We will assume a wheel of 70 teeth drives a pinion of 7. The proportion is therefore 10 to 1. The distance between the centre of the arbors is divided into eleven equal parts, ten of these are taken as radius of the driver, and one part of the radius of the follower, which makes ten rotations to one of the driver. These circles, which would just touch and represent the acting surfaces if they were rollers, are called the pitch circles. The acting part of most wheel teeth is beyond the pitch circle, while the acting part of the pinion is within the same. It is therefore quite obvious a wheel and pinion gearing, together to be the same relative proportions should measure the same distance from tooth to space along ts pitch circle. Although the pitch of a pinion might be correct for the wheel, the space is often much greater than the tooth.

Fig. 48 shows a general fault with the pinion leaves too thick for the teeth. There should be shake at every point. No advantage would be gained by pitching such a depth shallow. The pitch of the pinion is correct for the wheel; the fault lies in the thickness of the teeth. The pitch circles are dotted. Thinning the wheel teeth as shown by the dots would give sufficient shake to attain a sound depth.

The part of the tooth beyond the pitch circle is called the addenda, which should be so formed to give, as far as possible a rolling action when in contact with the follower. This form is, or should be, an epicycloid, a curve generated by rolling one circle on another. The leaves of high-numbered pinions are frequently made with semicircular addenda, when employed as followers, but with low numbers, where the action takes place before the line of centres, the epicycloidal form is adapted to ensure a safer depth. To allow of sufficient shake the leaves of the pinion are less in width than the spaces.

To draw an epicycloid cut the sizes in proportion in cardboard and place them on a sheet of paper. A point fixed on the circumference of the rolling circle will describe the curve, which is employed as the acting part of the wheel tooth.

When a pinion is not the correct size it is usual to place it in the depth tool with the driver to ascertain if it is possible to obtain a sound depth. A pinion a little large will frequently pitch correctly on the deep side, that is, the tooth pushes or rolls the leaf at a greater distance. Try the tooth at every position, there must always be a slight freedom between the leaves. If the inaccuracy is great it will pay to replace it. A pinion too small will record itself by a rubbing roughness, and a series of a slight drop, which means extra friction and wear on the pinion. It is advisable to replace a pinion too small, unless the depth can be pitched sufficiently shallow to improve it. Teeth too wide, giving an insufficient freedom of the depth is not uncommon, and a source of trouble, stopping with a slight particle of grit. A cut with the tool taking most away at the roots would cure this fault.

Assuming it is necessary to re-pitch the third and fourth depth—that is of course the third wheel and fourth pinion, broach the fourth holes, and stop them with solid brass wire. Place the wheel and pinion in the depth tool and adjust the screw to the correct depth. Remove the wheel and pinion, hold the tool perfectly upright with the point of one runner resting in the third wheel hole, and for this purpose slacken the screw of one runner. Then make a circular scratch with the point of the other runner across the fourth hole stopping. It is now quite obvious any point on the circular scratch will give a correct third and fourth depth, assuming the tool is true and accuracy is maintained with the rest of the work. It is then necessary to place the escape pinion and fourth wheel in the tool and adjust the depth, and mark it off on the plate in the same way, resting the point of the runner in the escape wheel hole, and making a scratch on the plate to cross the one already made. At the point of intersection, make a dot with a sharp marking tool or the point of a graver. Then carefully drill the hole straight.

The hole is next opened to fit the pivot, the plate fixed in the mandrel head, and the hole pegged true, the top plate screwed on, then catch the centre with the point of a sharp graver, and drill it with a drill less in diameter than the pivot.

A rounding-up tool is a great asset to a repairer, and with the rough class of work on the market of to-day, the possession of this tool renders the workman master of any depth difficulty. About 25 per cent of trouble in cheap grade watches comes from badly sized, or roughly cut wheels. The operator is not only able to top any wheel too deep, but a new wheel a shade larger can be reduced to the correct size, which would be useless without the tool.

Why do brass teeth cut a steel pinion ? is a question often asked. Because the wheel teeth, with continual grinding, charged with dirt, has a grinding effect on the pinion.

Precisely the same rule applies to the brass hole and steel pivot, the softer metal charged with grit and oil cuts the steel. When a pinion is badly cut and a sound depth seems hopeless, the best plan is to shift the wheel to run in a new part of the pinion or replace with a new one. A wheel and pinion depth too shallow near the escapement is liable to stop, and start off with a slight shake. When fitted with brass holes the depth can be corrected by drawing over the hole.

Escape pinions of six are now employed in nearly all wristlet watches. There is the disadvantage of the action taking place before the line of centres, but they have an advantage of more shake and consequently not so sensitive to stop with dirt.

## ENGLISH LEVER ESCAPEMENT

The Lever escapement, invented by Thomas Mudge about 1760. Later, was detached with a crank roller and has since been improved to its present form.

Many old movements have badly constructed escapements. It is impossible in such cases to get sufficient motive power to attain a vibration large enough to give good results.

The following is a good method of examining a full plate escapement. Try all the endshakes and make a note of any holes that are worn. Imperceptible endshake of the balance staff is unsafe. It will often cause a falling in the vibration when the case is shut.

Hold the movement in the left hand resting the edge on the board so that the action of the escapement can be seen between the plates, place the first finger on the rim of the balance, while a peg is pressed against the fourth wheel teeth to give extra power, and move the balance slowly until the tooth drops, and notice how far the tail of the lever is from the banking pin. This distance is called "run". When the tooth drops the roller pin should be leaving the notch. Try the shake of the tail to see if the guard pin is free of the edge of the roller. When the lever has reached the banking pin, move it away with the peg and notice if the tooth draws the lever over to the

banking pin. Repeat the operation with the lever
on the other side. If it is free to move a good
distance from the banking pin with the peg, the guard
or lever pin is too shallow, and should be bent upright,
or slightly nearer the roller.

The next test is to move the balance until a tooth
drops as previously described, pressing the fourth
wheel teeth slightly at the same time with a peg.
Immediately a tooth drops, release the balance, if

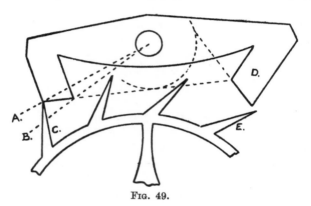

Fig. 49.

the tooth misses locking the balance will rush backwards. Try the balance both ways and every tooth
of the escape wheel. A wheel that misses locking is
not safe, the falling off of the vibration would probably
cause a stop. Escape wheel "misses locking" is
one of the most common faults. The cause is usually
the pivot holes or teeth of the wheel being worn, which
obviously gives a shallow depth with the pallets.

Fig. 49 shows a pair of pallets with 9 degrees of
impulse, which is the angle measured from the dotted
lines AB.

The tooth C has just dropped on the corner of the impulse face. Instead of drawing the pallet in, the tooth would push it out and bring the safety or guard pin against the edge of the roller. The vibration of the balance would fall off and if the guard pin was shallow, the balance would probably stop. The drop is shown from the corner of the exit pallet D to the tip of the tooth E. When the escape wheel holes are brass and worn, new ones should be fitted, or the depth

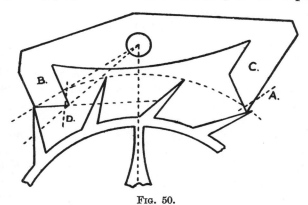

FIG. 50.

re-pitched. If the pallet holes are brass with escape jewelled, the former can be broached towards the escape wheel and the holes re-pushed. In the case of escapement fully jewelled, the safest plan is to fit a new wheel.

Move the balance round as previously described, and immediately a tooth drops, move the balance *slightly in the opposite direction* and try the shake of the escape wheel with a peg. Repeat this operation on the other pallet. It is just before a tooth drops off the locking corner the wheel may bind between the pallets (see Fig. 50). This is called "no outside shake". If the escape wheel is out of round, one fitted with teeth more radial would get over the difficulty, but the general rule is to grind a piece off the corner of the pallet, which is indicated by a dotted line A.

If there is "no inside shake", that is the back of a tooth binding on the inside of the entering pallet B. When a tooth is about to leave the locking face of the pallet C, grind the corner of the pallet B in the same manner shown by the dotted line D. When there is no inside, or outside shake, little ruts are generally worn on the *backs* of some of the escape wheel teeth.

The next step is to examine the action of the lever and roller. The impulse pin should have just perceptible shake in the notch, this can be tested with a peg on the lever, when the latter is mid-way between the banking pins. The balance arc is the angle the roller pin describes while engaging the lever notch measured from the balance staff centre, and is equal to the locking plus impulse and run. It is understood to mean the portion of the vibration of the balance during which period it is in contact with the escapement.

"Run" is needed only to get the guard pin safely away from the roller edge. Unnecessary run is a common fault and a loss to vibration, as the balance obviously on its return journey has to overcome the resistance of the tooth drawing the pallet and lever to the banking. The amount of run, plus locking is, therefore, energy utilized from the balance before the ruby pin receives impulse.

In a single roller escapement the difficulty is generally to get the guard pin deep enough to be safe, especially if the set arbor is out of round and has to be on the tight side in order for the hands to carry. If the guard pin is loose or rough, fit a new one. To fit a guard pin, file a piece of pin-wire on the filing block and burnish it, push it through the hole in the lever, make two marks on the pin with a sharp knife, one slightly below the lever, the other to represent the end of the pin. Place the pin on the block, hold the edge of the knife on the top mark while you twist the wire to cut a circle, and break off the waste piece. Next groove the other mark in the same way, give the pin a touch with a burnisher to rub down the rough marks, push it into the hole in the lever, and break it off.

A rough or rusty roller edge will sometimes cause trouble. To polish the edge, mount the roller on an arbor in the turns and adjust the front runner so that the top comes in a line with the edge of the roller to form a rest for the polisher.

Too much run is sometimes found when the ruby pin is still in the notch after the escape wheel has dropped, assuming the pin is upright it is usual to shorten the notch, or soften the shellac and push the roller pin back, the latter procedure is the safest, assuming the alteration desired is small.

The roller pin is sometimes found to be in the notch after the tooth has dropped *on one side only*, and left the notch too soon on the other. The lever in this case would be " out of angle ", that is, it would not form the same angle on each side from the line of centres immediately the tooth has dropped.

Place a wedge of cork between the tail of the lever and plate. Move the balance round both ways until the pin enters and leaves the notch. This test will show the exact amount of contact. If a tooth fails to unlock on one side, but the lever is moved over

towards the banking on the other, it is " out of angle ".
In such an instance push out the steady pins and move
the lever slightly in the direction it requires for the
tooth to unlock (the pallet staff will keep them in
position), then grip the lever and pallets with a pair
of brass-nosed pliers or sliding tongs, slightly broach
the holes and fit new pins. The run could then be
reduced by closing the banking pins, which would
give a better vibration.

The line of centres is an imaginary straight line
drawn from the pallet staff to the balance staff centres.
A lever and roller of 3 to 1 is the distance between the
line of centres divided into four ; one-fourth is taken
as radius, and a circle struck from the balance staff
centre, on which is planted the centre of the roller pin.
This is a very good proportion and one generally
adopted.

A single roller with low angle pallets is much favoured
for close timekeeping on account of the greater detach-
ment. But with a small balance arc there is obviously
a smaller intersection for the guard pin, and for this
reason it is sometimes very difficult to get a sound
safety action. All the advantages are attained with
low angle pallets when they are fitted to a double-
roller escapement. Pallets of 11 and 12 degrees are
often fitted with round ruby pins. The pin, of course,
does not intersect the notch at its greatest diameter,
unless a large balance arc is used in order to get a proper
intersection of the notch with an unnecessary amount
of run, and for this reason round roller pins are unsatisfactory except for very high angle pallets with a lever
and roller of about $3\frac{1}{2}$ to 1.

A round ruby or impulse pin often rubs on the wing
of the lever before entering the notch, causing a falling

off in the vibration in a certain position.   A new pallet hole would overcome this difficulty, but it is preferable to flatten the ruby pin.

The majority of round roller pins are glass or garnate, and are easy to cut under ordinary conditions.   To flatten a pin, soften the shellac and remove it.   Heat a piece of rod brass until shellac melts on one end, then press the rod firmly on the pin, and grind it on a fine emery wheel until one-third of the diameter is reduced.   An emery buff would answer the purpose.

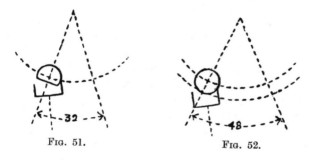

Fig. 51.                Fig. 52.

Next polish the flat with diamantine and a soft metal polisher.

A rough or worn notch is often traced, causing a bad vibration.   The pin should have a rolling action with a little or no friction.   To polish a notch, hold the lever in the thumb and finger while the notch is resting on a piece of soft wood.   File a polisher to pass freely in the notch, and grind it smooth with oilstone dust.   A little care is required to prevent the polisher binding, which might result in a crack at the weakest part.   Diamantine, or a burnisher would give the required finish.

Fig. 51 shows a flatted pin just entering the notch, with a balance arc of 32 degrees minus run.

Fig. 52 shows a round pin with a similar proportion escapement requiring a balance arc of 48 degrees necessary to get an intersection of the notch at the greatest diameter of the pin. It is therefore a disadvantage to use round pins with low angle pallets, and quite obvious that to get the pin safely out of the notch immediately the tooth drops, an intersection of less than the diameter of the pin would be obtained.

Too much shake in the notch means loss of impulse. Move the balance round until the centre of the lever is in a line with the balance staff, and try the shake of the tail which should be just perceptible, if more, fit a larger pin. When the hole in the roller will not permit this, and is too hard for a broach to cut it, file a piece of steel taper, to pass freely through the hole, and grind it with oilstone dust.

To fix a roller pin is a simple operation. File a piece of steel wire taper about 3 or 4 inches long to fit the staff hole in the roller, fasten it in a handle, or a piece of pegwood would answer the purpose, and keep it for future occasions. Clean the roller and pin in petrol. The roller is then mounted on the wire described, with the pin adjusted into position, and a small piece of shellac about half its size resting against it. Hold the part of the wire between the handle and roller in a small spirit flame until the wire conducts the heat to the shellac. As soon as it melts move the pin slightly to bring the shellac into the hole. Flaked shellac warmed and rolled into a stick will be found reliable.

There are several methods for removing rollers. A pair of brass-nosed pliers is generally employed, but it is a dangerous tool unless used by an expert.

It is very easy to slip off the edge of the roller if it happens to be tight. The screw remover is very effective. The safest, home-made tool is shown in Fig. 53 which is the actual size. The writer has had this tool in use for many years, and the tightest roller always yields to a blow from the hammer.

To make a table tool roller extractor, select a piece of flat steel about one-sixteenth of an inch thick, drill a small hole in the centre, and four holes near each corner for the feet. Turn a sink in the centre about three-quarters of the distance through the metal large enough to take

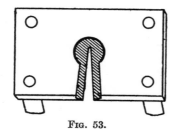

Fig. 53.

a large roller and file a taper slot to the edge to free a balance staff. The large slot is then filed level with the sink, and the edges of the smaller slot to a knife edge, so that the staff can be forced in position when the roller is flush with the flange. Turn four good stout feet about three-eighths inch long, and rivet them to the table. The small slot should terminate beyond the centre of the sink to form a resting-place for the small roller of a wristlet.

To extract the roller, slide the staff along the slot with the balance under the table, hold a hollow punch upright, resting on the cone of the pivot, and give the punch a sharp blow.

It occasionally happens the lever is split, or has been badly repaired, and in such instances a new one is necessary. Before proceeding to make a new lever we must satisfy ourselves that the roller is correct. If the roller pin hole has been broached to such an extent it is flush with, or burst through the crescent, or the edge stoned close to the pin hole allowing insufficient depth for the guard pin it would be useless. To fit a lever to such a roller would be time wasted.

If the lever is damaged it will serve as a guide to determine the guard pin and notch holes. Assuming

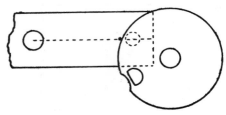

Fig. 54.

there is no accurate lever to work from, select a piece of thin flat steel a trifle thicker than the finished article. Escapement makers use strips made to the required dimensions, obtainable from any material dealer. When the steel is urgently needed, cut a strip off an old French clock mainspring. This steel is always reliable.

Scratch a line down the centre of the steel, drill a hole in the centre and broach it until it fits the pallet arbor. Place it in the frame together with the other parts of the escapement, adjust it for angle, and mark the guard pin hole on the line just free of the roller edge when a tooth has dropped (see Fig. 54). The lever must be pressed tightly in angle on the staff, and before drilling the hole be certain the dot is free of the roller edge on both sides.

Another good plan is to measure the distance from the lower staff jewel-hole, to the pallet hole in the depth tool, mark the distance on a strip of brass and scratch a line between the centres, remove the roller, measure the distance from the centre to the middle of the crescent in the depth tool and mark it on the strip of brass. This will give the distance from the pallet staff centre to the centre of the crescent. Mark it off on the lever with the depth tool and drill the guard pin hole very small. A hole for the notch a shade smaller than the impulse pin is drilled on the centre line free of the guard pin hole.

A little care is next required in filing the notch and wings. File the latter so that the corners are nearly level with the top of the notch hole. The easiest plan is to rest the edge of the lever on a piece of soft wood in the vice and file the hole square with a notch file until the roller pin fits without shake. Escapement makers cut the wings and notch with a circular mill cutter, the nose is the shape of the notch, and the sides cut back at an angle to form the wings. Two or three levers are clamped together and cut at one time. The sides are curved back and front, which are also milled in the same manner.

The lever is next fixed on the pallet staff and placed in the depth tool with the roller, adjusting the tool to the distance between the balance and pallet jewel-holes. It is then possible to judge how much requires filing off the wings so that the pin passes freely in and out of the notch. The runner receiving the pallet arbor will, of course, come inside of the balance. Unless this is observed it will press on the rim when the tool is closed to attain the depth.

The escapement is next placed in the frame with the fourth wheel and the lever adjusted for angle. Move the balance round in alternate directions, with the first finger of the left hand and apply power on the fourth wheel teeth with a peg. Immediately a tooth drops on each pallet the roller pin should be leaving the notch. A wedge of cork will be found best for this test as previously described. If the teeth drop on only one pallet move the lever over until the teeth drop on both.

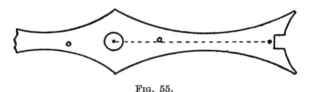

Fig. 55.

When the lever is correct for angle and depth, drill the steady pin holes. They can be marked with a drill through the holes in the pallets. The shape of the lever is quite a matter of fancy, the coffin shape and cheese cutter mark different periods ; curved front and back is now most generally used. This pattern is shown in Fig. 55, and is quite simple to file true with a crossing-out file. There is no theoretical length for the tail, it is usually made about the distance from the pallet hole to the guard pin hole, and then shortened with the pallets and lever on the arbor, until they are in poise.

It is then removed and placed on a piece of soft wood in the vice, and filed on both sides to thickness.

If there is any difficulty with the lever gripping, drive two or three small brass pins in the wood for the lever to rest against. A large smooth file will be found best for the thinning operation.

The lever is then hardened and tempered to a dark blue. The notch and wings are polished first. Swing tools are often employed for this work, but are not necessary for repairing. Rest the lever on its edge on a piece of soft wood in the vice. Select a soft steel polisher, and oilstone dust the notch, giving the lever a rolling motion to attain a rounded surface. Then finish with a little diamantine.

The top and bottom of the lever is polished on a piece of soft wood. Grind out the file marks with a piece of plate glass, a soft steel polisher, or bell metal block charged with oilstone dust mixed with oil. Cut the wood clean to attain a new surface, and finish with bell metal, or zinc and diamantine. To polish without scratches, use a brisk circular motion. Cleanliness is the main feature. File the polisher clean with a smooth file before applying more diamantine. (See Polishing.)

**To make a new roller** is a more simple matter, the old one is, as a rule, a guide. When the pin hole is broken through the crescent, the outer diameter or edge can be measured in a gauge. If, however, the roller is lost, drill a small hole in a piece of rod steel to nearly fit the balance staff and turn it off in the lathe.

Broach the hole to fit the staff tightly, then mount the roller on an arbor, and turn the face and back true. The edge is next turned free of the guard pin when the lever is over to the banking pin. To test this fit the roller on the staff and place it in the frame with the cock screwed on. When the roller is nearly small enough the guard pin will bind on the edge.  It is then turned until the pin has a little shake.

The ruby pin hole is next drilled.  Measure the distance from the pallet staff hole to the balance staff hole in a depth tool.  Scratch a straight line on a strip of brass and mark the measurement from the tool with the male centres (making two curves).  Make two dots at the intersections of the straight line.  Then measure with the tool the distance from the centre of the pallet staff to the bottom of the lever notch and mark it off from the dot on the centre line.  The distance is then taken with the depth tool from the balance staff hole on the brass to nearly the bottom of the notch (which was the last mark made) and mark it off on the roller from the centre hole.  This will give the outside edge (nearest to the crescent) of the ruby pin hole.  Select a drill that will fit the lever notch with a little shake, and make a centre on the roller half the diameter of the drill nearer the centre of the roller than the scratch.

Broach the hole upright.  Harden and temper it to a dark blue.  The roller is mounted on an arbor, the edge polished and then the crescent cut.

Select a piece of round steel wire about one-third the diameter of the roller to grind the crescent.  A stud polishing tool would be suitable to hold the roller.  Drill a hole in a small piece of brass so that the steel wire enters freely, screw the roller in the clamp of the stud tool with the piece of brass so that the hole is free of the roller edge.  Place the wire in the hole, holding it perfectly at right angles with the edge of the roller, and make a dot at the other side of the tool close to the wire.  A hole is then drilled and a long-headed screw fitted to steady the wire.  The latter is then charged with oilstone dust and moved with a forward and backward motion until the crescent is cut.

The crescent is polished in the same manner with diamantine, and the face of the roller on a metal block.

**New Pallets.**—To fit pallets send the escape wheel to a material dealer for size. To test broach the hole until it fits the pallet staff arbor, place it in the depth tool with the wheel, try the locking, the in, and outside shake. A pair of pallets having been obtained it does not follow the escape wheel will be suitable, as a new one is generally supplied with them and in most instances advisable to use this wheel.

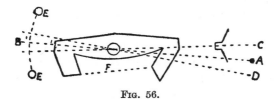

FIG. 56.

Place the pallets on the arbor with the lever and adjust them in the frame for angle. When the tooth drops on each pallet the lever should be the same relative angle on each side of the line of centres (see Fig. 56). A is the balance staff jewel-hole, B the line of centres, C the centre of the lever when a tooth has dropped on the entering pallet, D the centre of the lever when a tooth has dropped on the exit pallet, and E the banking pins. Assuming the banking pins are correctly placed, would give the same amount of run to each pin. Hold a straight edge to come in a line with the balance and pallet jewel-holes, then measure the distance from each banking pin, which should coincide. If they are unequal a new banking pin

hole should be drilled. The run should be sufficient
to give clearance between the safety pin and roller
when the tooth has dropped. When there is too much
run to the banking the greater will be the resistance
to the unlocking and a poor vibration can often be
improved by reducing the run.

Low angle pallets are employed for three-quarter
plate and better class escapements. A straight edge
placed on the impulse face of a pair of 10 degree would
touch the locking corner of the exit pallet, assuming
the angle of impulse to be 9 degrees.

Having adjusted for angle, we hold them in a pair
of brass nosed pliers, together with the lever and select
a drill which will pass freely through the steady pin
holes of the lever and drill through the pallets. Broach
the holes and fit two burnished pins rounded off at
both ends. Escapement makers use swing tools for
polishing the edges of levers, rollers, and the belly of
pallets. The time saved by using such tools is only
a consideration in the case of quantity. The repairer
who has only an occasional pair to fit will find resting
them on a piece of soft wood quite simple to polish.

**Tool for Polishing Pallets.**—Watch pallets making
and stone polishing is a trade in itself. When English
pallet stones are badly worn or chipped the best plan
is to send them to a pallet maker, together with the
escape wheel and frame.

The first consideration is the condition of the escapement. Stones slightly worn or rutted by the wheel
teeth will allow polishing without alteration to the
pallet depth. This operation can usually be
accomplished in a pair of brass-nosed pliers, a polisher,
and diamantine.

The principle of adjusting the English lever escapement is much the same as the Swiss. To polish the ruts from the acting faces of English pallets, it is necessary to remove the pallet staff and knock out the steady pins to separate the lever. A clamp for holding the pallets is sometimes used, but they can be ground quite easily with mixed oilstone dust, and a metal

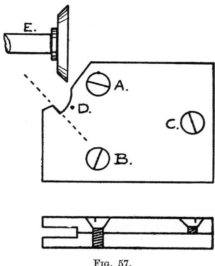

FIG. 57.

polisher, held tightly in a pair of brass-nosed slide tongues, or pliers, then finished with diamantine.

Fig. 57 shows a home-made clamp for holding a pair of English pallets while grinding the wear marks out in a lathe. Select two pieces of sheet brass about $\frac{1}{16}$ to $\frac{1}{8}$ in. thick. File them flat and place them together. Drill the plates and fit two chamfer-headed screws to hold them, shown at A and B. The bottom plate being tapped and the top receives the screw heads. A third screw, shown at C, is only tapped in the top plate ; the end of the screw is intended to press on the bottom plate to keep them parallel. File away one corner of the plates, then file a notch, with the side about the same angle as the locking face of an exit pallet shown by the dotted line. The locking face of the exit pallet to be ground should project slightly beyond this line to meet the face of the lap. A groove is then filed on the inside of each piece of brass, the space to be slightly less than the thickness of a pair of pallets. A hole is drilled for a pin to go through the pallet hole at D to keep the pallets from moving. A polishing lap, E, to screw in the chuck of the lathe is cut back at the same angle as the dotted line so that it comes flush on the locking face of the exit pallet. The pallets are then adjusted with the face in position, pinned through the hole D and screwed down. The clamp is then fixed in the slide rest and adjusted so that the face of the lap will come parallel with the face of the pallet to be ground and polished.

**Fitting an Escape Wheel.**—A lost wheel and pinion is only one of many reasons for fitting a new escape wheel to an English watch. " Wheel misses locking " is perhaps the most common, and with movements of jewelled escape holes there is no alternative.

When the escapement is run in brass holes it is often possible to draw-broach a worn hole over and so set the escapement deeper, assuming the wheel is the correct size and teeth the right angle for the pallets.

In the absence of a wheel gauge, a set of lathe step chucks will be found convenient for gauging a wheel from stock. As the steps in each chuck are different sizes, the one nearest approaching the old wheel should be taken as a guide to determine the required size. With a little practice accuracy will be attained in selecting a wheel a shade larger than one which just failed to lock.

When opening the hole in the wheel to fit the collet, place the old one on a sharp-cutting broach as a guide and broach the new wheel, turning it round alternately to see if it is flat. When it is broached to meet the old wheel try it on the collet.

The inertia of the escape wheel plays an important part in the timekeeping of a watch. The wheel should therefore be as light as possible. A heavy one is the original fault found in badly-constructed escapements.

Rest the teeth of the escape wheel on a cork held in the vice, holding the opposite teeth in a vertical position by the finger. File the crossings with a smooth escape crossing-out file, leaving the arms adjoining the rim the same thickness as the latter, and finish the crossings with a peg charged with oilstone dust. Cut the peg the same shape as the file to reach the corners, and move the peg in a circular direction until the file marks are removed. Clean the wheel in petrol and finish the crossings with a small half-round burnisher.

The wheel is reduced to thickness on a wide flat blue stone. The latter should have a perfectly even surface, which may be obtained by rubbing it on a larger stone. The wheel is mounted on a piece of flat cork held in the vice. The stone is then charged with oil or water and rubbed with a circular motion over the wheel. Another good plan is to place the wheel flat on the stone and rub it with the finger in a circular motion, using a good supply of oil and moving round alternately and reversing the sides to obtain a flat surface. It is then carefully cleaned with bread kneaded with oil, and washed in petrol ready for polishing.

There is more art in polishing brass than one would imagine. Many well-known authorities have their favourite combination of metal and polish, but this is simply a matter of fancy. Tin or zinc blocks are best charged with diamantine or " red stuff ". The polisher in all cases must be softer material than the work to be polished. To obtain a smooth surface free from scratches, the block must be frequently filed or scraped to keep a clean and flat surface. Cleanliness is of vital importance during the whole operation. Polishing material should be kept covered when not in use. The rest is practice.

There are many methods of polishing an escape wheel, and the writer finds the quickest is the easiest. It is quite palpable the old style of fixing the wheel to a block with resin or shellac, which occupies extra time, is quite unnecessary. Place the wheel on a clean cork held in the vice and cut away at an angle round the cork so that the flat surface is the same size as the wheel. Rest the block, charged with diamantine or " red stuff ", flat on the wheel, and rub briskly with a circular motion. Clean the wheel and scrape the block before applying more polishing material, and re-cut the surface of the cork for the seat of the wheel. On no consideration use two kinds of polish on the same block without filing the surface clean. When the wheel is free from scratches, clean it in petrol and burnish it with a smooth burnisher rubbed on a board with " red stuff ", and cleaned in a piece of tissue paper. The wheel is reversed, and the other side treated in the same manner. It is finally pressed on the brass collet, a hollow turned in the form of a rivet, and the wheel rubbed on. The rubber can be formed on the end of a small burnisher with a half-round end. Rest the rubber on a tee rest with the point over the rivet as the lathe runs, lubricating the tool with oil.

## THE DUPLEX ESCAPEMENT

The Duplex escapement was invented about 1770—credited to Dutertre, an ingenious French watchmaker, and was improved to its present condition by other French horologists. It derived its name from the fact that the escape wheel has twc sets of teeth. One set press on the roller of the balance staff, and so lock the wheel, the other being cut vertical with the rim of the wheel to give impulse to the balance by falling on the pallet.

Although the Duplex escapement is a French invention, it did not become popular in that country, but met with favour among English watchmakers.

The best of the Duplex much resembles the Chronometer escapement from the fact that it receives impulse at every alternate vibration, but the balance of the former is never detached—the locking teeth resting on the ruby roller during its excursion in both directions.

A slotted ruby roller is fitted on the arbor of the Duplex balance staff, and planted so that it engages the path of the locking teeth. Fig. 58 shows a locking tooth just leaving the notch of the roller. As the roller A moves in the direction of the arrow, a tooth passes into the slot, and is then released, thus allowing an impulse tooth B to drop on the pallet. When the impulse tooth is released the next locking tooth C drops on the left side of the roller.

The impulse teeth stand up from the rim of the wheel so as to meet the impulse pallet. On the return vibration of the balance the locking tooth enters the roller slot, and is pressed back slightly to its original position on the roller edge. The roller notch has to pass well beyond the line of centres before the locking tooth enters. It is therefore quite clear on the return

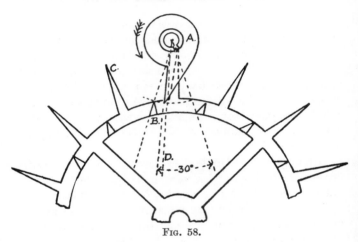

FIG. 58.

excursion the tooth will be forced back against the left-hand side of the roller.

The diameter of the roller should not exceed one-third the distance between the points of one locking tooth and the next. The drop on to the impulse pallet is about 8 degrees, shown in sketch, and the actual impulse on the pallet about 30 degrees measured from the centre of the staff.

Fig. 58 illustrates a locking tooth just leaving the notch, the distance the impulse tooth B falls on the

pallet equals the drop about 8 degrees, and the amount
of intersection of the pallet to the path of the impulse
tooth equals the impulse, shown by the dotted curve.
It is important the intersection of the pallet should be
perfectly safe.   This is a common fault in the Duplex,
and when the teeth or pivots are a little worn with
wide holes; it is often advisable to move the pallet
round a little to give more drop, shown by the dotted
line D, which means the tooth would drop safely on
the pallet.

The Duplex escapement requires exact adjustment
in all its parts.   A wide hole that might be passable
in a lever escapement would be fatal to its correct
action.   The roller slot must be in a relative position
with the pallet, so that it will release a tooth at exactly
the right moment.   If a locking tooth is released too
soon the impulse tooth will miss contact with the pallet,
because the latter will not have entered the path
described by the tooth, which means no impulse will be
given.   Then, again, if the tooth does not reach the
slot quick enough, the result would be too much drop
on the pallet, the impulse shortened and a poor vibration
to the balance.

The balance staff requires to be planted with exact-
ness, and one cause of trouble is the wearing of the
balance pivots.   In such instances the pivots having
been burnished, new holes should be fitted.   A little
experience is required to decide how much side shake
is passable.   The roller being nearer to the bottom
pivot should have the first consideration when there is
any doubt.   It often happens a pivot can be burnished
to attain a new surface without removing all the wear
marks ;   this is usually the best course to adopt.

Lead   the   balance   round   in   alternate   directions

with a peg to try each locking tooth and see that every
impulse tooth falls safely on the pallet, if some are
shallow move the impulse pallet round so as to give
more drop.

The vibration of the balance falling off when it
is inclined towards the escape wheel is often the cause
of the pallet catching on the corner of the impulse
tooth.  This can sometimes be traced to a staff jewel-
hole too large.  When the pivots fit correctly, polish
a very little off the corner of the pallet with diamantine
and steel.

A loose roller is occasionally the cause of stoppage.
In such a case the roller and staff should be cleaned
in petrol, and fixed with shellac.  Heated pliers will
be found convenient for this purpose.  Oil should be
applied at the roller notch, but not on the impulse teeth
or pallet.  To set the escapement in beat a locking
tooth resting on the notch should be on the line of
centres.

Theoretically the balance of a Duplex should be in
poise, but many authorities argue it should be slightly
out to overcome the liability of the escapement to
" set ".

## THE  MAINSPRING

The mainspring is the motive power.  The strength
should be the height, thickness, and length to give
sufficient number of turns to the barrel attaining as near
as possible a uniformity of pull in the four centre
turns used to drive the train.  Assuming there is
no stop work, the top turns are employed in driving
the mechanism.  There is a tendency to fit too strong
a mainspring.  The idea of applying a stronger power

to overcome some fault looks simple enough. But to rectify it by this principle is creating a greater.

The correct size for the body of the arbor is one-third of the inner diameter of the barrel. When the arbor is less there is usually trouble with mainsprings continually breaking. A quick and efficient method of overcoming this difficulty is to wrap the eye of the old spring round the new one when the latter is hooked in the barrel.

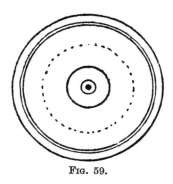

FIG. 59.

When a mainspring is run down there should be as much unoccupied space as the spring occupies when it is lying against the rim (see Fig. 59). The dotted circle divides the space from the spring. The spring will, therefore, occupy the whole of the unoccupied space when it is wound, and should be the correct length in order to obtain the greatest number of turns in the barrel. This is necessary to attain an equal adjustment.

The difference between the number of coils of the mainspring when it is wound to the top, and the number when let down resting against the rim of the barrel is exactly the number of turns the barrel will make.

The barrels of most modern watches, especially
the " wristlet ", are fitted without a stop work. The
safest form of spring attachment for this watch is the
riveted or turned-up end. Fig. 60 shows the latter,
which is quite simple to make. It takes the strain off
the hook and permits a uniformity in the uncoiling of the
spring. Hold it with a pair of pliers about half an inch
from the end in the left hand. Heat the nose of a small
pair of pliers in a spirit flame. Make the end of the
spring to a red heat and bend it over while in the flame
(Fig. 60 A). Another heating process will be necessary

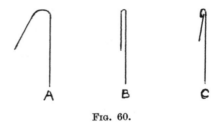

A          B          C

FIG. 60.

to bend it flat when the operation is repeated, the jaws
of the small pliers in this case embrace both pieces of
spring (Fig. 60 B). The spring is then cut near the
end with a slitting file and the piece broken off. This
leaves a hook-shaped end (Fig. 60 C). The piece of
waste spring is next broken off about three times its
width, with one end filed to a sharp edge to grip the
barrel hook.

Wind the spring in the barrel and push the hook end
round away from the barrel hook with the point of the
tweezers. Then push the loose piece down the end in
the spring first. When it is flush with the bottom
of the barrel press the tweezers behind the hook and

push it until the loose piece is tight between the two hooks. Wind it to its full length to try number of turns, gripping the arbor in the sliding tongs. When the square is very short a large pair of nippers will be found safer.

The riveted brace is usually employed where a large number of turns of the mainspring is required and the barrel is on the small side. Space is obviously a consideration, and the "riveted" form occupies space equal to twice the thickness of the mainspring, while the "loose piece" takes an extra thickness of spring. The riveted brace is simply an extra piece of mainspring the same size and acting the same as the "loose piece", only riveted to the end of the spring. The holes should be the same size counter sunk each side, so that the rivet should be secure and not project beyond the surface of the spring.

A mainspring winder should be furnished with three or four different sized chucks. The chuck selected represents the size of the barrel arbor for the spring to be wound. If it is larger or smaller the spring is liable to break. Most winders are without a chuck small enough to wind a wristlet spring. It is best to turn one in the lathe for size necessary.

The pivoted brace is another form of attachment commonly used in going barrel mainsprings without stop work. Because mainsprings stocked in the shop are not provided with a brace is no reason why another form of attachment should be fitted. Numerous holes in the barrel weaken it. To stock all the sizes with a brace fixed would mean a large and expensive assortment, which in time would deteriorate. These braces can be bought separately, and, taking into consideration nineteen out of twenty with care can be removed from the old spring and fixed to the new, a dozen pivoted braces of various sizes should last a long time.

To transfer a brace from an old spring to the new is a simple matter. File away the rivet on the mainspring side. Insert a knife between the spring and the brace, when the latter will fall away. Place the rivet on a hollow stake held in the vice, and with a sharp blow, using a punch the same size, drive it out. File both sides of the brace flat. Punch a hole near the end of the spring and file the end square so that it lies tightly against the shoulder of the brace with the two holes opposite. In this position they are broached the same size.

Fig. 61.

The fixing of the brace to the spring is an important feature. The rivet should fit tightly. Unnecessary hammering will tend to split it or stretch the hole and alter its shape. A brace is often rendered useless by excessive hammering. Iron properly fitted will hold a brace as tight as steel, and is much easier to rivet. File a piece of iron wire taper to fit the hole. Screw it in the vice, press the spring and brace on. Cut off the end and drive them down the wire, using a hollow punch. Cut off the wire nearly flush with the brace, file it flat and rivet it. Deal with the other side in the same manner and stone over the surfaces flat. Fig. 61 shows the end of a spring and the brace ready for pinning.

A barrel hook should stand out from the rim the same

height as the thickness of the spring. Any length beyond this not only weakens the hook, but diminishes the actual space utilized in the barrel. A hook is often made too high because it is too large in diameter. The smaller the hook the stronger.

Fig. 62 shows part of the rim of a barrel with a small hook of suitable dimensions. This hook has a long hole with many threads, therefore a firm grip on the barrel. Fig. 63 illustrates a large hook in the same size rim, showing the barrel space wasted between the eye of the spring and the first coil. When a mainspring breaks in a barrel with the large hook, the sudden strain of the outer coil comes a violent blow against the end

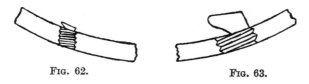

FIG. 62.            FIG. 63.

of the hook tending to drive it through the barrel. When it is not expelled, there is insufficient threads to form a hold and resist the strain, with the result the hook becomes loose. It is therefore quite apparent which hook is the stronger, both to resist the pull of the spring and the breaking strain.

It is quite simple to fit a barrel hook. Drill a hole in the barrel small enough to tap it with a number 13. File a piece of steel pallet wire, taper, and thread it in the screw-plate with a full thread, nip the wire off on the side which has not been tapped close enough to make a hook. File it with the wire in the screw-plate ; undercut the hook with a slitting file, for the eye of the spring to grip, and file the top back away from the undercut (see Fig. 64). Unscrew the hook the same way it was screwed in, and screw it in the barrel *from the inside*, holding the small piece of wire which has no thread and will pass freely through the hole, and screw home to the hook. Nip off the piece on the outside, and file it flush with the barrel (Fig. 65).

A mill cutter, as a lathe accessory, is a very useful tool for reducing the height of a barrel hook. When a large hook is sound but occupies too much space, it is advisable to cut it down. A fine tooth steel ratchet wheel squared on an arbor to fit a split chuck and hardened, will reduce any hook without damage to the

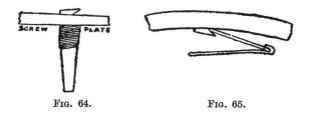

FIG. 64.                    FIG. 65.

barrel. Hold the barrel firmly on the rest so that the ratchet touches the top of the hook. A few rotations of the flywheel will accomplish the work. (See Home-made tools : The Lathe.)

There are various forms of mainspring trouble. The strongest spring the barrel will take is sometimes fitted without examining the stop work, train or escapement ; these parts, by chance, might be correct, but with a fault at the motive power its timekeeping will be rendered useless.

When the body of the arbor is too small a good plan is to turn it down in a split chuck and drive on a brass collar or piece of bush wire and turn it to size. The hole for the hook should be drilled well into the steel less than a right angle so that the pull of the mainspring tends to draw the hook tight, and also preventing the brass collar from slipping (see Fig. 66). File the pin which is to form the hook almost straight, allowing a little drive.

Many mainsprings are left too hard in the eye, with the result they break when the eye is bent to the shape of the arbor. There is nothing gained by this, from the fact that no elasticity is required in the first half-turn. Some repairers make certain before bending the eye by holding it over a very small spirit flame.

FIG. 66.

Loss of power is often difficult to find when it is not constant, and can be traced to a worn or " dead " mainspring.

When the mainspring is removed from the barrel it should be examined. The life of a spring varies. If it assumes a cramped position (see Fig. 67), discard it for a new one. If it has worn bright in places and appears " lumpy ", wind it in the barrel, try the turns with the sliding tongs, allowing it to run back slowly between the thumb and fingers ; to notice if the pull is unequal or " jerky ". Oil fails to reduce coil friction to any great extent in such a spring ; the vibration is sure to fall off at the weak pull, and a new one is the easiest way out of the difficulty. A spring sometimes

binds through being out of flat, and can be improved
by bending the coils.   Another and not uncommon
fault—" coils foul of barrel cover ", or bottom of barrel ;
this is generally owing to the spring being too high or
the cover or bottom of the barrel being out of flat.
In such an instance, turn the bottom of the barrel in
a step chuck, or if the cover, a cut with the slide rest
from the centre nearly out to the edge.

When the loss of power is traced to the barrel and the
mainspring appears free, remove and try the freedom

Fig. 67.

and endshake of the arbor by holding it in the sliding
tongs.   If it is not perfectly free, turn the boss of the
barrel or cover in a step chuck ; a rough hole may be
round-broached.   A worn barrel arbor pivot should be
polished and the hole rebushed.   A barrel out of flat
can sometimes be trued by turning the cover round,
but when this fails fit a new hole and upright the barrel.

Uniformity of pull in a mainspring is essential to
close timekeeping, and for this reason it is cheapest
in the end to use the best quality.

## WRISTLET WATCHES

The club tooth wheel is now employed in all wristlet lever escapements. The wheel is not so fragile, less drop is required, the oil is easily retained on the acting surfaces of the teeth, and the pallet stones are readily adjusted.

The cleaning of a wristlet watch is a simple matter. More trouble in regulation arises from this style of watch than any other. It is difficult to know exactly what is the cause of a stop or bad timekeeping in any particular watch. It is mainly a matter of experience. It is quite a common practice for an owner to bring in their watch with a request for regulation, and in nine times out of ten the cause is the want of repairing and cleaning. In most instances customers are open to reason, and will agree to have the piece overhauled.

Assuming the watch has been cleaned, a general examination should reveal the faults. It is a great mistake to fit a stronger mainspring. More wristlet watches are taken in for regulation with this fault than any other. A mainspring must be weak enough to give five turns in the barrel, and perfectly free of the bottom of the barrel and cover. A mainspring fitted too strong might cause the watch to " set ".

In many cases regulation is confined to alterations of the balance and spring, but when the variation is inconsistent it is usual to look for a fault in the escapement and examine the whole of the movement to find the cause. It is a general, but unwise, policy to open the index pins with the regulator over to the " slow ". A quick method no doubt to get a watch slower, but the wider the index pins the greater the variation between the long and short arcs. The safest procedure is to let the spring out at the stud, or in case of a Brequet place two washers behind a pair of opposite screws in the balance.

When a watch is wanted immediately unpin the spring at the collet and stud and stone down the surface on an oilstone with a piece of cork. A spring showing signs of rust is a hopeless case, and should be replaced.

Wristlet watches are more subject to a knock, and although many customers are inclined to excuse themselves, they are often ignorant of the cause of the damage. It is advisable, therefore, to examine the balance staff pivots, and if they show the slightest sign of wear or damage to burnish them for a new surface. Remove the jewel-holes and clean them ; any sign of chip or crack would be noticed.

To test the vibration of the balance for escapement errors, notice exactly the position of the balance arms at the end of each vibration, dial down. Place a mirror on the board and hold the movement a few inches above. (See Inconsistent Timekeeping.)

Faulty escapements not only utilize a large percentage of the motive power and cause a bad vibration, but the power so wasted is occasionally irregular, thus rendering the piece useless for regulation.

" What is the correct amount of locking and how is it measured ? " In theory we are taught the locking should be from $1\frac{1}{2}$ to 2 degrees, measured from the pallet staff centre, but in practical work, especially with the club tooth, 1 degree is generally attained. Assuming the wheel to be perfectly true, a little less will be sufficient, with a decided draw on the pallet. It is quite simple to understand. An imaginary line is drawn from the pallet staff centre to the locking corner of the pallet ; cast your eye from the locking corner to the pallet staff centre, and the distance the tooth drops on the locking face from the corner represents the locking measured in degrees. Circles are divided into 360 equal parts, called degrees. A right angle, which is one-fourth of a circle, is 90. When speaking of the locking we assume a circle struck from the pallet staff centre to cut the locking corner of the pallet, and the distance of the tooth from the locking corner immediately

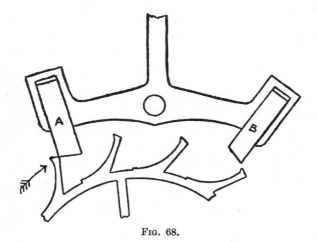

FIG. 68.

the tooth drops is the angle called locking. The distance the tooth slides up the locking face is termed "slide-lock", and should be sufficient to bring the safety pin free of the edge of the roller. The slide lock is equal to the "run", and when these are excessive the greater will be the resistance to the unlocking. The slide lock should not exceed the actual locking.

The escape wheel misses locking is quite a common fault in this style of watch. It will usually record itself

by a falling of the vibration of the balance, caused
by the safety piece rubbing on the roller edge. Lead the
balance round slowly with a peg in alternate directions
to see if the wheel teeth drop safely on the locking face.
If the wheel is out of round, a new one will give the
best result. The lock should be deep enough to draw
the pallet in and the fork over to the banking. Fig. 68
shows a tooth just missed the locking corner on the
entering pallet A.  We therefore draw the stone B,
assuming the escapement to be in angle. When it is
unsafe, the best plan is to place the pallet on a clamp,
or an old barrel with a hole to take the pallet staff,
and a piece of brass wire bound round the edge with the
ends looped and twisted to form a handle. An old wristlet
watch plate makes a very useful clamp for holding the
pallets while a stone is shifted. It leaves both hands
free to adjust the stone. To make a clamp, knock both
pallet jewel-holes out and file the under part of the cock
away until the cock grips the top of the pallets when it
is screwed down.

The pallets are placed in the clamp. The cock screwed
down with a small knob of shellac on the plate, and the
latter held over a spirit flame until the shellac melts.
The clamp is then placed flat on the board, and the two
hands are free to adjust the stone to the position
required. A fine needle point will be found suitable to
insert between the top of the stone and the steel to
slightly press the stone forward.

When there is too much drop on the pallets the stones
are too narrow or the club ends of the wheel teeth are
too short and should be changed for a new wheel.
When there is too much drop on the entering pallet
and scarcely any on the exit, the pallet stones are too
close together, and if the drop is excessive on the exit

pallet and practically none on the other, the pallets require closing. This is generally accomplished by softening the shellac and pressing the stone over.

Immediately a tooth drops the pin should be leaving the notch. If the shake of the lever is no greater when moved over a little further the pin is still in the notch. The roller pin would therefore require pushing back from the notch.

Roller pins of wristlet watches are usually oval, or flatted, fitted in a hole of the same shape. When the pin is upright and fits the hole it affords no room for pushing back. Under these conditions remove the pin and grind the hole. This is by no means a difficult procedure and less risk than shortening the notch. Remove the roller and pin, file a piece of steel wire taper to fit the pin hole. Grip the roller in a pair of brass-nosed slide tongs and rest the latter on a cork, or piece of soft wood held in the vice. Charge the wire with mixed oilstone dust and grind the pin hole with a forward and backward motion, pressing the wire on the side nearest the centre of the roller.

With the roller pin and notch depth shortened the banking pins are then closed. The sides of the pins nearest the lever should be parallel so that the same amount of run is attained with the end shake up or down. When the pins are small the best plan is to knock them out and broach the holes to fit larger ones or if they require bringing much closer, to draw file them in the direction of the lever and fit new pins to the holes.

Another method of pitching the roller pin the correct depth is to bank the escapement to " drop ". Remove the balance and close the banking pins until the teeth only just escape without run. If on replacing the balance the pin fails to enter the notch, it is too deep.

Press the pin back, or grind the hole in the roller with oilstone dust and re-cement the pin. When it passes freely in and out of the notch in the plates, open the banking pins slightly for freedom or " run ".

Should the roller pin be oiled ? This question has frequently caused discussion. In many instances no doubt friction occurs at the lever notch. The best results would be attained in reducing the friction by polishing the notch and fitting a new ruby pin. A nicely polished notch with a roller pin suitably fitted, should give a rolling action with a little or no friction. The late Mr. Charles Curzon said emphatically no oil is required. The operation of oiling the roller pin does more harm than good, as soon as the oil thickens the vibration must surely suffer. It will pay to spend a little more time polishing the wear marks from the notch and fitting a smooth impulse pin, than attempting to overcome a difficulty by means of oil, which only proves useless.

The guard pin or safety depth is sometimes mistaken for the roller pin, and when banking pins are employed they are opened. The repairer is under the impression the safety nose is too deep, whereas the fault lies with the roller pin. Opening the banking pins should be avoided, there is nothing gained. The wider the bankings the greater the resistance to the unlocking, and the greater the balance are. Opening the banking pins might overcome one fault, but it creates another.

Escapement out of angle is another form of trouble. In the club tooth it is mostly attributed to the lever being bent. The impulse should be conveyed to the roller pin on the line of centres. Therefore, the smaller the pin the nearer this object is attained. An escapement " out of angle " will obviously give impulse to the roller pin at a greater angle on one side than the

other. The pin would leave the notch too soon on one
side, and appear too deep on the other. The arc of
vibration would consequently suffer. It is quite simple
to remedy this with a few light taps from a flat punch.

It is inadvisable to bend the lever when it is straight
in order to get it in angle called " bending the fork ",
unless there is sufficient draw on the opposite pallet.
Fig. 69 shows the lever in angle, with the balance
removed, showing the staff jewel-hole. The mainspring
should be wound a few teeth. The dotted lever notch
shows the relative position of the lever when a tooth
drops on the opposite pallet. Move the notch slowly

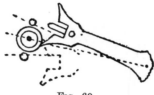

Fig. 69.

with a peg until a tooth drops, and if it is in angle it will
assume the position shown by the dotted notch. The
side of the notch is the same distance on each side of
the centre dotted line. The jewel-hole will act as a guide.
Cast your eye in a line with the side of the notch shown
by a dotted line ; it will come close to, or on the edge
of the jewel setting.

Fig. 70 shows the same escapement " out of angle ",
causing the ruby pin to leave the notch when it assumes
the position of the dotted notch before the impulse is
completed. In this case there would be unnecessary run
to the banking, as shown, and too much " slide lock "
on the pallet B. Obviously we get a loss of impulse.

The vibration would be increased, and the escapement put in angle if we draw the pallet stone B, and push in the stone A the same amount.

Escape wheel " setting " on the locking or impulse faces is a common fault in wristlets, and when the ' set " is on both pallets it is a source of trouble and liable to stop at any time.   The cause is usually too much draw on one or both pallets.  The mainspring too strong.  A rough lever notch.  Balance too heavy, too much " lift " or an escapement too heavy, and out of proportion. These badly designed escapements should be sent to the maker.

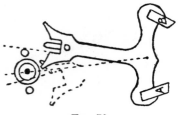

FIG. 70.

No " inside " or " outside " shake means the wheel is without freedom within three teeth between the inside corners of the pallets when a tooth is about to escape from the exit pallet, or four teeth between the outside corners of the pallets, when a tooth is about to unlock from the entering pallet.  Insufficient drop is practically the same as no inside, or outside shake, and the remedy is the same.  The slot for the pallet stone requires grinding to bring the stones closer, or wider as the case may be.

Rollers of wristlet levers are usually on the double roller principle, and both made in one piece.  A table tool is the safest method of removing them. The small roller being thickest, is placed in the sink of the tool, with the staff inverted, and a hollow cone punch used to rest on the cone of the lower pivot. One sharp blow is then required to remove them. (See English Lever Escapement.)

Faults in the balance spring are often attributed to the escapement. (See Faults in the Balance Spring.)

Many forms of unsuitable tools are often employed to remove spring collets, and these are largely responsible for scratched balances or springs distorted at the eye. Fig. 71 shows a home-made collet remover, in the form of a spade from a piece of round or flat steel. The

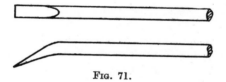

FIG. 71.

tightest collet will yield to this tool without fear of damage to the balance or spring. Select a piece of steel about three or four inches long, soften it and bend the end to form the angle. File the spade as shown in the sketch, harden and temper it to a deep straw. Then sharpen the end to a knife edge. With the latter inserted between the collet and balance, the downward leverage of the tool will remove the collet.

Many " wristlets " are made without a crystal bevel to the bezel, and for want of knowledge a crystal glass is often fitted. It is quite obvious the amount of room for freedom is decreased. Many such instances have been brought in for regulation. To overcome the difficulty change the glass to one which the bezel was intended.

The "pull out to set hands" watch is now quite general. The idea is right, but in many instances the construction wrong. About nine watches out of every ten returned to the repairer with the button and shaft pulled right out are on the principle of the new style. It is quite clear that side shake permitted in a shaft and button of the push piece type would be altogether unsuitable for the pull-out variety. The depth of contact allowed for lock is so slight and the shoulder of the notch often the wrong angle, that any slight side play will have a tendency to force the lock piece pivot out of the notch.

There is more strain on this style of shaft than the old form of push piece. It is therefore necessary they should be perfectly free from shake of any description. If the sides of the notch are rounded, the shaft can be placed in a split chuck and the notch turned square or slightly undercut with a flat-ended or chisel shape cutter made especially for this purpose.

When a winding shaft has too much side shake the best plan is to turn a new one. Too much shake is either the pivot of the shaft made too small for the hole, or the body of the steel turned too small for the hole in the plate. In the latter instance the rocking would obviously lessen the amount of lock at the notch. This is especially noticeable in miniature wristlets. It is therefore important a new shaft should first be turned to fit the hole in the plate without shake.

The continual pulling out and in of the shaft has a tendency to loosen any lock piece screw, either a right- or left-handed thread, even if it screwed down tightly. Many repairers in despair have riveted over the end of the screw, but such a procedure obviously becomes a trouble to the next horologist who has to dissemble the watch. An extra piece is necessary to prevent the screw from turning. The slot of the screw could be filed a little wider with parallel sides, and a finger piece made from a bit of old mainspring to fit the slot, and fixed with a small screw, in the plate. Another method is to file a flat on the side of the screw head about one-third the diameter. Then file a thin plate with a slot to fit over the screw head, flush with the flatted part, from a piece of thin mainspring. Drill and tap a hole in the brass to fix a screw for holding the lock plate. The whole fixture can be made small with the screw head about the same size as the lock piece head. Its object is simply to prevent the lock piece screw from turning.

A tightly fitted screw to the lock piece is no guarantee against the shaft pulling right out, if it has side play with the button at the pendant. In this instance the quickest plan is to turn up a brass collar from a piece of clock bush wire, and drive it on the boss of the button to just fit the hole in the pendant.

Another original fault emanates from the lock piece screw having endshake. It is quite clear in such a case the lock piece would move with it, and the shaft might be pulled right out in the act of setting hands. The lock screw as a rule is on the pivoted principle, with a body in the middle which is supposed to fit the sink in the plate. As there are so many different sizes and shapes in these screws, the chances are the nearest tool shop pattern would occupy as much time in alteration as it would to turn a new one. To overcome the difficulty turn the socket of an old wristlet hour hand to fit over the bottom arbor of the screw, and come flush with the body, thick enough to fill the sink and stop the shake (see Fig. 72). A, the lock piece ;

B, the screw; and C, the collet, fitted to stop the shake.

There is often a difficulty in getting the square of the winding shaft in the castle wheel without the shifting sleeve riding out of its place, if the dial happens to be screwed at the edges of the plate. In such instances it is quite clear the dial must be screwed on before the movement is fixed in the case. The best plan is to fix the shaft first, screw down the lock piece, see that the oil has run in the slot and teeth of the winding wheels,

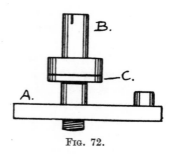

Fig. 72.

" pull out " in the act of setting hands, to examine the action, then release the screw sufficiently to slide the shaft out without moving the winding wheels. Screw on the dial, place the movement in position in the case when the shaft should slide in slowly without disturbing the position of the wheels.

The most senseless contrivance in a wristlet is visible dial screw heads with hidden collars for gripping the feet. It is often necessary to remove the dial before taking the movement out. This is only accomplished at great risk of cracking the dial. The fit of the screw collars, and dial feet, in such cases are tight, which makes it more difficult, because, as the screw is slowly moved the foot omits to drop when opposite the crescent. The blade of a knife forced gradually between the dial and plate while the dial screw is turned will release the former when the crescent comes opposite the foot. For future occasions make a dot on the edge of each screw head, and one on the plate opposite, to mark the position when the feet are free to fall through the holes.

**The Motion Tension.**—"Snapping on" a cannon pinion is old-fashioned. There is no doubt the idea originated from the English full-plate key-winding watch. There was a logical reason for such a device in this style—the path described by the balance intersecting the centre of motion of the centre wheel.

Many wristlets not only show a weakness in design by reverting to this old notion, but becomes a source of trouble in regulation. To be satisfactory the fit of the pinion must be perfect, and the solid arbor dead true. An error in either would cause trouble. Then, again, it is not an easy matter to tighten the tension of the cannon with a new bur, unless it is the correct spot to come opposite the groove in the arbor. The whole thing is small and obviously becomes loose with wear. Many repairers in despair form spiral burs on the arbor. This procedure is useless because it not only disfigures the arbor, but with the action of setting hands the cannon would ride up the arbor and bind the hour wheel.

The cause of the trouble arising from this device can be summarized as follows : The pinion arbor out of round, taper backwards. The groove in the arbor to receive the bur out of truth, or too deep. The shell of the pinion in most instances is too thin to raise a bur strong enough to be forced over the arbor, and hold sufficiently tight to carry the hands in all places. When a wristlet watch is made with a hollow centre pinion, and a cannon pinion driven on a friction tight set arbor in the usual way, a defective set arbor is soon replaced, but not so with a solid centre pinion.

When a large bur fails to take effect, place the centre pinion in a split chuck and oilstone-dust the arbor mostly near the end to give it a slightly taper shape, which will also reduce the groove. This will make the pinion appear very loose, but with a new bur raised it will have no difficulty in reaching the groove to form the correct tension necessary to carry the hands at all parts.

The bur should be formed with a small centre punch, while the pinion is pushed on a broach for safety and placed on a brass grooved stake in the vice. Two or three grooves are filed different sizes to accommodate the diameter of the pinion. Refrain from using steel nosed pliers for removing a pinion. Any rough mark left from such a procedure would ultimately cause the pipe of the hour wheel to bind and stop the watch. Brass or copper nosed pliers are used for taking off steel parts with polished acting surfaces.

An old pair of pliers can easily be faced with brass. They must be rigid, and therefore a large pair is preferable to a small. Soften the jaws, and file the insides away about one-third, leaving a shoulder. Fit the brass chops flush with the shoulder and slightly thicker near the ends, so that they close flush at this part. Two holes are next drilled through each jaw, chamfered on both sides to take the rivets. Brass pins are fitted tightly with a little riveting from a round-faced hammer, to fill the chamfer holes. This tool should be in use when taking down, or assembling any watch; it prevents scratching polished steel surfaces.

These snapped on pinions carry the minute hand fitted on to a shoulder, and in many instances the pivot is too short and too thick at the shoulder to afford a hold for the socket of the hand. There is usually plenty of room, but the fault is original, and consequently the minute hand works loose. The best plan is to fit the pinion on an arbor and turn the shoulder back, and the seat for the hand almost straight, with a very sharp graver. A very little is required to give the effect and the pinion should run perfectly true on the arbor.

When the shoulder of the pinion is below the top of the hour-wheel, and there is not sufficient metal to lower the hour-wheel pipe (with the same short arbor for the minute hand) the safest plan is to collet the boss of the minute hand, and turn the boss small enough to free the inside of the hour pipe to fit flush against the shoulder. A brass collet would be effective for the new boss, and the hour-wheel endshake adjusted from the minute-hand.

Another difficulty experienced in many cheap grade lever wristlets is when the top of the " snapped on " cannon pinion is not high enough from the dial to give sufficient freedom for the hour hand with the minute. There is usually plenty of room to fit a much higher pinion, which would give the best result. When the price for the repair will not allow a new pinion, the shoulder of the pipe can be turned back to give a longer bearing. Half the thickness of metal is then turned away and a new pipe driven on to come above the top of the pinion arbor. An old cylinder shell would be found suitable.

**Inconsistent Timekeeping.**—To get a watch going and to regulate it to time are two very different matters.

When the variation is on the gaining side we usually

look for a fault in the escapement. The inconsistent variation is the most troublesome. But to accomplish our task with an irregular gaining and losing rate we must search beyond.

A great deal of inconsistent timekeeping emanating from wristlet watches can be traced to faults in the hands and motion work. A seconds hand is quite unnecessary where luminous hands are fixed. To get three such hands perfectly free of each other, the dial, and glass, is frequently the work of an expert. The centre wheel is often a little out of upright, which would cause any of these parts to run foul, and obviously tell on the performance of the timekeeper. In such instances the safest remedy is to upright the fourth wheel. When the luminous hour and minute hands are too thick for the necessary freedom between the dial and glass they can be placed on a piece of soft wood in the vice and planed with the side of a sharp graver.

The loss of power through one hand rubbing on the dial, glass, or foul of another hand would account for a variation in timekeeping. A slight endshake for the fourth wheel is necessary. The latter is often jewelled and out of upright, or the dial out of thickness. When the fourth wheel is run in the same bar as the third or escape, upright the fourth wheel by turning a new setting and fitting a new jewel-hole.

Turn the hands round slowly to observe the freedom at different parts of the dial. If the point of the minute hand is close to the dial one side with plenty of space on the opposite, the centre wheel is out of upright or the centre arbor bent. Close the bezel and see if the minute hand touches the glass. A bent set arbor is easily straightened with a few light taps from the hammer.

The hands are often damaged on removal. The tool

selected is usually a pair of nippers, the result is a
cracked hour pipe or a bur under the minute hand socket.
There are many useful hand removers on the market,
and a very safe tool can be made by filing the jaws of
a pair of pliers to a V-shape (see Fig. 73). The tightest
hand will yield to this tool without fear of damage.

The boss or centre of the hand usually marks a ring
on the glass when foul. This might be tested with red
stuff.   When the glass is a flat crystal and there is

Fig. 73.

insufficient room to lower the hand the glass should be
changed for a hollow or flat-concave crystal.

The hour hand must have a little side shake at every
point. The endshake of the hand is proportionate to
the endshake of the hour wheel, or adjusted by the
minute hand. For instance the hour wheel might have
too much shake, but this is sometimes reduced when
the minute hand is driven home.   If the hour hand
appears tight take off the minute hand. When there is
no alteration remove the former and try the shake of
the hour wheel. If the wheel has no shake unscrew the
dial and the fault is visible. A wheel too tight on the
cannon pinion should have a touch with a broach,

or polish the arbor of the pinion if it appears rough. A wheel tight in the depth requires topping. When the wheel is free with the dial off turn away a little of the shoulder to give it shake. Sometimes the hour wheel is perfectly free with the hand removed ; there are two courses open, turn down the boss of the hour hand to free the hole in the dial or file the dial hole.

When the dial feet are bent or buckled through a fall affords another instance of increased friction. The hour or seconds pipe runs foul of the dial at the holes. It is advisable, therefore, to examine the dial feet when a watch shows indications of a blow. Straightening the feet is a simple matter.

Many wristlets would be more satisfactory without a seconds hand. The only alternative to the excessive handshake nuisance is to reduce it even at the cost of a new jewel-hole or stopping. A thin collet turned off an old seconds pipe gripped in a split chuck to fit against the shoulder of the seconds pivot is a quick method of reducing the endshake of the seconds hand. A thick one should be replaced.

Luminous hands as a rule are thick, and afford very small space for freedom. It is often necessary to shorten the end to free the seconds hand. While these hands will not stand bending where the luminous substance adheres, it is quite possible to bend the tip of the minute hand to a curve to free the glass, by gripping the end flush with the coloured filling; flat, with broad-pointed tweezers and bend the tip gently with the pliers.

When the operator has a good stock of hands it is a simple matter to replace them with a thin pair. Steel hands are often thinned by resting them flat on a piece of soft wood. This procedure requires careful manipulation, or the colour is liable to be scratched. The safest operation is usually the best. To avoid risk of breaking shellac a hand to a strip of brass which is placed on a piece of soft wood in the vice. It is then easily filed to the required thickness and boiled out in methylated spirit. An hour hand is placed on an arbor and the back of the boss turned flush with the part already filed.

The most common fault is the rocking of the hour hand, which inevitably causes it to foul the minute or seconds hand. This irregular movement can usually be traced to a badly fitted hand, a split pipe, or the centre arbor bent. The pipe of the hour hand too taper or slightly taper backward, or the hole of the hour wheel too large with too much shake. Any attempt to tighten a hand with the hour wheel socket the wrong shape is courting trouble. The hour hand will become too loose when pressed home if the wheel pipe is too large on the end. Too large at the root or too taper forward with the centre arbor bent is a common combination of faults. When the hour hand is pressed home it only grips the wheel in one place, while the boss of the hand occasionally rubs against the minute socket and quickly works loose. In this instance mount the wheel on an arbor, turn the socket slightly taper and fit a new hand.

A bent centre arbor is generally the cause of an accident. Many cannon pinions are fitted too tight, that is with too much drive, and instead of easing the hole of the cannon it is driven on the arbor too tightly.

A brass hammer is indispensable to a watchmaker; in fact, when applied to its many uses proves a time-saving appliance. One sharp blow is sufficient to remove any cannon pinion without damage to the set arbor.

The important thing is to hit straight. Steel minute hands are driven on without scratching the socket, thereby dispensing with the old style of hollow punch. A piece of an old clock pillar would be a convenient size for a hammer and prove excellent practice in filing. When the top of the cannon pinion comes flush with the top of the centre arbor of a hollow centre pinion the usual procedure is to drive the set arbor out with a blow from a flat-ended brass punch. Refrain from using steel, especially a point ; it not only disfigures the end of the arbor, which is always visible to the wearer, but bulges the end of the arbor and in time cracks the seat of the minute hand. A thin brass punch should be kept especially for this work, and in its place ready for future occasions.

It is essential the centre arbor should run true : on this depends the running of the hour and minute hands. Where the freedom is small a bent arbor will account for the minute hand fouling the glass, dial, or seconds hand. When an arbor is badly disfigured, it is best to replace it. It is a difficult matter to get the hand to carry safely at all points of the dial without being too tight if the centre arbor is not true in the round.

A very useful tool for tightening hour hands can be made from an old hollow steel stake. Soften it and broach all the holes slightly with taper broaches, the stump ends usually form the best angle. The socket of the hand is placed on the hole which should just admit it ; a flat punch and a blow from a hammer closes the socket. Hands treated in this manner should only be closed when they are a trifle loose. The hour hand should only have just perceptible endshake. When the latter is excessive a motion collet placed over the hour wheel pipe will prevent the hand running foul. These collets are obtainable in 3 or 4 sizes of all material dealers. No oil is required to the motion work except the minute wheel stud in a keyless watch.

Motion work trouble is best located with the dial off, the hands replaced, and the watch set going ; one is able to locate any fault in the motion work when the watch stops. By careful examination of the different shakes and depths the cause of trouble is visible.

**Bent Pivots.**—A great deal of trouble in regulation can be traced to a damaged balance staff pivot. The injury is often insufficient to cause any noticeable alteration in the arc of vibration. Most watches lose in the short arcs. A small mirror will indicate any variation in the arc of vibration. For the " dial up " test hold the movement two or three inches above the mirror and notice the exact place where the arm of the balance reaches at the end of a vibration. This should coincide with the vibration when the watch is placed flat on the board (dial down). Then top plate at right angles to the mirror, which represents " pendant up ", and compare the arm of the balance at the termination of each vibration. The movement is inclined slowly until it assumes the " dial up " position, keeping our eye on the arm of the balance, which will here record escapement errors with the watch at different angles. Continue holding the piece close to the mirror to represent " pendant right ", " pendant left ", and follow the same inclined test in each case. Any inconsistency of the arc of vibration in a certain position is usually an indication of escapement errors. The angle and position of the movement when the vibration falls will give an idea of the nature of the fault. If the balance is inclined towards the lever we might expect to find a wide staff or pallet hole causing insufficient freedom for the guard or impulse pins. A slight falling in any position would indicate an escapement error, or possibly a damaged staff pivot.

A pivot worn rough or damaged through a fall is easily burnished smooth on a Jacot tool. In Fig. 74 we have a pivot spread out on the end; the metal being compressed, the pivot obviously becomes a trifle shorter. It is necessary, after burnishing down a bull-headed

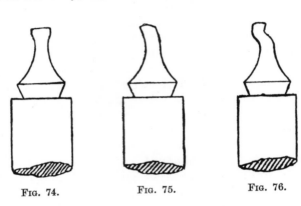

FIG. 74.  FIG. 75.  FIG. 76.

pivot, to try if it comes through the jewel-hole so that the end reaches the endstone while the pivot is free in the hole. It is by no means uncommon to find the pivot riveted in the jewel-hole. When the latter is intact, and a slight pull fails to withdraw the staff, remove the jewel screws and endstone, turn the plate over with the balance hanging, press the balance with the thumb of the left hand, the fingers holding the plate so that as much of the pivot comes through the jewel-hole as possible. Select a sharp, long-pointed graver, cut away the rivet cutting with the point of the graver round the edge until the pivot is free to fall out of the hole.

A slightly bent pivot, causing increased friction, is another reason for the arc of vibration falling in one position. All pivots with a single bend (Fig. 75) can be treated in the same manner. Some watchmakers straighten staff pivots by placing them in a hollow runner and employ a polisher as a lever. A watch bouchon placed over the pivot and inclined in the direction to straighten it is a method favoured by many.

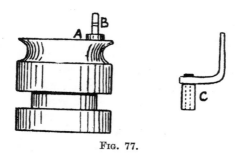

FIG. 77.

From experience a small pair of heated pliers is the safest. The secret is to grip the pivot at the start of the bend and bend it in the right direction.

Fig. 76 illustrates a crushed or double bent pivot. This form is a hopeless case and means a new staff. There are many who will take exception to this statement and advocate a new pivot to the old staff. It is not advisable to drill a balance staff unless the pivot inserted is dead true. It is not an easy matter to accomplish. The writer has replaced a great many balance staffs drilled for pivots a trifle out of true because the original performance of the watch was disorganized.

A good light is essential for pivoting ; daylight is a lesser strain on the eyes, therefore the quickest.

In Fig. 77 we have a useful home-made centrifugal carrier for a Jacot tool which adapts itself to any radius from the runner hole. The pivot supplied in the pulley is turned down to a shoulder A, with a slight nick B turned on the pivot. A piece of steel is drilled to form a pipe and snapped on the arbor at B. A short pivot turned on the end of the pipe C. A piece of steel wire or a Geneva minute hand bent at a right angle and the hole riveted to the pivot at the end of the pipe.

After straightening a staff pivot with the heated pliers, it is necessary to give it a rub on a Jacot tool to remove any roughness.

Loss of power in the train would account for inconsistent timekeeping, and a loss of vibration to the balance. Remove the barrel, the balance and pallets, and move the centre wheel gently with a peg. This test will reveal any defect in the train. (See Correcting Bad Depths.) Reverse the plates and repeat the operation. The centre wheel foul of bar, or keyless wheel is quite a common fault. When the wheel is not out of flat, or will not stand bending, the best plan is to fit a new centre wheel hole, uprighting it from the opposite one.

The troubles arising from the centre wheel being out of upright are nearly as numerous as faults in the escapement, and can be summarized as follows :—
Insufficient freedom for the hands ; the centre wheel foul of the barrel, the bar, the winding wheel, the third wheel, bar, or the balance. This latter fault will often cause a deal of trouble when the centre wheel is out of flat. It is always advisable to examine a watch immediately it stops. If there is no apparent fault,

remove it from the case, and try the vibration in different positions ; the balance will " stop " or fall off, inclined towards the centre wheel. Such a fault would be difficult to locate if the watch were allowed to run until the lowest part of the centre wheel was the other side of the balance.

The usual procedure is to true the centre wheel. Remove the escapement and let the train run slowly to see if the wheel requires bending up or down in order to bring it free of the other parts. A general survey is also required to see which hole requires uprighting. It is a matter that requires a little knowledge to decide how the centre wheel and pinion depths shall be altered in relation to the great wheel and third pinion. When the centre wheel is leaning towards the balance, a new top hole uprighted from the bottom would pitch the depth with the great wheel deeper, and if, as it some-times happens, the centre wheel would foul the barrel with too much endshake, upright the top hole, leaving the new hole flush, then fit a new lower hole to stand above the plate and reduce the endshake to let the wheel run free of the barrel.

If the centre wheel, out of upright, inclines toward the balance, and runs foul of the keyless wheel on the barrel bar, upright the top centre hole from the bottom, but if the centre pinion is too deep with the great wheel, fit a new bottom hole uprighted from the top. The same consideration must be used when the centre wheel is out of upright and inclined toward or away from the third pinion.

To upright the top centre hole, broach it from the inside, fit a solid stopping and slightly rivet it over. Screw the pillar plate in the mandrel, and peg the hole true. Screw down the centre bar, catch the centre with a sharp pointed graver, and drill the hole with the lathe running, using a drill a trifle smaller than the top centre pivot.

To upright the bottom centre hole, broach the hole in the plate from the inside, then force the broach in tightly to make five little slots (this will help the stopping to hold when riveted), and fit a solid stopping tight. It is then riveted from both sides. A round face, or riveting hammer, should be used for this operation, and a little care is required with the hammer so as not to disfigure the plate. Rest it on a solid stake in the vice during the riveting stage and give the stopping a number of quick, light blows in preference to heavy ones. The latter will have a tendency to buckle the plate and give endless trouble. Next screw on the centre bar, fix the plate in the mandrel, and peg the top hole true. The bar can be unscrewed and removed without shifting the pillar plate. Catch the centre with a graver and drill the hole the same as the preceding method adopted for the top hole. Before removing the plate from the mandrel, test the hole for true with the peg, and if it is out turn it true with a hand cutter having parallel cutting sides and small enough to enter the hole. These home-made cutters are easily made on the taper ends of old files. Remove the plate and fit the pivot with a broach. Try the wheel in the frame. A little may be turned off the stopping for endshake if necessary with a flat-ended hand cutter.

Many watches have the centre and third wheels intersecting the path described by the barrel. In this calliper movement the freedom between the wheels and barrel is obviously very limited, and a wheel a trifle out of flat will often run foul of the plate, barrel, or another wheel. It is advisable in such cases to try the barrel and train in the plates to examine the freedom. Truing a wheel is a simple matter, and can be accomplished by placing it in the callipers or a split chuck in the lathe. It should be observed in which direction, up or down, the wheel requires bending to attain its freedom. When a wheel is proportionately thick and runs true try the endshake, and if it is foul in any position it might be thinned by holding the wheel on a cork held in the vice. The wheel is gripped on the edge by the thumb and finger, rotated between each stroke of a very smooth cut file, using the safe edge towards the pinion. The file marks are removed, repeating the operation, but substituting a blue stone and oil for the file and using a circular motion. The bottom of a wheel should be thinned, not the visible side, which would disfigure the watch. For example, if the top of the centre wheel is foul of the bottom of the third, thin the third wheel. When the thickness will not permit reducing, fit the wheel lower on the pinion or fit a new hole. A worn pivot or wide hole will often account for a wheel driven out of upright and foul.

The loss of motive power is often due to coil friction. The molecules of the spring only rub each other with the smallest possible friction when the steel is not too soft, perfectly free from roughness or lumps, clean and well oiled. Coil friction is reduced with the uncoiling of the spring from the centre. " Waltham " mainsprings give nearly an equable pull. What is the advantage of the steel barrel ? are questions often asked. Because with a higher and thinner spring which uncoils from the centre the pull is more uniform and the friction reduced. The steel barrel adopted by the Waltham Company is not only lighter and stronger, but only rotates when the spring is wound.

When the watch is going the boss or body rotates, which is fixed to the great wheel, therefore allowing the spring to unwind from the centre, and thus reduces coil friction, while the barrel remains stationary.

The wristlet is perhaps the most general of to-day. The barrels of these watches being small, care must be taken in fitting a mainspring, to attain the maximum energy in a comparatively small space. It is advisable to observe the barrel holes and arbor pivots. When any roughness appears, a round broach and a polisher employed will reduce friction which would require a stronger mainspring giving a lesser number of turns.

**Fitting Jewel-holes.**—A cracked or broken jewel-hole is removed with a tap from a hammer and a piece of pegwood used as a flat-faced punch. When the hole is ejected the setting is generally opened sufficiently to receive a new stone.

After removing the old one, if the setting is deep and undercut, rub it round with the point of the tweezers or end of a D-shaped burnisher to receive the new stone without shake and form the new setting. It occasionally happens there is insufficient setting to secure a new stone. The cock or plate should be fixed to a cement chuck and pegged true with the hole while the shellac is soft, and a new bed and setting turned to fit the stone. (See Lathe. Shellac Chuck.) In the case of a thorough hole (without endstone), the thickness of the stone must be the same as the old one to attain the right endshake, or a thicker one might be used if there is sufficient metal to lower the seat. The thickness of the stone is not so important where an endstone is employed.

It is not an uncommon occurrence to find the only holes the correct size to fit the pivot are unsuitable in the brass setting. In such cases turn a setting in the lathe from a piece of rod brass and set a loose stone which exactly fits the pivot. (See Lathe.)

Balance staff pivots through wear or damage may sometimes be corrected by sinking a jewel-hole and endstone. When it is found advisable to sink the setting of a hole, it is pegged true on the cement chuck and the shoulder turned back the desired amount. Sunk screw heads to the endstones should be re-sunk. Rough pivots are polished before the jewel-holes are fitted.

Jewellers polish their holes with the finest diamond powder on a copper wire. Stones are reduced to the required thickness and polished on laps charged with diamond powder with the lathe running at a high speed. It is not advisable for horologists engaged in the repairing branch of the trade to attempt grinding or polishing stones. It is a trade in itself. Worn or rough jewel-holes should be replaced.

**Faults in the Balance Spring.**—There are perhaps more instances of indifferent timekeeping attributed to faults in the balance spring than any other part of a watch. To locate any fault and to manipulate the spring is usually the last stage to accomplish in watch repairing. There is as much practice required in the manipulation of a balance spring as to turn or polish flat surfaces. It is quite customary for an instructor to touch the springs for a young watchmaker after he has assembled his watches.

A general survey of the balance spring will reveal its performance. The truth of moving in the round and flat are first located. The attention must be arrested on the play at the index pins and the freedom in general. The latter we will deal with later. A

spring pinned too close or flush with the collet and too
far away on the opposite side is a general fault. Such
a spring would appear out of centre with the collet,
and an attempt at regulation would prove useless.
To bring the spring central without unpinning insert
a round pivot broach between the spring and collet
at the hole shown in Fig. 78 by the dot A and press
the point of the tweezers beyond the broach to bend the

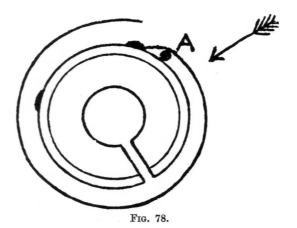

Fig. 78.

spring in, indicated by the arrow. The sketch shows
the spring bent in ; A the round pivot broach.

Two or more coils are often bent out of round or
flat near the centre of the spring, the result of an
accident. The extent of the bends vary considerably,
and with experience there will be no difficulty in
deciding if the spring is worth the time necessary to
bend it true. The spring shown in Fig. 79 is what we
might expect as the result of careless brushing. To
locate the first bend trace the spring round starting

from the collet. It will be noticed the first coil to
deviate from its correct course is bent in, and the start
of the bend is indicated by the dots. The commence-
ment of the other bends which are on the outer coil are
also marked, with two dots. Unpin the spring at the
stud and place it on white paper on the board. The
white being a contrast from the spring the coils of the
latter show more distinctly. Two pairs of fine pointed

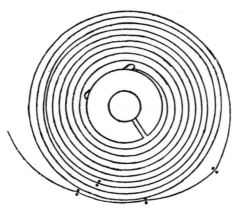

Fig. 79.

tweezers, or a pair and a steel point should be used to
bend a balance spring. The selection is quite a matter
of fancy when performing on these circular operations.
Grip the spring at each place marked by the dots with
the tweezers and bend the coil to assume its circular
course. By bending the coil out in the first case will
close the wide space on the opposite side and thus bring
the coil central with the others.

A spring is often dipped in petrol, placed on a piece
of tissue paper on the board and tapped carefully with

a brush as a means of cleaning.  This is safe enough
for experts, but there is always a liability of bending
a coil in brushing.  A very safe method can be made
in the shape of a box for the drying process.  A circular
or card box will be found convenient with a piece of
wire gauze fixed in the centre to form two compart-
ments.  Put a little boxwood dust in the box.  After
immersing in petrol the spring is placed in, covered
with the lid, and shaken gently.  Hold the box upright
before removing the spring and the gauze will separate
the spring from the box dust.

A fault is often the result of an accident in brushing,

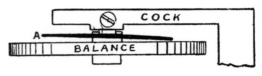

Fɪɢ. 80.

and the outer coil or coils runs out of line with the rest.
When the freedom of the spring is close between the
cock and the balance the coils run foul when the movement is inclined in a certain position.  This will record
itself with a falling off in the vibration of the balance.

To locate the place of bending necessary to bring
the spring true in the flat, hold the movement in a
horizontal position and sight the spring in motion
to assume a straight line.  Any deviation of the spring
from its correct line will then be detected.  The part
of a coil that starts the upward or downward bend from
the body of the spring is the place to grip with the
tweezers.  Fig. 80 shows the elevation of a wristlet
balance cock, stud, balance, and spring.  Although

the spring is out of flat it might free the balance in
the dial up position, but cause a falling in the vibration
with the spring inclined towards the balance. The
spring runs parallel with the balance after leaving the
stud, and commences a downward bend just beyond
the index pin. It is at this point A a slight bend with
the tweezers is necessary to bring the spring flat. The
safest plan for beginners is to remove the spring from
the balance and fix it on the cock. A better idea can
be formed of the relative position of the spring in the
true and round. The cock can easily be moved to any
position and the spring manipulated without fear of
damage to the balance or staff pivots.

The cheap grade " wristlet " without jewel-holes
is a source of trouble to regulate and a good example
of spring imperfections. In this style the spring is
roughly pinned disregarding any effective alteration from
the index. The stud hole is generally a much greater
distance from the pivot hole than the index pins,
sometimes it is less. Unless the outer coil is circular
with the curve described by the path of the index
pins (which is seldom the case) the spring will be thrown
out of centre. Any attempt at regulation by the index
under such existing conditions would only prove futile.
In these instances remove the spring from the balance
and fix the stud on the cock. Bend the spring in close
to the stud, so that the outer coil comes central with
the index, and move the index through its whole path
to see if the spring collet remains central with the
pivot hole.

Wristlet watches are more exposed to the danger
of water coming in contact with the movement.

With regard to the damage it mostly depends on
the fit of the case and the time in the water. The

form of treatment also differs, but the main object is to perform the operation immediately.

In most instances the water finds its way in at the pendant to the keyless parts, and perhaps the barrel, but fails to reach the escapement. A general survey is then necessary to see how the parts are effected, and with a little experience the operator will be able to determine how long the water has been in the movement.

Assuming it has been in the sea, unscrew the lock piece screw, and take out the shaft. When the rust has sufficient grip to render this difficult, it will be advisable to let down the mainspring and take off the barrel bar. If the shaft is rusted tightly, remove the balance, flood the shaft with olive oil and warm it with a spirit flame. The keyless parts being in this condition, a paraffin bath will be found best for cleaning, and boil out in olive oil. Rust which has started on the brass work is easily removed with stiff brush, or a peg-cut wedge shape, and the hollows in the plates can be reached with a small scratch brush.

Rust on the keyless parts is ground out with an emery-stone, or failing this, an emery buff. Rest the wheels and flat pieces on a piece of soft wood in the vice. Two or three brass pins driven in the wood will act as a fixture to prevent the parts slipping. Finish the top and sides of springs lengthways with the stone to attain the grain in the position of bending. A cross grain would be liable to break. The teeth of the wheels are cleaned with a scratch brush, or file cleaner. A lathe will be found best to finish the wheels with a circular grain, and for grinding the winding shaft.

When the water has flooded the movement, or found its way to the escapement, discretion is necessary to

decide if the watch is worth saving.  As a rule with
badly fitting cases the pinions and escapement fail to
survive the destruction from rust in two or three hours.
The timekeeper, however, may be brought in for treatment under these conditions within an hour or so.

In such instances there is a fair chance of saving the
timekeeper.  Take out the movement, remove the
hands, dial, and balance.  Shake off any superfluous
water.  Place the balance and spring in box dust, brush
it dry, and immerse in methylated spirit.  The
movement is then dried in box dust and dissembled.
The usual petrol and chalk brush formula follows,
or the parts may be washed in spirit and brushed.
Either is a matter of fancy.  Rust settling in the keyless
work is not so detrimental, and after placing it in oil
the writer turns his attention to these parts last as
described.

Slight rust on the pinion leaves can be removed
with fine emery mixed with oil.  Knock the wheel
off, and rest the pinion on a block.  Cut a strip of box
wood to fit between the leaves.  The wood is charged
with emery and the leaves ground free from rust.  Clean
the pinion and polish with diamantine.  When rust
has settled in a pinion it should be replaced by a
new one.

**The Harwood Self-Winding Watch.**—This ingenious
invention (Fig. 81) fulfils all its claims.  The wrist motion
winds the watch ; it cannot overwind.  The mainspring is
wound on the same principle as a pedometer winding
invented by Louis Recordon in 1780.  There is a
weighted lever pivoted at one end, and kept in its
normal position against the upper of two banking pins
by a long curved spring so weak that the ordinary
motion of the wearer causes the lever to continually

oscillate between the banking pins. Pivoted to the
same centre as the weighted lever is a rachet wheel
with very fine teeth, and fixed to the lever is a pawl,
which engages with the ratchet wheel. This pawl is
made weak, so as to yield to undue strain caused by

FIG. 81.

the endeavour of the lever to vibrate after the watch
is wound.

In the Harwood device the weighted lever has been
improved with recoil bankings. The setting of hands
is accomplished by rotating the bezel round in either
direction. The inside of the bezel is cut with teeth
gearing with the set hands wheel. A red dot is shown
through a hole in the dail. After setting the hands it
it necessary to turn the bezel in the reverse direction
until the red dot reappears.

Fig. 82 shows the winding, which comprises a weighted
segment pivoted in the centre of the watch and
oscillating round the outer edge of the movement,
and fitted with spring buffers to absorb any shock.

Near the centre of the segment is a pivoted pawl
engaging the teeth of a flat wheel with spur teeth and
which performs the double office of ratchet and gear
wheel and in turn communicates its rotation through
two wheels and pinions to the winding wheel on the
barrel arbor.

Fig. 82.

In setting hands the bezel drives a constate wheel
shown in Fig. 82. It is furnished with a stem on
which slides a castle cam pinion. The upper part is
cut away, at an angle to throw in or out of gear with
the set hands wheel.

**Oysters.**—Rolex Oysters are now made of a slightly
different construction. This difference lies in the way
the metal rim surrounding the movement is held inside
the frame of the case. The first of these rims were
made to rest upon a ledge inside the case, and the back
was screwed up first and the bezel second.

A pin is now fixed into the rim surrounding the movement, and this pin fits into a slot (elongated hole of the
inside case) so that the movement no longer rests upon

a ledge but is just suspended by means of this pin between the pendant and the slot. In this way the screwing up of bezel and back which grip the threaded rim surrounding the movement moves the movement up and down the slot until the final tightening of the back gives it its definite position. An extra hard turn is then given to the *back only* with the tool supplied for the purpose.

When an Oyster is opened by a watchmaker he must make sure whether he is repairing one of the earlier models, which require the bezel unscrewed first. In the new style the back first, a steel tool can be obtained from the maker. Oil the flat surfaces of bezel and back before being screwed up against the frame of the watch case. Ricinus oil does not change in any climate and is recommended by the maker for this purpose. A new glass must be perfectly round and fit the bezel tightly. A small amount of bees-wax should be applied to the groove before fitting the glass, and in order to melt the bees-wax hold the bezel, with the glass fitted, over a spirit flame for a few seconds, and in this way act as a double security to exclude water.

## TURNING BREGUET OVERCOILS

Much has been written on the balance spring, mostly based on theory. It is, perhaps, the favourite subject with non-practical writers, and although their theoretical rules and calculations might appear uninteresting to the average apprentice, theory combined with practice is absolutely necessary to a practical man if he wishes to succeed and master the difficulties appertaining to the balance spring. The calculations and manipulation of a balance spring, sometimes called hair spring, are very perplexing to a beginner. When only he has gained sufficient experience to know the number of different variations in timekeeping are attributed to the balance and spring does he realize what a great deal he has to learn ?

Nickel-steel springs are now fitted to many foreign watches, which are largely responsible for the fine performance of these timekeepers. They have advantages over the steel spring, the inability to rust, a small co-efficient of expansion, and non-sensitivity of magnetic influence.

Infinitely better results are obtained with a quick moving train. English makers, realizing this fact, have emulated the Swiss, with the result that the 18,000 train is used in all modern watches.

Breguet springs are now quite common in the general run of watches. There is no question of doubt as to their superiority for timekeeping, assuming other depending properties are correct. Flat watches are occasionally made with insufficient room between the stud and the balance for reasonable freedom of the flat and overcoil. Unless such a movement falls into the hands of a repairer experienced in the art of springing, its timekeeping property is likely to be rendered useless.

There are many firms who send their Breguet springing to a trade shop. This is attributed to the fact that only a certain standard of ability is engaged, and, while this scheme might work well, there are times when accidents will happen to an overcoil which would save great inconvenience if the operator was capable of bending a bent Breguet spring to its normal shape.

Wristlet watches fitted with a Breguet are no doubt the most difficult " to time ", not because they are small, but are often fitted with insufficient freedom between the balance, coils, overcoil, and cock. More watches of this style are brought in for regulation than any other, with one of the parts mentioned foul in one particular position. One bend, occupying a few minutes, is all that is necessary to complete the work.

The writer has often heard springers arguing, each imagining his idea was the correct way, but members of this class have some method in which they make a speciality.

Two or three springs of approximate strength are often selected. Some prefer to pin the spring in the collet before finally counting it. The point of attachment at the collet should be in a horizontal position with the jewel-hole when the movement is " pendant up ", that is, the centre of gravity. The pinning-in process is, therefore, important, and it will be found easier if we hold the spring in position on the balance, by pressing the collet down, and count the number of vibrations a minute to a centre-seconds watch or a chronograph. An 18,000 train gives 300 vibrations per minute, and, as we count every alternate vibration, the spring should count 150 while the watch records a minute, or, for a preliminary trial, 25 for 10 seconds. Hold the spring in the tweezers and raise it so that the lower pivot touches the glass of the watch and start the balance revolving with a slight backward and forward movement of the wrist. A little practice will be required to start counting the spring at exactly the minute. The best plan is to start the balance a few seconds before the seconds hand reaches the 60, carefully observing that the balance is vibrating exactly at even seconds, and at

60 we start.  For convenience, most horologists count in sequence of 20's, finishing the minute with 10.

When the spring counts exactly 150 to the minute, the part gripped by the tweezers should represent the centre of the overcoil between the stud and index pins. Next break off the waste end, leaving sufficient to reach from the index pins to the other side of the stud.

Precisely the same process applies to pinning in a flat spring to the collet.  We now carefully break away the centre of the eye of the spring, holding the latter with

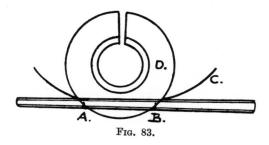

Fig. 83.

a pair of tweezers and bending the waste end towards the centre with a sharp point.  Two pair of tweezers will be found convenient for bending the elbow, which should be the same angle as the hole in the collet.  Place a piece of tissue paper on a broach and rest the collet on it.  File and burnish a pin, with a flat (about one-fourth of the diameter), and fit it to a piece of waste spring in the collet hole, with the flat part against the spring, shown in Fig. 83.  Now it is quite clear if the part of the pin in the hole of the collet is holding the piece of waste spring tight, the same part of the pin would hold the eye of the spring exactly the same when it was placed in position on the collet.  Make a mark on each side of the pin flush with the collet A and B, remove the pin, nick round both marks on a block with a knife, break off the waste end and burnish down the burs. Next place the spring in position on the collet, press the pin in and break it off. The piece of waste spring is shown at C and the collet D.

Having pinned a spring to the collet, it is next placed on the balance and the test made in the truing callipers for true in the round and flat. Many springers mount the collet on an arbor and true it in the lathe. A peg cut to a wedge shape will be found best for truing it in the flat. It is very important the spring should be perfectly true ; any bending should be done on the inner coil nearest the pin.

The bending of the overcoil is the next stage. There is a difference of opinion on the rise. Some prefer an abrupt, but English makers generally favour the gradual. Many horologists who apply the former, place the spring on a piece of hard wood or lead and give it a few taps with a thin, flat punch having a notch to fit over the ribbon of the spring. The spring is then turned over and treated in the same manner at the part that is to finish the rise and bring the overcoil parallel with the flat of the spring.

The writer prefers two pairs of tweezers for bending a gradual rise. Two bends only are necessary to bring it parallel with the flat of the spring. It will be found good practice for a beginner to bend up a temporary overcoil on a spare spring, starting with a little over three-quarters of a coil for the rise, and mark this distance on the permanent spring from the end which is to come through the stud-hole with a little " red stuff ". Bend the overcoil of the temporary spring with the part embraced by the index pins circular with the jewel-hole. Next hold the temporary spring central over the permanent one with the start of the knee bend rise to come exactly over the " red stuff " mark, and it will indicate the point to form the elbow of the eye for pinning in the collet. In most open-face watches the point of attachment to the collet would be slightly under even turns with the stud-hole.

To bend the overcoil, grip the outer coil firmly with one pair of tweezers at the " red stuff " mark and lever

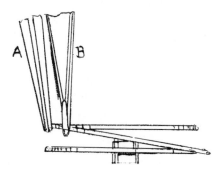

Fig. 84.

the coil up with the other pair to form the incline. Next hold the spring tightly at the end of the incline and bend the terminal up until it is parallel with the flat of the spring. See Fig. 84, which shows the tweezers on the left, A, making the second bend parallel with the coils of the spring. The other pair, B, is simply to hold the outer coil, and the points should be rather on the flat side for strength to enable the spring to be gripped firmly without fear of buckling. The less amount of bending a spring is subject to, the greater the chance of it giving an equal performance in the long and short

arcs.   It  is,  therefore,  preferable  to  bend  a  spring
insufficiently  than  to  bend  it  back  again.

The  next  step  is  to  test  the  height  of  the  rise.   Press
the  spring  collet  on  its  seat,  place  the  balance  in  the
frame,  screw  on  the  cock,  and  notice  if  the  overcoil
is  in  a  line  with  the  stud-hole

Overcoils  with  an  index  are  more  difficult  to  bend
accurately  than  " free  sprung ".   The  curve  encircled
by  the  index  pins  must  be  perfectly  circular  with  the
jewel-hole.   The  terminal  should  be  a  gradual  curve,
free  from  corner  bends, and  a  pair  of  tweezers  with  curved
points  (known  as  corn  tongs)  are  generally  used  to  bend
the  spring.

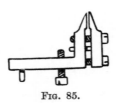

Fig. 85.

A  little  practice  is  necessary  with  the  " corn  tongs "
to  keep  the  curve  parallel  with  the  flat  of  the  spring.
Select  a  pair  of  thick,  broadpointed  tweezers,  file  one
point  concave  and  the  other  convex,  having  the  same
curve  as  the  former.   Round  the  inside  of  one,  and  hollow
the  other  so  that  the  points  form  two  curves  of  the  same
radius.   It  is  important  the  points  should  be  smooth  and
parallel  or  there  will  be  a  difficulty  in  bending  the  spring
straight.   Care  must  be  taken  in  bending,  springs  unnecessarily  manipulated  are  sure  to  cause  excessive
acceleration  in  their  rate,  and  become  a  trouble  in
regulation.

A  very  useful  little  clamp  of  brass,  in  the  form  of  a

minature vice, by Mr. T. D. Wright, for holding a spring
while turning the overcoil is shown in Fig. 85.    The
jaws are curved to the outer coil of an average spring.
The base, which is rectangular with the fixed jaw, has
a screw and steady-pin for fixing to a table tool.    The
loose jaw has two screws, with a steady-pin between ;
the top passes through a clearing hole in the loose jaw,
and tapped into the fixed one.    The bottom screw is
tapped into the loose jaw for the purpose of keeping
the opening parallel.

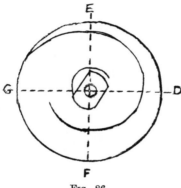

FIG. 86.

The turning of an overcoil with this tool will be
comparatively easy.    Fix the outer coil in the clamp at
the " red stuff " mark, which represents the start of the
overcoil, and bend the terminal with the corn tongs to
the shape of the temporary spring, or sketch of a
theoretical curve.    A good plan is to bend the end of the
overcoil to the stud-hole before finally shaping the
circular part to suit the path of the index pins.

The coil in the flat of the spring that comes directly
under the overcoil will be a guide in bending

circular with the pins. It is advisable to practise on
a few old springs until the student feels confident.

A good plan is to draw two lines on a piece of paper
at right angles, AB and CD, and hold the movement
in such a position so that the pendant is in a line with
the vertical line AB, and the centre of the cock jewel-
hole coincides with horizontal line. We shall then see
exactly where to pin the spring in the stud so that the
point of attachment at the collet comes on the horizontal
line. Fig. 86 shows the relative position of the point of
attachment at the collet to the stud. CD is the horizontal line, and EF parallel with the line drawn through
the pendant AB. Before pinning the spring in the
stud, place the cock on its back, with the end of the
spring in the stud-hole, and notice if it is perfectly
central with the jewel-hole, the hole in the collet will
serve as a guide ; any slight alteration to the overcoil to
bring the spring true in the round should now be made.
Pin the spring in without the balance. The pin holding
the spring in the stud should be smooth, flatted, and
pressed home with a small pair of pliers or strong
tweezers.

The index pins should receive careful attention.
Place the balance in the frame with the spring, and
move it round slowly in both directions until a tooth
drops ; this angular distance of the balance can be taken
as a guide to see if the spring leaves each pin alternately
and touch flat. If either is out of upright the spring will
jump, throwing the outer coil slightly out of flat as it
strikes the pin. A loose pin should be replaced by a new
one. Pins too far apart is another error ; the play
should be just perceptible. It is impossible for any
watch to keep time in the long and short arcs if there is
much play between the pins. A Breguet index should

have only a short, circular contact with the spring, and as close to the stud as possible, the pins to terminate with the spring. This would avoid any tendency to jump the pins, which is more prevalent in flat springs. In fact, the index could be abolished to advantage in all class of watches. Fixing four screws in the balance would cost no more than making an index, and, when made for cheapness, creates faults in other directions.

We now try the watch for mean time ; it may be brought to about one minute a day by adding to or taking weight from the balance. The general rule is to remove two or four opposite screws and replace them with heavier or lighter ones, as the case may be.

When the curve is correct the spring should be " set " by heating. Place it on a bluing-pan until a drop of oil near it begins to smoke. After pinning in the stud the spring should not be altered for mean time adjustment.

There are now two courses open to us—first to adjust for temperature, and the isochronism, the position and mean time trials, of course, to follow. Many springers take the isochronous test first and " set " the spring. The writer prefers this latter method, as any alteration to the screws for temperature should make no material difference to this test.

**Isochronous.**—The long and short arcs of the balance to be performed in the same time. The time of vibration of a pendulum to be the same, regardless of extent of arc. The general method of making the long and short vibrations isochronous is by altering the shape of the overcoil ; as a rule, watches will be found to lose in the short arcs. There is no doubt the correct length of a spring plays an important part regarding isochronism. The late Mr. Glasgow suggested the whole question lies in the theoretical length, and argued that if a spring

is too short the short vibrations will be fast and the long
ones slow, and that all manipulation with an object to
obtain isochronism are only attempts to remedy the error
or alter the effective length of the spring.

M. Phillips, a French mathematician, laid down
certain rules governing the action of the balance
spring.  Their theoretical curves were reduced to
greater simplicity by Jules Grossman, and produced
in book form into the horological world by L. Lossier
in the *Journal Suisse d'Horologerie*, and later translated and published in the *Horological Journal*.

A theoretical terminal curve would be correct if
applied to a perfect balance, but there is always a
small error, and, therefore, the perfect balance is
imaginary.

It is no uncommon occurence for the operator to find
the spring not exactly central with the index pins when
the balance and spring are placed in the frame.  Move
the index from end to end, and if the spring moves,
although the deviation be slight, give the overcoil a
slight bend near the stud in or out, as the case may be,
with tweezers or a steel point.

The start of the overcoil must be perfectly free of the
outer coil of the flat, and the spring concentric in its
expanding and contraction.

Approximate tests for isochronism may be made at
short intervals.  Trials of four or six hours will be found
convenient, but the different periods should be reduced
to 24 hours for comparison.  Many springers check
their watches at odd times, recording the duration
of the trail in minutes, which are worked out to 24 hour
period by the aid of a slide rule or list of tables, to save
unnecessary calculations.  To a beginner, system is an
important factor in making calculations, and for this

reason 24 hour trials will be found more reliable when the rate becomes close. A book should be kept for watch trials, entering the number of the watch, the various trials, with their daily rate, and what alteration made. It will pay in the end to keep a record of the work done for further reference.

There are many methods for obtaining isochronism ; the most general is altering the shape of the overcoil. The short arcs may be quickened by altering the point of attachment at the spring collet, or by using a shorter and thinner balance spring with more open coils, by closing the index pins until the spring is just free, or by altering faults in the escapement. The inertia of a heavy fourth and escape wheel is likely to render such a watch difficult to time, and in these cases a stronger mainspring should bring the piece faster in the short arcs. Many adjusters contend that isochronism is more effective in altering the form and position of the spring attachment in short springs.

The theoretical terminal would fulfil the required conditions, assuming the balance and other depending properties were perfect. We shall conclude, by a trial, that it is generally necessary to deviate from its course in order to obtain a uniformity in the long and short arcs. It is usual to examine the escapement at this period. Look for any fault likely to cause an error between dial and pendant up. To poise a pair of pallets refers to the lever and pallets which are pinned together. This is usually accomplished when the lever is run to depth and pinned. It does not follow that because the pallets are in poise when made they will remain so when fixed to another depending object.

Many errors in timekeeping can be traced to " lever and pallets out of poise ". This is usually an original fault, and by no means uncommon in escapements of a cheap class.

A springer on making his tests for isochronism will invariably test his lever and pallets from the direction of his error. A very little will make a noticeable difference for position in a fine watch. The form of procedure is much the same as poising a balance. Rest the pallet staff pivots on a poising tool, or a pair of callipers would answer the purpose. As a rule, the tail of the lever is left too heavy, and a little can be stoned off the end, leaving it the same shape, then polished. When the fork end falls to the bottom on the poising tool, rest the fork on a piece of soft wood in the vice and stone away the curves behind the wings to form a deeper hollow to the curves. Clean the escapement if it is at all dirty. Screw on the balance cock, hold the balance upright over the cock, with the pivot central over the jewel-hole, so that the impulse pin comes on the line of centres with the balance and pallet holes, and notice which screw in the balance, or part of the rim, is on a line with the balance staff hole and stud screw hole. The stud hole should now come in a line with the balance staff hole and the imaginary line on the rim of the balance to be perfectly in beat.

We next take a four hour trial. Start in the morning and wind the mainspring one turn. We then attain the shortest vibration. The watch should be set to mean time to coincide with a reliable regulator or chronometer and placed dial up at 8 a.m. At the end of the trial the time is observed. We will assume it has lost four seconds. The variation is noted in book : 12 noon P. up — 4. The watch should then be wound about two turns and placed pendant down. After another four hour trial it is found to be 9 seconds slow ; that is, it has lost 5 seconds during this trial. We make a note of this, 4 p.m. P. down — 9, and wind the spring full to get the greatest vibration, and place it dial up. At the end of four hours, which would be 8 p.m., it is found to be 6 seconds slow, having gained 3 seconds. We note this trial, 8 p.m. D. up — 6, and extend another column, multiplying each variation (which represents four hours) by 6 to attain the variation in 24 hours. We then have P. up — 24, P. down — 30, D. up + 18. Add the two former trials together and divide by two to get

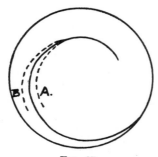

Fig. 87.

the mean variation in the short arcs, 24 + 30 = 54 ÷ 2 = 27. As one quantity is minus and the other plus, we add them, which gives us 27 + 18 = 45. The short arcs are, therefore, 45 seconds slow.

When the short arcs are slow, the overcoil is bent flatter towards the centre with a little more of the flat added to the overcoil as would apply in this case (shown in Fig. 87 at A). When the long arcs are slow, the overcoil is bent away from the centre to quicken the long arcs. The alteration to an overcoil should be very gradual. The watch is again set to time and 24 hour trials taken.  A is the overcoil altered when the short arcs are slow ;  B represents an alteration when the long arcs are slow.

Sometimes a second trial is necessary for isochronism. We proceed in the same manner, except trials of a longer duration are more reliable as the watch becomes closer. When the variation of the long and short arcs coincide, the spring is said to be isochronous.  However, we will assume the result of our trials show only a small difference, which may probably be an escapement error.

Next we take a trial for compensation for temperature. It is usual to give the watch a few hours' run in the oven before starting the trial, to let the balance and spring settle down to the change.  An oven with a temperature of 85 to 90 degrees, and usually a refrigerator or ice-box, is required for temperature adjustment.  Trials in the cold chamber necessitates a little more trouble.  It is customary to make temperature adjustments after the piece has been subject to 24 hour tests in the oven and a lower temperature.  The balance and spring should be carefully cleaned in petrol after each trial, or through condensation they are liable to rust, and except for marine chronometers and high-class watches the ice-box as applied to repairs might be dispensed with.

We will assume it has lost 5 seconds in the oven.  The watch is then wound and placed in the same position, dial up, in a cold receptacle, and at the end of 24 hours it is + 7, that is, it has gained 12 seconds.  Note this in the book under the isochronism trials.  The tests now show that the balance is under-compensated, and the screws require shifting nearer the free end of the rim. When altering the screws of the balance they should always be moved exactly the same relative position on each side and screwed home to the rim, or the balance will be thrown out of poise. When the trials show the watch to be gaining in the oven, it is over-compensated, and the screws should be moved nearer the fixed end of the rim. Shifting a screw one hole nearer the free end of the rim will make a greater difference than a one-hole alteration nearer the fixed end, and the entry should be made of the number of the holes into which the screws are replaced for future reference.

As the rate between the two temperatures becomes close, 48-hour trials will be found more reliable, and as the daily rate between the two temperatures reduces the error to about 3 seconds, we will consider the trial satisfactory.

It is advisable, after completing the temperature trials, to test the balance for truth, poise, and then set it.

The balance usually requires poising after the temperature trials. Moving the screws always make a slight difference. The reduction should be made from the end of the screws where the balance is heavier, and polish the ends on a screw-head lap or in the lathe, but on no condition alter the weight or relative position of the four quarter screws, which are used for final mean time adjustment. Two opposite, or the four screws are turned slightly in for losing, and out for gaining, as the case may be. Unscrewing the four quarter screws one turn each should make the watch lose about one minute a day, but, of course, there is no rule, it depends on the proportional weight of the screws to the balance. Thin washers of various thickness and assorted sizes are used by repairers to fit between the screw-head and the rim when the piece is gaining. These will be found very useful, and can be obtained from your material dealer. Best balances are fitted with steel quarter nuts instead of screws, the gold adjustment head having a slot at each end and at right angles to each other. A screwdriver with a notch cut to free the screw thread is kept especially for this work.

A pair of callipers, with one arm screwed in the vice, is employed by many timers for poising a balance. It is then rubbed gently with a smooth round file. Modern shape callipers, provided with an adjusting safety screw, a weak spring, male and female centres. are more simple to manipulate, and jewelled V shaped centres are preferable. For poising a balance, the poising tool is now generally used. It is more accurate, less dangerous, and quicker to indicate the error of the balance.

The balance is next " set ". It is placed on a hot metal block (with a hole in the centre to free the roller) until the free ends of the rim close the slit and touch the fixed ends. Then remove it to a similar cold metal block until the rim assumes its normal shape, reiterate the process three or four times, and the position and mean time trials follow.

When adjusting for positions, the balance should have a vibration not less than a turn and a quarter in the long arcs. Wind the watch and take 24 hour trials in all the positions. Assuming it has gained 14 seconds dial up, pendant up it has gained at the rate of 12 seconds a day, pendant right we find its daily rate is + 11 seconds, and left + 15, pendant down + 10 seconds. Now we may conclude that when any two of the closest quarters are slower or faster than the others, or any one quarter or position shows a decided deviation from the rest, there is probably a slight escapement error, such as lever and pallets out of poise, a defective jewel-hole, impulse pin too tight in the notch, guard pin too close, a badly-shaped pivot.

If there is no apparent escapement error, we may

conclude the balance is too heavy at the part that is opposite the VI and IX, when it is at rest. We should in this case slightly screw in the quarter screws or timing nuts, opposite the VI and IX, or unscrew the opposite ones.

## APPLYING A FLAT BALANCE SPRING

Assuming the old spring is useless for reference, the train might be 16,200 vibrations per hour, or possibly 14,400. However, an 18,000 train is easily located, which gives us 300 per minute, while the fourth wheel makes one rotation. Any number train makes 30 vibs, for one turn of the escape wheel 300 divided by 30 equals 10. The difference, therefore, between the escape pinion and the fourth wheel for any 18,000 train is 10. An escape pinion of 6 would have a fourth wheel of 60, a pinion of 7 would have a wheel of 70, or 8 of 80, a suitable combination.

The ratio of the escape pinion to the fourth wheel of a 16,200 train is 9. Therefore 7 and 63 would be correct numbers. A 14,400 train would show a product of 8. This rule applies, of course, assuming the watch has a seconds hand or a seconds train. (The fourth wheel makes one turn in a minute.) It occasionally happens in an old fusee the train is an odd number ; it is advisable in such cases to count the number of teeth in the wheels, multiply them together, and divide by the product of the three pinions multiplied together, which would give us the number of vibrations per hour We will take as example an old lever train. Centre wheel 63, third 60, fourth 60, escape 15, with third pinion 8, fourth 8, and escape 7. As there are two vibrations for each escape wheel tooth, we multiply the number of teeth in the wheel by 2. We then have—

$$\frac{63 \times 60 \times 60 \times 30}{8 \times 8 \times 7} = 15187$$

vibrations per hour. This is an example of an odd number that would cause trouble if we attempted to spring it without counting the train.

We will take an ordinary 18,000 train wristlet watch. The strength of the spring depends on the length, width, and thickness. Place the cock on its back on the board and select a spring a little larger in radius than the distance from the centre of the jewel-hole to the index pins. The strength of the spring for this radius to coincide with the weight of the balance is determined by counting it with a watch going to time. A centre seconds or chronograph watch with a flat crystal glass is most accurate for this operation.

The balance spring holder obtainable at any material dealer will be found very useful to those who find a difficulty in vibrating the balance with the tweezers.

To count the vibrations without fear of damage to the spring, place the latter on the balance with the collet pressed down sufficiently to hold it.

Grip the spring with the tweezers at the coil that comes opposite the index pins, lifting it so that the lower balance pivot just touches the glass of the watch for support, and start the balance vibrating with a slight backward and forward movement of the wrist, while the fourth finger and edge of the wrist is resting on the board to keep the hand steady. A little practice will be required to start counting the spring at exactly the minute.

A good plan is to vibrate the balance a few seconds

before the chronograph reaches the 60, carefully observing that the balance starts its vibration exactly at even seconds, such as 56 or 58, and at 60 start counting for 10 seconds. If the spring is correct it should count 25. When the number counted in 10 seconds is more, it is too strong and should be replaced in the packet and the next number weaker tried in the same way. Refrain from touching steel springs with the fingers, and opening more than one packet at a time.

When a spring counts a little less than 25 in 10 seconds, move the tweezers about half a coil round nearer to the centre and recount it. A spring that counts correctly will usually have a coil or two of waste beyond the point where the tweezers gripped. Break off a small piece of the end.

The pin having been made to fit the piece of waste spring (see Breguet Overcoils), there will be less danger of distorting the inner coil when pinning the spring to the collet.

It is not advisable to pin a spring to the collet before determining if its diameter coincides with the distance of the index pins to the centre of the jewel-hole. Many watchmakers take preliminary trials to ascertain this calculation with a small knob of bees-wax to hold the centre of the spring to the balance. There are occasions when the collet fails to hold sufficiently tight except when pressed down flush with the balance arm and the bees-wax method would then become useful, which is as follows : Take a small piece of bees-wax, about the size of a spring collet, roll it in a ball, flatten it, then press the end of the coil into the bees-wax and push the staff pivot· into the centre.

The centre of the spring is next broken off to form the eye. Place it on a sheet of white paper for this operation.

A thin, pointed pair of tweezers and a needle point will be found most suitable for this work. Hold the spring over the collet to compare the amount of waste spring that intersects the collet, allowing for the elbow. Grip the inner coil with the tweezers and bend the waste piece towards the centre with the point, holding the latter close to the tweezers to form a sharp corner, bend it back, and it will break off. When more than a coil requires to be removed, it will be found safer to sever it in three or four pieces to avoid bending the inner coils. The spring should fit easily over the collet with a little shake before forming the elbow.

There are many methods adopted for forming the elbow ; they all aim at one object—to produce the curve with one unabrupt bend, perfectly flat with the coils of the spring. A needle, with the end filed up, using the eye as a slot and fixed in a handle, is a favourite tool with many springers to lever the elbow the required shape.

Two pairs of tweezers, or one pair with a needle point, are two safe forms of procedure. The main feature is to hold them upright, and form the bend level with the coils of the spring, pointing the same angle as the hole in the collet. This can be tested by holding the spring over the collet, and notice if the elbow comes over the centre of both ends of the hole.

The next stage is to place a piece of tissue paper on a broach and press the spring collet on tight. Let the spring down flush with the collet and guide the elbow into the hole. This is easily accomplished without bending it by bringing the inner coil farther away from the elbow to rest on top of the collet and touch the broach. The end of the elbow is then guided in with the tweezers. Before pushing the pin in, a general survey of the spring with relation to the collet is necessary. Notice if the elbow is right in the hole, and the spring looks true in the round and flat. Although the spring is quite likely to go out a little in pinning, a great deal depends on this step. A spring badly pinned will often result in a futile search for the cause of indifferent timekeeping. When the spring is setting correctly on the collet, push the pin in, which was described. (See Breguet Overcoils.)

We now press the collet on the balance and count the spring for half a minute to the chronograph, or stop-watch, in the same manner as the short trials of 10 seconds. For half a minute it should count 75. When nearly accurate count a full minute, which should record 150.

Many factories employ a vibrator. This tool is used to determine the time of vibration of a spring by observation instead of counting. The vibrator consists of a balance and spring accurately vibrating to time on a platform with an arm, which holds the spring distended and used as a standard. The balance and spring to be tested is started vibrating in unison and by the side of the standard. The difference is soon visible and the necessary alteration adjusted for fast or slow.

Truing the spring in the flat and round is the next procedure. This operation not only requires a trained eye, but a little experience to attain satisfactory results. A beginner will benefit by a little practice on a few old springs pinned to their collets. To true a spring in the flat, mount the collet on an arbor with a horse-hair bow and fix it in the turns. Many of the " old school " place the arbor or the spring collet on the balance in the callipers. The lathe is quite capable of accomplishing the work, and the turning arbor minus its collet would

be held in a split chuck. The course adopted is quite a
matter of fancy. Hold a pair of tweezers, or a peg cut
wedge shape, on the rest to act as toucher. Move the
bow slowly and observe the deviation of the sprine
from the flat or straight line. The observation should be
confined to the first coil as it leaves the pin-hole, and all
bending should be performed at this part with the peg
or tweezers to bring it in a vertical line, as shown by the

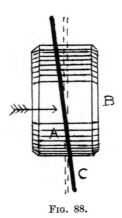

Fig. 88.

dots in Fig. 88. The arrow is the part at which the
pressure is applied, A is the pin-hole, B the collet and C
the spring.

Having pronounced the spring true in the flat, the next
stage is truing it in the round.

To bend a spring approximately true in the round is
by no means difficult, but to get it perfectly true is
quite another matter, the latter is only attained with
practice. The most difficult proposition is perhaps to
determine the correct part for bending. All bending

as a means of truing a spring should be accomplished within the first third of a coil from the collet hole, and the less a spring is bent the better the chance of obtaining isochronism.

A balance spring is said to be isochronous when it causes both the long and short arcs of the balance to be performed in the same time. Most watches lose in the short arcs, the error varies with the imperfection of the spring. Although the term isochronism might be suggestive of theoretical calculations, it is important the students should understand its meaning in practical work, and aim as far as possible to attain it. Isochronism is often misunderstood to mean position errors. The latter is due to escapement faults and bad jewelling. A watch may be perfectly isochronous and yet have position errors. The long arcs are understood to be dial up, the short pendant up or hanging.

The short arcs may be quickened by closing the index pins so that there is only perceptible play, or by fitting a stronger mainspring. A spring to be isochronous must be pinned up at even turns, that is the end of the eye at the collet comes opposite the stud hole. Adjustments can be made by altering the shape or point of attachment of the eye. A spring pinned to the collet out of round or flat, kicking and jumping while in motion like the waves of the sea, is a hopeless case of sochronal adjustment. Such a watch would be inconsistent in timing in the long and short arcs, and the spring should be re-pinned at the collet.

Truing a spring in the round is accomplished at any required point from the collet hole to the first quarter coil of the eye. The main object is to bend the spring at the right place, and the correct amount. Unnecessary bending distorts the molecules of the spring, and under

these conditions regulating for timekeeping would prove
a fiasco.    Fig. 89 shows the place of bending necessary
to bring this spring true in the round indicated by the
arrow.

We now come to the pinning stage.    Fit a pin to
the stud in the same manner as the pin to fit the
spring collet.  Push a pivot broach in the stud-hole and
hold the cock in a horizontal position to see if the
broach is parallel with the plane of the cock.  If the
hole is out of level, a slight twist of the broach inclined

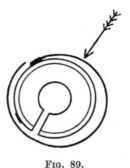

FIG. 89.

in the opposite direction will bring it correct.  The cock
is next placed on its back, and the end of the spring
passed through the stud-hole ready for pinning.

Circling and levelling the spring is the next procedure.  The part of the spring embraced by the index
pins should be a curve central with the jewel-hole.
Move the index to its full sweep and notice if the spring
is thrown out of centre during its path.  If the spring is
moved in any direction by moving the index, the part
embraced by the latter is not central, and a slight bend
near the stud would correct it.

The index pins play a more important part than many horologists imagine. The futility of neglect in this direction displays the lack of knowledge in timing, resulting in the loss of time and fruitless attempts at regulation. Badly fitted, rough, or pins out of upright will cause a variation in the long and short arcs. The spring on striking a pin out of perpendicular would be thrown out of flat, or causing the coils to tremble with the same result. It will pay in the end to replace defective index pins. Drive out the old stumps from under the index with the latter resting on a hollow punch, held in the vice. File and burnish the new pins, fitting them tightly from the top of the index allowing a little for drive. Stone and burnish over the tops. Rest the index on a hollow punch held in the vice, with the pins in the hole, and drive home with a flat punch flush with the index.

The second coil jumping the index pins is another source of trouble. The quickest and easiest remedy is to shorten the pins flush with the spring, close them so there is only perceptible freedom, and finish the ends to a curve wedge shape on the Waltham principle. It is then absolutely impossible for any coil to find a resting place.

Place the cock on its back with the spring pinned in the stud, to see if any slight alteration is required. Any slight bending here takes place before starting its trials. It frequently happens, the centre of the spring is a trifle out of centre with the jewel-hole. One slight bend only will be found necessary to get it central. When the jewel-hole is sighted in the centre of the collet-hole, we know it is correct.

We will assume the watch has run its first trial with the new spring and the variation noted in a book kept

for springing and adjusting watches.  Enter the name
of the customer, the number of the watch, the date, and
any alteration made to the balance or spring.  Such a
book will prove useful when a customer brings the watch
back on future occasions.

Short trials will be found convenient in the preliminary
stages, and these should be multiplied to give the variation in 24 hours.  To " take up " or " let out " the spring
is easily accomplished when the collet is removed from
the balance and the stud fixed to the cock.  It is not
only avoiding risk of damage to the staff pivots, but
easier to keep the spring true in the round and flat.
When the gaining or losing rate is within five minutes
a day, the balance should be poised.  Many springers
prefer this procedure before starting the first trial.

Balance collets are invaluable for screw balances in
bringing a watch to time when the piece is gaining with
no spring to " let out " at the stud, or with a Breguet
spring and the index over to the slow.  It is not usual
on such occasions to alter a Breguet at the stud.  To open
the index pins is by no means a more successful
operation ;  all possibility of close timekeeping in the
long and short arcs is frustrated.  Except by horologists
who are expert at springing, it is a safe maxim to refrain
from altering a Breguet spring as a means of regulation.
Different sizes and gauges of balance collets are obtainable at any material dealer's.  A pair the same diameter
as the screw head fixed on opposite screws will show a
difference in timekeeping from half a minute to six
minutes a day, according to the thickness or gauge of
the collets.

It is often necessary to poise a screw balance by adding
weight.  This is easily accomplished with an assortment of balance collets.  Single collets of suitable gauge

placed behind the heads of adjoining screws will accommodate instead of the orthodox method of fitting new screws.

A compensation balance out of true in the flat can be trued by trying it in the callipers with a toucher and bending the two sides of the rim with the thumb and fingers. " Out of round " is not such an easy matter. The usual procedure is to adopt the calliper test with a toucher. If the bend is equal and on both sides from the fixed end, it is usually trued with a slot cut in a piece of rod brass fixed to a handle. The slot deep enough to take the rim, with a little shake. When the bend is not regular, or away from the fixed end, the safest plan is to remove the screws, placing them in their relative position in holes on an old barrel or stand. Rest the rim of the balance on a boxwood block cut hollow in the vice, rub the inside of the rim with a half round burnisher to bring it inwards, and the part outwards with the tool described.

The general method of poising a balance consists of removing weight at the heaviest part. Many of the old school use the callipers for this test, but a poising tool will be found quicker and safer for beginners. In a plain balance or cylinder pocket watch it is advisable to leave the part of the balance farthest away from the pendant when the escapement is at rest, slightly heavier. This should give a gaining rate of half to one minute a day in the short arcs when going to time dial up, and so that as far as possible equalizing dial up and when carried in the pocket. In most watches this would coincide with the position of the banking pin shown in Fig. 90 ; the part of the rim at B would be parallel with a vertical line through the pendant. The circle represents the rim of a balance on a poising tool at rest slightly

heavier at A, with the banking pin about 30 degrees
to the right.

When a balance easily comes to rest on the tool with
the part of the rim much heavier at A, chamfer a hole
on the under part of the rim at A with a graver, or an
old round file sharpened as a three-edge chamfer.  To
cut the hole a little care is required to avoid bending
the balance.  Hold the rim of the balance reversed in the
thumb and finger, and rest the rounded edge on a boxwood block, or any smooth rigid object ;  the cutter

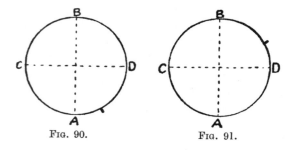

FIG. 90.                    FIG. 91.

must be sharp or a slip might prove disastrous.  Try the
balance on the tool if it is still too heavy with the
banking pin nearer to A, cut a smaller sink between
B and D to bring the smaller sink nearer the top and the
pin back to its original position.  Sometimes it will be
found necessary to cut several small holes before the
balance is in poise slightly heavier with the banking pin,
as shown in Fig. 90.

Fig. 91 shows a balance out of poise with the pin a
quarter of a circle out from the required position.  As
the balance comes to rest with the heaviest part at the
bottom, a little practice will be required to determine
how much metal to take off and the correct place to

remove it. The heaviest part is A, and we require the rim at D to be slightly heavier. We might possibly get the balance perfectly in poise by cutting away one hole at A, but our object is to lighten the weight at C in order to let D fall to the bottom. Therefore chamfer a hole at A and a smaller one at C, and try the balance on the tool. It is quite possible a small hole would be required between A and C, but between these points the operation should take place. It is advisable to repeatedly place the balance on the tool until the student feels confident of the amount to cut away. Remember you can always take off a little more, but too much excavating would mean altering the balance spring, and it might mean a new one.

The same angular rule regarding the weight applies to the poising of a screw balance. The four quarter crews are used for timing purposes ; the others may be reduced by shortening the heads flat in a screw tool and polished. Always try to emulate the original.

**Polishing Flat Surfaces.**—Although there is not a great deal to learn in polishing, which is mainly a question of practice, there is a certain fascination in adorning horological work with its finish which marks its rank of quality.

Blocks of bell metal, zinc, and tin are the principal metals employed in polishing. The most convenient sizes are $1\frac{1}{2}$ or 2 inches in diameter. The blocks must be filed perfectly flat and scraped clean with every additional application of polishing material. Studs, indexes, rollers, levers, pallets, and the sockets of minute hands are the principal pieces that require polishing in a modern watch. The escapement parts usually require attention through rust.

The stump of a fusee or centre hole size broach fixed

in a file handle will be found convenient for holding a minute hand during the polishing operation. Grind the end to a flat or obtuse point. When the socket of a minute hand has been punched, or appears out of flat, the quickest method is to file it flat, resting the boss on a piece of soft wood in the vice. Place it on a bell metal block charged with oilstone dust and rub with a quick circular motion, gripping the hand at the hole with the broach tool. If, as it frequently happens, the stem touches the metal block, the rubbing should be confined near the edge or the blue will be polished away. When the file marks are removed and the edges "up", clean the hand with bread kneaded with a little oil, or immersed in petrol and brushed, finally pegging the hole. Cleanliness and quickness are the chief features in polishing. If the slightest particle of oilstone dust or dirt remains on the hand, it is impossible to give it the final polish free from scratches. The socket is next polished in the same manner on a zinc or tin block charged with diamantine ; a very little of the latter should be applied. Rub briskly with a circular motion until the polishing material is almost dry ; reverse the motion occasionally.

Diamantine is the quickest cutting and most popular polishing material for steel. It can be used on soft steel, bell metal, zinc or tin polishers. (See " Turning a Balance Staff in the Turns ".) Refrain from using a graver or other sharp tool to deposit the material on the polisher. For polishing screw heads diamantine mixed with about the same proportion of oil will give a more uniform colour when tempering the steel.

Pallets and levers are polished in the same way, or could be placed on a piece of soft wood in the vice, and the block moved with a circular motion. Studs and indexes are generally shellaced to a larger piece of flat brass to form a steady base and polished on a block, while a graver point grips the brass to give the revolving motion.

The same rules apply to polishing brass surfaces. The polisher, of course, must be softer than the metal to be polished. Tin is therefore selected for escape wheels, and boxwood strips mostly employed for lathe work. After various trials the writer finds soft paste diamantine equal to any for brass work.

## THE VERGE ESCAPEMENT

The verge is perhaps the first form of recoil frictional rest escapement. The balance has therefore no free or detached arc, the escape wheel is continually pressing on the verge during any part of the vibration. The balance staff which forms the verge is set nearly at right angles to the escape wheel arbor, and the pallets are the same distance apart as the diameter of the escape wheel, each pallet engaging on the opposite side of the wheel.

The pallets should form an angle of about 95 degrees, or slightly more than a right angle, but, unfortunately, many pallets are found to have 105 degrees, and some-times more. With these wide angle pallets we get a larger vibration and less recoil, which is considered by many unsuitable to attain the best results. Many old horologists who would be considered authorities on the verge have stated that 95 degrees is sufficient. With a smaller angle we obviously get a smaller vibration and a greater recoil. Closing the pallets is easily accom-plished by holding the centre of the arbor between the

two pallets over a spirit flame, and with a pair of hot
pliers twist the bottom pallet slightly round in the
direction of the top.

The escape wheel, sometimes referred to as the
" balance wheel " or " crown wheel ", has various
numbers of teeth, but 13 is the general. It should be
pitched perfectly at right angles to the verge, with the
potance pivot hole in the centre of the verge staff, or
the drops will not be equal. The follower at the other
end is used to regulate the depth. The escape wheel
teeth are cut back at an incline to free the pallets as the
wheel recoils, and the recoil continues until the balance
has completed its vibration.

The verge is practically obsolete and bears no comparison with a lever or even a well constructed cylinder
for timekeeping. The earliest form of verge was
employed before the introduction of the balance spring.
Some years ago there was a good business done in con-
verting verge watches into lever escapements, but the
modern watch has to a great extent robbed the escapement maker of many a verge-conversion.

There is generally trouble in regulating the verge ;
the wide variation is more prominent when wound and
three-parts down. Sometimes it will be found necessary
to set up or let down the mainspring, but assuming this
is right, the escapement must be theoretically correct.
The least amount of drop should be attained, and to
ensure this is equal on both pallets, the escape wheel
hole in the potance must be in a line with the centre of
the verge staff. If the drops are greater on the lower
pallet, draw out the brass slip slightly which contains
the escape wheel hole. Occasionally the drops are
unequal on different teeth. In this case the escape wheel
should be trued.

Perhaps the quickest way is to put the wheel in the callipers, holding a toucher near the teeth, and when the wheel rotates you will notice if the points of some teeth are higher than the others. Mount the wheel in the turns, holding a blue stone well oiled firmly on the rest so that it just touches the teeth. Give the bow long sweeps until the tips of all the teeth are true. Notice the points of some teeth are much thicker than others. It would, therefore, be necessary to file the backs of the teeth in order to bring the points the same thickness and equal distance to each other. For this purpose a smooth " crossing-out " file is suitable. Try the escapement in the plates with the contrate wheel ; put a little power on the latter with a peg, and slowly move the balance round in alternate directions until the escape wheel drops.

When a verge requires a new hole, the safest plan is to knock out the plug in the cock and upright it from the bottom hole.

The plug is often true with the bottom hole, however, fix the top plate in the mandrel and peg the lower hole true. Screw on the cock and test the cock hole for truth with a peg. If it happens to be out, turn it true with the slide rest, or a hand cutter to pass freely through the hole.

Place the verge in the plate, screw on the cock, and mark the distance the top pivot enters the plug hole in the cock, that is the distance from the bottom of the new plug, to the end of the pivot. This distance can be measured in a gauge or on the end of a piece of pegwood.

Turn a new plug in the lathe to fit the hole in the cock from the outside, catch the centre true with a graver, and drill the pivot hole the same depth as recorded on the pegwood. This is a simple matter, as

the point of the peg can be used as a gauge to try the
hole for depth without removing the work from the
chuck.    When the hole is the correct depth, alter the
end of the drill to a chisel or flat shape, to finish the end
of the hole square.    Turn the plug off to length and
drive it in the cock from the outside until the endshake
of the verge is correct.

## ASSEMBLING  A  REPEATER

Repeating watches were invented in the seventeenth
century.    At that period they were invaluable for
ascertaining the time in the dark, but since the improvement in electricity, the switch electric dial has found
public favour at a much smaller outlay, consequently
repeaters are quite uncommon as a repair in most shops.

Cleaning and repairing a repeater affords much
opportunity for developing the brain.    There are several
different styles of arranging the parts, although the
mechanism is much after the principle of striking work.
Naturally it is more fragile and easily deranged by careless manipulation.    Many early forms repeat by pressing
in the pendant, but the slide in the band of the case is
now generally used.

It is advisable to examine the action of the repeating
parts before taking it to pieces.    The repairer will learn
much by careful examination of the different parts.

A quarter repeater is perhaps the most general.
When the slide in the band of the case is pressed home
the mainspring is wound and the hour rack pressed down
until the tail reaches the snail.    The teeth in the hour
rack pass the pallet, which trips and returns immediately

to its original position by a weak spring. The slide also moves the "all or nothing" piece which releases the quarter rack, and it is thrown on the quarter snail by a weak spring. When the slide is released, the train of wheels are free to run, and each tooth lifts the pallet for the number of blows struck for the hour. After the hours are struck a pallet on the barrel arbor square engages the quarter rack, bringing it back to its original position, while the two sets of ratchet teeth lift the pallets in passing, causing the quarter to be struck. The number of quarters to be struck is determined by the tail of the quarter rack falling on the quarter snail, which is central with the cannon pinion. The hammers are pivoted in the ordinary way with a second long pivot or stud passing through a slot in the pillar plate, and by this stud the hammer is regulated to rest free of the gongs by two springs screwed to the plate, one acting as a stop banking. The speed of the train is regulated by a wheel and pair of pallets on the principle of an alarm clock. Many of the old style of repeaters have the pivot holes of the last wheel in the train eccentric in a screwed-in bush, and by altering the depth the speed is adjusted.

It is customary in some shops to put a watch away partly finished and proceed with a clock or other work more urgently needed, but when working under such circumstances it is advisable to ascertain that all work required the same day is cleared up to afford the repairer the chance of finishing his repeater uninterrupted. It is an easy matter to lose a piece when putting a repeater in pieces away hurriedly. Young horologists, with a very limited experience at such work, require the whole of their attention displayed on the complicated mechanism.

The repeating train is sometimes in a separate bar. This should be put together first, together with the hammers, barrel, centre, third and fourth wheels, screw on the top plate, and complete the escapement, oiling all the necessary parts in the going train and the pivot holes in the repeating train. There is no orthodox method for the next procedure. Many horologists get most of the repeating parts together before putting the movement in the case. A three-armed holder will be found very useful at this stage to grip the pillar plate. The writer prefers to fix the movement in the case, as it leaves both hands free to manipulate the various parts as the case lies on the board.

Screw on the two hammer springs and the two banking pieces which keep the hammers from touching the gongs when at rest. Place the hour rack on the square of the repeating barrel arbor, which has a mark or dot to indicate the right square, and put on the winding pinion. Next put on the two pallets and springs, the hour snail and star wheel, the jumper and spring. Place a key upon the winding pinion of the repeating barrel arbor and wind it about two turns until twelve teeth have passed the pallet, and hold it in position with your left hand while you put on the winding rack so that it falls on the twelve step of the snail. Release the key and let the train run so that the twelve teeth are gathered up.

The quarter rack and spring are placed into position, the quarter snail, the " all or nothing " piece, and the finger piece on the barrel arbor which brings the quarter rack into its position, and pin it on. Screw on the gongs and try the repeating work at the hour and quarters. The hour and minute wheel follow. Set the hands forward until the flirt piece jumps the star wheel round. Put on the dial and hands exactly at the hour after the one that previously struck.

Rusty gongs generally give a bad sound. They should be cleaned with a strip of emery cloth wrapped round pegwood. Then brush and polish with diamantine and bell metal, resting the gong on a piece of clean cork. Be careful not to mix screws when taking it to pieces. A screw put in a wrong place will often foul another piece and cause trouble.

See that all springs press well home the pieces they drive. The hammer pivots, studs, and ends of the acting springs should have a little oil. The case slide should be quite clean but not oiled, as it would collect dust.

## THE CHRONOMETER ESCAPEMENT

A chronometer is an instrument for measuring accurate time. It is generally understood to mean an escapement with a spring or pivoted detent where the impulse is given direct from the escape wheel tooth to the balance staff. The chronometer escapement was invented about 1760 by Le Roy, for marine time-keepers to keep Greenwich time for the purpose of obtaining the longitude at sea.

It is stated that Earnshaw and Arnold perfected the escapement about 1780. In John Arnold's escapement the detent moved towards the centre of the wheel to unlock, the arms and rim were sunk to free the locking stone and the teeth were said to be epicycloidal curves ; however, they required oiling, and were subsequently abandoned. In 1781 Thomas Earnshaw substituted the spring detent for the pivoted form. His detent moved away from the centre of the wheel to unlock on the same principle as they are now used.

The chronometer escapement is very delicate, and although occasionally employed in high-class watches, it only gives satisfaction when in the hands of careful wearers ; with rough usage, it is liable to " set ". As the pocket variety and the marine are practically alike, the same form of procedure is adopted in repairing.

The escape wheel has 15 teeth. The rim and arms are turned out for lightness, leaving a thin edge to support the teeth. When the escapement is at rest a tooth is on the locking stone which is fixed in a pipe of the detent, and lies against the screw head of a banking stud. The foot of the detent is screwed to the plate. Fitted to the balance staff are two rollers, which should only be removed in case adjustment is necessary to the escapement. The impulse pallet in the large roller should be opposite an escape wheel tooth when at rest. When the balance is moved the small roller or discharging pallet engages the gold spring which is fixed to the detent and projects slightly beyond the end. The detent is thus moved by means of the gold spring. Until the tooth is released from the locking stone, the wheel being now free, the impulse pallet should be in front of a tooth, so that it drops safely on the pallet and gives impulse to the balance. As soon as the drop on the impulse occurs the discharging pallet should be leaving the gold spring, when the detent springs back to its original position against the banking stud ready to receive the next tooth of the escape wheel. The impulse roller is planted as near as possible to intersect the path of the escape wheel equal to the distance between two teeth, so that the impulse pallet may attain a safe intersection when the tooth drops on to it. The tooth engages the impulse pallet until it leaves the path of intersection of the roller. The drop on to the locking should be very slight, daylight between the edge of the roller and tooth is sufficient.

The end of the detent does not come quite up to the gold spring, therefore the discharging pallet on its return vibration simply bends the gold spring without moving the detent, although the unlocking only takes place every alternate vibration, the escape wheel makes one rotation in exactly the same time as a lever escapement, which is an advantage, as locked, the wheel advances one tooth.

The chronometer is more detached than the lever escapement which is an advantage, as the unlocking and impulse takes place at every alternate vibration of the balance. No oil is required on the pallets, escape wheel teeth, or any part of the escapement except the pivot holes. When properly constructed and nicely made, its performance seldom fails to give satisfaction.

Marine chronometers require very careful handling. A clean board is essential. It is a mistake to attempt to clean a chronometer unless the operator has sufficient time to finish the job uninterruptedly. Unscrew the lock nuts and remove the brass box from its gymballing. Unscrew the bezel, turn the box upside down, so that the movement falls gently into the right hand. Remove the hands, dial, motion work, and " up and down " pinion. A pair of brass-nosed pliers will be found best for the pinion, which is fitted friction tight on the lower fusee pivot.

Next examine the escapement. When the balance is at rest the impulse pallet should be opposite a tooth of the wheel. Move the balance round gently with a peg until the discharging pallet unlocks the detent, and notice the drop on the impulse pallet. Immediately the tooth drops, move the balance very slowly in

the opposite direction, you will then be able to judge
by the time it falls, if the intersection of the pallet
in the path of the wheel is safe (see Fig. 92).    The
discharging pallet A is just on the point of unlocking
the gold spring.    When the unlocking is completed
the impulse pallet B will have passed well into the
intersection of the path of the wheel to receive impulse.

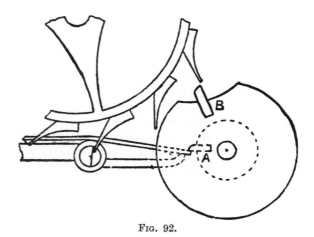

Fig. 92.

It is advisable to make a note of any alteration to
the escapement in a book for further reference.    If
the tooth of the escape wheel has insufficient grip when
it drops on to the impulse pallet, it is not safe, and the
discharging roller requires to be shifted round a little
nearer the impulse pallet with brass-nosed pliers, so
that the latter attains a greater intersection of the path
of the wheel when the tooth drops.    When the drop
is excessive, the discharging pallet should be moved
in the opposite direction (that is to give a greater angle

between the two pallets), which would increase the vibration.

The freedom between the tooth and path of the impulse pallet should be the same as the back of the next tooth and edge of the roller. We can observe the roller edge through the hole in the top plate, and if there is insufficient clearance from the tooth and too much from the roller edge and the escaped tooth, it will record itself by the amount of drop on to the locking stone. This may be equalized by shifting the locking stone slightly nearer the balance staff centre. Slacken the screw of the detent foot and press it forward. If there is no perceptible shake in the steady pin, give the foot a slight tap from a strip of ivory or soft metal punch and a light hammer. Great care must be exercised with this alteration ; the slightest movement will show a marked difference.

The locking and impulse stones are usually fixed slightly out of upright in alternate directions so that the bearing of the escape wheel teeth is different on each pallet, and, as far as possible, equalize the wear of the teeth. Occasionally the roller and escape wheel depth is found to be shallow. Where the pivots have been polished down through wear a new jewel-hole would deepen the escapement or press over the potance.

Our attention is next diverted to the detent. Lead the balance round with a peg until the gold spring drops, and then move the balance slowly the reverse way and notice how far the detent engages the discharging pallet after an escape tooth drops from the locking stone. This distance must be slight, and the detent should spring back sharp to the banking screw in time to receive the next tooth on the locking stone. The discharging pallet should, on its return journey, lift the gold spring

the same angle, and it can be observed by watching
the distance the balance travels over the top plate.

When the detent is at rest, the free end of the gold
spring should lay flat on the end of the horn pointing
to the centre of the balance staff.  If the discharging
pallet engages the gold spring, with a greater angle in
" passing the spring " than in the opposite vibration
of unlocking, the horn of the detent requires to be bent
up slightly to bring it in the line of centres with the
balance staff, shown by the dotted line, Fig. 93.  We
first remove the gold spring, which is screwed or
occasionally riveted to the detent.  Soften the end of

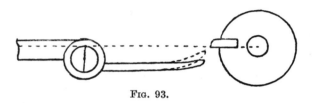

FIG. 93.

the horn to avoid any risk of breaking, grip it near the
pipe with a pair of flat-nosed tweezers, and bend the end
with a small pair of heater pliers.

The gold spring requires careful observation ; it is
made thicker at the free end, so that most of the bending
takes place beyond the pipe.  The free end is left square
and burnished to lay flat against the horn.  Any signs
of a burr or roughness should be burnished out, or
the spring may " kick " as the result.  Invisible
difficulties of the escapement will frequently be traced
to the gold spring.  We are able to notice the freedom
during its action by observation between the plates,
and any inclination to foul the impulse roller noted.
The fixed end should be rigid.  Oil at any place of contact

will cause trouble. It is the safest plan to remove a buckled spring to burnish it flat on a boxwood block, and in the event of a crack, to replace it with a new. Gold discharging wire is obtainable from a material dealer, or could be made from a piece of rolled or hammered round wire.

Many attempts have been made to repair a chronometer detent. The only alternative of overcoming the difficulty of a broken detent to attain a good result is to replace it with a new one. It is perhaps the most difficult piece of work in the horological sphere, and splendid practice for the ambitious workman. Many chronometer makers have their favourite methods of procedure.

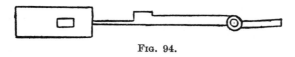

Fig. 94.

Select a suitable length of fine-grain steel, mark off, and drill two holes, one for the foot screw, the other for the locking stone ; the former is filed to a slot for adjustment. It is then roughly shaped out (Fig. 94), a trial brass locking pin fitted, and screwed to the plate to observe the relative position of the locking pallet when the steady-pin hole in the foot is drilled. Next drill and tap a hole for the screw to fix the gold spring. The detent is now hardened and tempered, the blade, pipe and foot finished to size and polished. Finally, the spring is thinned down with emery or oilstone dust and polished with diamantine. A brass pin is next filed to fit the pipe ; it is then reduced to about half the diameter, so that it holds the locking stone when placed in a position and fixed with shellac. Heated pliers held against the pipe will be found safe for running the shellac.

Having tried the detent in the plates with the complete escapement and pronounced it satisfactory, we then remove it and block the train with a wedge of cork at the fourth wheel. Slacken the stud screw, unscrew the cock screw, and lift off the cock. Remove the balance from the rim with a pair of tweezers and place it under a cover with the detent. These fragile parts are always liable to accident if left exposed.

The mainspring is wound and the stop work examined. Attention now calls for the maintaining work. Notice if the maintaining spring is free and the fusee detent drops well into the ratchet teeth. Remove the dust cap, replace the adjusting rod, and keep the spring tight while the cork wedge is withdrawn, the third wheel bar unscrewed, to lift out the wheel. Replace the bar and let down the spring gently with the adjusting rod, observing and noting the difference between the pull of the mainspring at each turn.

We note any variation in the pull of each turn of the mainspring. It is not advisable to alter the " set up " except when the variation is great between the first and last turns. The ratchet and square are marked with a dot for reference in setting up, but when these indications fail to coincide it is a safe plan to note the number of teeth " set up ". Next remove the chain, barrel bar, barrel, and release the fusee detent.

With the power off it is a good opportunity to examine the holes and wheel depths ; the teeth being nicely cut, a hole which is a little worn should not materially affect the depth. When the chronometer is very dirty and the holes assume a sticky nature, it will be found advisable to try the train in the frame again after cleaning the pivots and holes.

The escape wheel is the first to be removed and the last inserted on assembly. This operation requires careful attention. Slacken the pillar screws so that the top plate is raised sufficiently near the escape wheel to free the pivots ; it is then gripped by the tweezers and withdrawn from the plates. The top plate is then removed and the remaining wheels taken out.

The fusee chain should be examined for defective links or rivets. To replace a loose rivet, rest the chain on a lead block and start it with a light tap from a flat punch the same size as the rivet at the small end. When it protrudes slightly beyond the chain, hold the latter on a hollow punch with the projecting end in a hole and drive it through with the flat-faced punch. A tempered needle will be found reliable steel for repairing fusee chains. Chains are usually cleaned in petrol or benzoline, placed in an oil tin, and wiped ready for winding on the barrel.

Theoretically, the mainspring should be removed from the barrel, but in this case discretion is the better part of valour. When it is necessary to remove a spring, it should be cleaned as it lies in its normal state when taken from the barrel ; any tendency to open the coils will distort the molecules, and is likely to break.

After cleaning the fusee, the maintaining and great wheels are left to ride easy without shake. Try the key on the square, hold the great wheel, and notice if the maintaining spring is pulled freely home.

Pivots showing signs of wear are polished on a bed in the lathe or turns with bell-metal and " red stuff " or diamantine, then burnished. When the roughness appears deep, the marks are turned away before polishing. The pivots having been repaired, the wheels are placed in the plates and tested for depth, endshake, and freedom. A rough hole will mark a smooth pivot and cause extra friction. It is expedient, therefore, to round broach the holes where the pivots have been polished ; this not only attains a smooth surface, but hardens the bearing for the pivot. When a hole is worn oval or appears too large for the pivot, causing a bad depth, it is broached from the inside of the plate, finally forcing the broach before withdrawing it to leave five notches for the new bush to hold when riveted. In the case of a third or fourth hole ; a piece of brass wire is fitted from the inside slightly projecting above the plate and oil sink ; the outside is riveted with a round-faced punch, while the plate rests on a stake held in the vice. The round-faced punch is then substituted for the stake, the plate reversed, and the flat side riveted with a round-faced hammer.

The new hole is drilled upright by centring the other hole in the opposite plate in the mandril. Test the hole for true with a peg, screw on the plate to be drilled, catch the centre with a graver, drill the hole and try it for true with a peg resting on the T rest. It is necessary in fine work the holes should be drilled true to keep the wheel upright. The hole is broached to fit the pivot and the wheel placed in the frame and tried for endshake. The plate is finally fixed in the mandril, the shoulder of the hole turned away for endshake with a polished cutter ; it is then reversed and the oil sink turned out with a polished half-round cutter. Fusee and centre holes are turned on an arbor, riveted to the plate, uprighted, and finished in a similar manner.

To clean plates, cocks, and bars, mix rouge with water into a thick paste and rub it over the parts with a smooth brush. If tarnished, dip them into a solution of cyanide, but to do this requires very careful handling. The plates require stripping of all steel work, and the parts have to undergo a further bath of water and another of methylated spirit. A more simple process is to place the parts on a bent wire and hold them under a running water tap immediately after the cyanide immersion. The force of the water will remove all trace of cyanide. The train wheels are served in a similar manner, and the parts dried in boxwood dust, and finally brushed with the holes pegged out.

Little need be said on the assembly of the parts. The mainspring adjustment should be tested. Handle the balance and spring as little as possible. Anyone inexperienced in chronometer work will profit by cleaning the pivots with pith and leaving the balance and spring in its tarnished condition.

To prevent accident to the locking detent, screw it on before any power is applied to the train. In most cases it is safe not to insert it until the last. To try the escapement for " beat ", lead the balance round with a peg in each direction until the gold spring drops from the discharging pallet. Release the balance immediately ; it should then start off. If the spring collet requires shifting, the train should be blocked with a cork wedge at the fourth wheel before removing the balance. Chronometer oil is preferable for all the pivot holes. Clock oil is suitable for the barrel and fusee.

The chronometer is given a 24-hour run before its daily variation is noted. A long trial will be found more reliable for obtaining an accurate rate. The variation of a chronometer from mean time is not so important from a captain's point of view as the

consistency of its rate.  He makes his calculations from
its rate, and if the variation from its rate is great the
piece is worthless as an instrument of navigation.

The variation of the chronometer must be noted.
When it is wide and several weeks are available for
rating, it is advisable to give the mean time nuts a slight
touch.  A screwdriver with a notch cut in the centre
to free the screw is necessary for this operation (Fig. 95).

In the marine chronometer balance two screws are
provided with nuts opposite each end of the arm for
regulation.  The nuts are slit at both ends forming right
angles so as to grip the screw thread spring-tight.  At

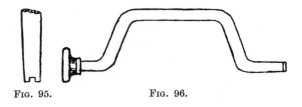

Fig. 95.                    Fig. 96.

a right angle to the timing nuts are two compensation
weights, which are shifted near or away from the fixed
end of the rim.  Each weight is held to the rim by a
small screw the head of which points to the centre of
the balance.  For loosening the screws that secure
the weights, remove the balance spring and make a
screwdriver with an arch-shaped stem long enough
to free the staff pivot and the opposite weight (Fig. 96).
A chronometer having an unreliable rate should be
tested in an oven of about 90 degrees, and again in
normal temperature.

New chronometers, instead of losing or gaining steadily,
go faster day after day.  There is no consistency in the

ratio of this "gaining". The acceleration is also noticeable when a balance spring has been unnecessarily bent or manipulated. The bending of a spring, although not absolutely crippled, disturbs the molecules, which effect the elasticity of a spring. It invariably takes an indefinite period to regain its elastic property and settle down.

A marine chronometer might prove satisfactory in extreme temperatures, and yet show an irregularity known as "middle temperature error". This problem has perhaps been the most perplexing to manufacturers. The loss in heat from the weakening of a balance spring is found to be uniform in proportion to the increase of temperature, while the balance is inconsistent in its expansion or contraction, being insufficient to counteract the change of the spring in all changes of temperature. With the compensation correct in the heat and cold we therefore find an error in the normal or middle. There are many forms of auxiliary employed to avoid the middle temperature error. Palladium balance springs not only give a smaller middle temperature error, but are free from liabilities to rust or become magnetized and for these reasons are more generally adopted.

In 1862 the Admiralty offered honorary prices for the two marine chronometers which stood first in order of merit at the annual competitive trials at Greenwich Observatory, provided that their performance during the trials was not below the standard of merit established in former years. Marine chronometers for the British Navy are purchased annually after tests at Greenwich. Prices offered vary according to the performance. The trials last about twenty-eight weeks. The chronometers showing the best record at the end of the trial will show the lowest trial number. The trial number is attained by the greatest difference between one week and the next, multiplied by two, plus the difference between the greatest and least weekly rates.

When a chronometer is dispatched to the docks it is expedient to screw up the symballing and carry it very steadily, the symballing is released with the piece free to swing when it is fixed securely in the captain's cabin.

**The Rate of a Marine Chronometer.**—The marine chronometer is usually made out for its daily rate—gaining or losing. That is, a trial is taken of a certain duration. The chronometer checked at certain periods, the variation noted from a regulator or chronometer with a known rate, and the average variation calculated to give the daily rate.

To rate a chronometer is not a difficult matter. It is mainly a matter of calculation to a practical man. It is necessary to have the Greenwich time by signal daily, or a good regulator with a close, reliable rate.

A little discretion is required to determine if it is necessary to clean a chronometer before giving it a rate. A chronometer might look fairly clean, but with the thickening of the oil the variation would not only be greater, but inconsistent, and to rate such a piece would be time wasted.

Shipping people who use marine chronometers depend on the accuracy of the rate. It is, therefore, more satisfactory to deliver a marine with a wide variation, if it is consistent, than to give a rate with a closer variation if it is not reliable. The captain makes his calculations from the rate supplied.

Many chronometer makers have rules of their own. Some use a slide rule to facilitate the rating. The simple method is the best to adopt for occasional use. Select a certain convenient time in the day to check the chronometer and stick to it. The horologist must work to a system if he wishes to be successful. If the time comes by signal, note the variation in the book, which should be kept especially for rates. Enter the number of the chronometer, the date in the first column, the variation in the second, and the variation from day to day in the third, with room at the end for any comment. When it is only possible to get the Greenwich time every three or four days, check them on these occasions, but wind them every day. An eight-day is wound once a week. Take, as example, the first observation is 1st March, and other dates 4th, 8th, 11th and 16th. The chronometer showed the following variations. We enter in the book as follows :

|  | | | Daily rate from day to day | Daily rate |
| --- | --- | --- | --- | --- |
| March | 1 | + 5 | — — | — |
| ,, | 4 | + 1 | — 1·3 | — |
| ,, | 8 | — 4·5 | — 1·4 | — |
| ,, | 11 | — 9·5 | — 1·7 | — |
| ,, | 16 | — 16 | — 1·3 | — 1·4 |

On 1st March we noted the variation was 5 seconds fast, and on the 4th it was one second fast. It had, therefore, lost 4 seconds in 3 days, which gives an average of one and three-tenths. For the whole 15 days the chronometer had lost 5 plus 16 equals 21 seconds, divided by the number of days 15 equals 1·4, or one and four-tenths. A longer rate is more reliable than a short one. If the observations are taken from a regulator with a close rate, the rate of the latter must be added to or substracted from the total variation of the chronometer, as the case may be, before dividing by the number of days to attain the rate. A chronometer is not set to Greenwich time before delivery.

## TRAINS

The following numbers of teeth in the wheels of watch and clock trains will prove useful as a guide to determine the right numbers where trouble occurs with getting the piece to time.

The general **English Bracket Chiming Clock** is as follows :—

Great wheel 96.
Centre wheel 84, pinion 8.
Third wheel 78, pinion 7.
Escape wheel 30, pinion 7.

### Chiming Train.

Great wheel 100.
Second wheel 80, pinion 8.
Chiming wheel 40.
Pallet wheel 64, pinion 8.
Warning wheel 56, pinion 8.
Fly pinion 8.

### French Pin Pallet Escapement.

Great wheel 80.
Second wheel 78, pinion 12.
Centre wheel 84, pinion 8.
Fourth wheel 70, pinion 7.
Escape wheel 41, pinion 7.

### Striking Part.

Great wheel 80.
Second wheel 72, pinion 12.
Pin wheel 70, pinion 8.
Pallet wheel 63, pinion 7.
Warning wheel 56, pinion 7.
Fly pinion 7.

## French Visible Escapement.

Great wheel 80.
Second wheel 80, pinion 12.
Centre wheel 84, pinion 8.
Fourth wheel 84, pinion 7.
Escape wheel 34, pinion 7.

The number of teeth in the escape wheel differs. For example, a short pendulum would have a greater number of teeth.

## Striking Part with ten pins in the pin wheel.

Great  wheel  80.
Second wheel 72, pinion 12.
Pin wheel 70, pinion 8.
Pallet wheel 63, pinion 7.
Warning wheel 56, pinion 7.
Fly pinion 7.

The gathering pallet wheel drives the warning pinion, and in all instances the number of leaves in the pinion must divide into the number of the wheel—here we have 63 divided by 7 equals 9 turns of the warning to one of the pallet. When a wrong number has been fitted, it will easily be located by counting the numbers of driver and follower to see if they divide equally.

The motion work of most clocks is differently arranged to those of watches. The tension wheel on the centre arbor (known to watchmakers as the cannon pinion) usually has 32 teeth, and drives another of the same number. The minute pinion has 7, with hour wheel of 84. The ratio 12 to 1 is therefore the same.

## Another Striking Train often used with 8 pins in the pin wheel.

Great wheel 84.

Pin wheel 64, pinion 8.
Pallet wheel 63, pinion 8.
Warning wheel 56, pinion 7.
Fly pinion 7.

All watches are now made with an 18,000 train.
The one generally used is as follows :—Centre wheel
64 teeth, third wheel 60, pinion 8.   Fourth wheel 60,
pinion 8.   Escape wheel 15, pinion 6.   The centre wheel
we know makes exactly one turn in an hour.   Therefore
the numbers of all the wheels multiplied together divided
by the numbers of all the pinions multiplied together will
give the number of vibrations of the balance per hour ;
that is, assuming we multiply the number of the escape
wheel teeth by two, because there are two vibrations
for each tooth of the escape wheel.

To calculate the number of teeth in a lost wheel
and pinion, we will assume the third wheel and pinion
are lost.   The pinion can be taken from the train of
the others, which are 8.   Call the lost wheel $x$.

$$\frac{64 \times x \times 60 \times 30}{8 \times 8 \times 6} \text{ equals } 18,000.$$

Therefore $x$ equals $\dfrac{18,000 \times 8 \times 8 \times 6.}{64 \times 60 \times 30}$

**Motion Trains.**—The number of teeth in the minute
wheel and hour wheel multiplied together and divided
by the numbers in cannon pinion and minute pinion
should give 12.   That is cannon pinion and hour wheel
of 12 turns to 1.

The train generally used is as follows :—Hour wheel
32.  Minute wheel 30.  Cannon pinion 10.  Minute pinion 8.

To work it out is quite simple : 10 divides into 30,
3 ; 8 into 32, 4 ; and 4 multiplied by 3 equals 12.

**Twenty-four Hour Train.**—A watch converted into a 24-hour dial would require a new motion train giving 24 turns of the cannon pinion to one of the hour wheel.

A suitable train would be cannon pinion 10, minute wheel 40 pinion 7, hour wheel 42, or a minute pinion of 8 and hour wheel 48. With a cannon pinion of 12, minute wheel 48, pinion 7 and hour wheel 42. Another 24 hour train cannon pinion 12, minute wheel 36, pinion 7 and hour wheel 56, or a pinion of 8 and hour wheel 64. The pitch in each case must be correct.

**Grandfather Clock Trains.**—Numbers in eight-day English long case clock trains, see page 249, and chiming train, see page 318.

Grandfather clocks with escape wheels of thirty teeth and a one-second pendulum, generally embrace six or seven teeth. The number of teeth embraced depends on the length of the pendulum. A shorter pendulum would embrace a lesser number because the vibration would be greater.

Invar pendulums with a little or no co-efficient of expansion are now fitted to all modern long cased clocks.

The average length of crutch to a Grandfather clock is four inches. Those with a heavy pendulum six and a half inches. Clocks with a short pendulum about one-third the length of pendulum.

The weight employed to drive a thirty-hour English clock on the endless cord principle should not exceed five pounds. Many are fitted with a much heavier weight, with the result that when the oil becomes dry the heavy weight drags the clock on tearing the acting surfaces into ruts until the timekeeper finally comes to rest, and requires a great deal of repairing—fitting new parts.

# CLOCKS

## ALARM CLOCKS

Alarm clocks are now in demand, and a large proportion will obviously be out of repair. Most of them are on the drum clock principle, but the alarm work is the same. Remove the two winders, the set hands and alarm buttons—the latter is a left handed screw—the two feet and the bell with the stop piece and two washers. The movement will then push out from the back, the alarm hammer will usually require bending a little to free the hammer from the slot in the case.

The hands are next removed, this is best accomplished with nippers, take off the dial which is pinned on, and the movement is visible for examination. Many faults are contracted in the escapement through worn acting surfaces and cause extra friction. Under such conditions the vibration of the balance must suffer.

Leat the balance round slowly with a peg in alternate directions until a tooth of the escape wheel drops. It should fall safely on the undercut or locking face of the pallet pin. When it is shallow, and falls on impulse face the cause is usually worn pallet pins, or worn pallet and escape wheel holes, sometimes both. Some clocks are made with the pallet arbor run in a separate cock. In such a case it is quite a simple matter to bend the cock over to deepen the escapement, assuming the pallet pins are not worn.

Needles tempered to a light blue will be found convenient for making new pallet pins. They should be left perfectly smooth, stoned and burnished to fit the holes ; and the old pins driven out with a small flat-ended punch, while the pallet rests on a hollow stake in the vice.

The illustration Fig. 96 A shows the alarm mechanism. The alarm spring A is screwed to the plate and its other end terminates in a right angle, going through a hole in the plate to engage an arm on the alarm pallet B. In the sketch it will be seen that the alarm is locked at B, A stud C on the alarm spring presses against the hour wheel. The latter is only free to rise when its nose piece D comes opposite the slot in the alarm wheel. The hour wheel then allows the spring to rise and free the alarm pallets E, then the alarm is let off.

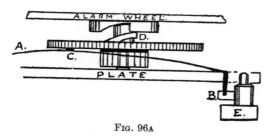

FIG. 96A

The nose of the hour wheel and edge of the alarm disc and the notch requires oiling. The alarm will fail to act if the hour wheel pipe is left rough, it should slide freely in the alarm wheel.

Examine the alarm spring, this sometimes gets bent, not allowing freedom to the pallets when the hour wheel is up to the alarm wheel. A rough mark on the end of the spring will often prevent freedom to the pallets when the alarm is let off.

The alarm pallets require oil in contact with the wheel. The stud should be perfectly smooth, and oiled where it rubs on the hour wheel. See that the seat of the hour wheel is resting on the cannon pinion when the former is locked. The end of the alarm spring should be at right angles to the plate to lock safely.

Fig. 96B shows the " silent tick " mechanism of a modern luminous alarm clock. It has a slow vibration of the balance with 100 to the minute. One flatted pallet pin only is furnished to deaden the sound. The escape pinion has twelve leaves. The escape wheel is shown at A.

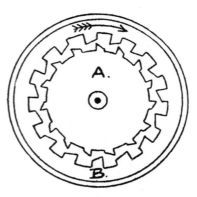

Fig. 96B.

Fitted loosely on the escape wheel arbor and kept in position by a weak balance spring is a disc escape wheel with internal teeth B. The escape wheel A advances a tooth at a time, and the pallet pin slides from the impulse face of a tooth on the wheel A on to the locking face of a tooth in the wheel B. This has the advantage of abolishing " drop " for a rubbing action, and therefore one pallet pin only is necessary.

The freedom of the wheel B, adjusted by the weak

spring, is only equal to about half a tooth. The action is therefore sliding from a tooth of one wheel on to the tooth of the other wheel.

## NICKEL DRUM CLOCKS

Nickel Drum Clocks, although roughly made, find their way into nearly every shop for repair. The repairing of the escapement is usually confined to a few details which, if neglected, will often contract a combination of faults.

It is bad policy to neglect such elementary work. Nearly every clock that requires cleaning has the balance staff pivots worn to a certain extent and to leave them in this state would mean bad timekeeping a falling off in the vibration in one position, or ultimately a stop. It is a safe maxim to stone and burnish the pivots in every clock. The centre is generally worn away, sometimes on one side or cut rough near the point ; in any case the object is to form a new, smooth burnished centre, the same angle. Remove the spring collet, and place the staff in a split chuck with the end near the pivot just resting on the tee rest for support. Most of these balance staffs are hard and require stoning to shape with an arcansas stone well oiled and then finished with a burnisher. The staff is then reversed in the chuck and the other pivot treated in the same way. Balance staffs to fit different size holes in the balances can be obtained from any material dealer. The quickest method to obtain the correct size is to punch out the old staff and send the balance for the size of the hole.

Numerous faults are contracted in the escapement through worn acting surfaces and cause extra friction, a loss of motive power, and obviously a loss of impulse. Under such conditions the vibration of the balance

must not only suffer, but an inconsistency to gain or
lose and time wasted in attempts at regulation.

Lead the balance round slowly with a peg in alternate
directions until a tooth of the escape wheel drops to
try the locking.  The locking corner, or undercut of a
tooth, should drop safely on the pallet pin (Fig. 97).  If
the impulse angle of the tooth falls on the pin it misses
locking and is unsafe (Fig. 98), the safety nose of the
lever would rub on the edge of the roller instead of being
drawn safely away.  Such a fault would mean an
inconsistent vibration to the balance, and is the cause
of the wheel and pallet pins being too shallow.  The

Fig. 97.                    Fig. 98.

amount of " drop " a tooth has on the pallet pins should
be equal and as small as possible.  Move the balance
round  in both directions until the roller pin is safely
out of the lever notch and try the shake of the lever,
which should be the same on both sides.  If the lever
is out of angle with hardly any shake on one side and
too much on the other, the shakes could be equalized
by pressing the lever round a little on the pallet arbor.
It is generally necessary to remove the pallets from the
plate for this operation.  Hold the pallets firmly in a
pair of pliers and press over the lever with the thumb
and finger at each end.

An escape wheel too shallow which " misses locking "
is usually the cause of worn escape wheel, or pallet holes,
worn pallet pins, and often both.  Few clocks are made

with the pallet arbor run in a cock. Assuming the parts mentioned are not badly worn, it is a simple matter to press over the cock slightly with a pair of pliers nearer to the escape wheel to get the escapement deep enough to lock.

When pivot holes are worn badly the pivots invariably suffer, and even if the escapement depths are not affected, the extra friction will absorb the motive power to the cost of impulse when the mainspring is nearly down. Those which suffer the most are the quick moving parts, and it will pay in the end to repair any pivots showing signs of wear or re-bush any escape holes worn wide if the escapement depths are affected.

It is not necessary to spend much time on this class of work to make it pay. In the event of no lathe being available, pivots can be repaired on a filing block. Grip the arbor in a pin vice, rest the pivot in a groove of a filing block, or an old emery buff in the vice would do, and rotate the pin vice while an emery buff is used to remove the rough marks, then finish with a burnisher. Balance staff pivots could be repaired in the same way.

The pallet pins wear as quickly as any part of the acting surfaces. When the ruts appear in the form of deep grooves, the safest plan is to replace them. Many faults can be traced to worn pallet pins, and to replace a pair is quite a simple matter.

The old pins can be pulled out with a pair of pliers, or driven out with a small flat-ended punch the same size as a pin. The pallets should be held over a hollow punch in the vice.

Temper a few needles to a light blue. This steel is always reliable and convenient for this work, new pivots, and repairing fusee chains. Screw a needle in a pin vice and file it on a block almost straight and exactly the same size as the old ones. Stone out the file marks and finish with a burnisher. Fit the pin in the pallets tight, cut it off to length, leaving a little for drive, and stone the flat end.

It is important that new pallet pins should not exceed the diameter of the old ones, and for this reason it is advisable to file them almost straight. The escape wheel teeth are not always cut or mounted true, and in such cases it is quite obvious pins slightly too large would cause the wheel teeth to have no in or outside

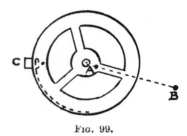

Fig. 99.

shake. The wheel would probably kick in one place and most likely stop.

The escapement depth too shallow is often the cause of worn escape wheel or pallet staff holes. The plates being very soft the escape holes wear in a very short time. When the escape wheel misses locking with either holes worn wide, broach open the holes from the inside of the plate, insert a piece of bush wire, cut it off and rivet it over. Then open the holes to just fit the pivots. Try the wheel or pallets in the frame separately as the case may be to see if the parts are perfectly free with endshake.

All clocks should be set perfectly in beat or they are liable to stop. A spring must be true in the flat, and round, if the clock is to keep good time. Hold the balance and spring over the balance hole as shown in Fig. 99, with the pivots central with the holes to see if the outer coil of the spring comes between the index pins and forms a circular curve to the stud hole. The outer coil must be free of the pins with the regulator over to the fast and slow, or the act of moving the regulator would throw the spring out of centre and obviously out of beat.

Two bends in the spring are often necessary to get it circular. Grip the outer coil opposite or farthest away from the stud hole with a pair of tweezers and bend it in or out with a point until it is free and central with the index pins. The next bend will probably be required between the index pins and stud in a similar manner, to get the part of the coil over at a slow free between the pins and in a line with the stud hole, so that when the spring is pinned in at the stud it is not thrown out of circle.

To pin the spring in the stud so that the clock is in beat is a simple matter. Hold the balance and spring over the balance hole as shown in Fig. 99 with the pivots central with the holes, and the balance or impulse pin A in a line with the pallet staff hole B. The part of the outer coil of the spring that comes exactly over the stud hole C is the piece to be pinned in the stud to be in beat. A dot should be made on the rim of the balance opposite the stud when the balance is in this position to indicate the exact part for pinning the spring. This is the relative position the balance pin should occupy in relation to the lever notch when the escapement is at rest.

## REPAIRING AN EIGHT-DAY ENGLISH CLOCK

The repairing of an eight-day English clock might appear simple. The cleaning is often regarded as the chief feature, with the result the clock invariably stops in a very short time.

As a matter of fact, cleaning is quite a secondary consideration. Not one such clock in twenty stops for the want of cleaning only.

The " grandfather " type, as a rule, is allowed to run too long without attention. The oil obviously evaporates, and the force of the heavy weights overcomes the extra friction at the acting surfaces, wearing them into ruts until the clock finally comes to rest. The principal repairs consist of worn pivots, holes, and pallet faces. An estimate submitted to the customer in such cases of the cost of the work required to put the clock in good order will be found the most satisfactory procedure to inspire confidence in the horologist.

The correct procedure is to repair a clock first and clean it afterwards, but as many appear in such a terribly dirty state, it would be difficult to examine the various parts without cleaning it first, and for this reason many clockmakers start with the grease brushing stage.

It is advisable to examine a clock before removing it from the case to ascertain the cause of stoppage. See that the hands are perfectly free of each other. Try the hour hand for shake in the hour wheel teeth. Notice if the striking work has failed and thus arrested the going part. The gut lines sometimes get " caught up ". Worn lines should always be replaced. They should be hung to run parallel and perfectly free of the seat board. When any rubbing takes place, free the line by cutting a slot in the seat board. The latter, which is a resting place for the movement, must be perfectly rigid. It is kept fixed or bolted to the board with two staples coiled round the pillars, passing through the board, with screwed ends and held tightly with two nuts. The seat board and method of fixing is often a source of trouble.

Hammering the threads and screw-holes of overturned nuts and bolts with the object of holding the movement to the seat board is time wasted. The average staple employed to fix the movement is too slight, and could be increased twice the diameter to advantage. The number of clocks that work " out of beat " after being wound can be attributed to the scanty bits of pin-wire which serve the purpose of bolts.

When there is no apparent cause of stopping in the case, we might assume the clock requires cleaning, and, therefore, remove the movement. The pendulum and weights are lifted off, and the seat board with the movement withdrawn. Unscrew the nuts and remove the seat board. Next release the motion collet pin, the collet and hands, the dial pins, and remove the dial. With the plates resting on the board an approximate examination of the escapement will reveal its condition.

A grandfather clock is usually fitted with a " recoil " escapement. It is so named from the action of the pallets, which produces a recoil or backward movement of the escape wheel after a tooth has dropped. Try the shake in the pallet and escape wheel holes. It is important these acting surfaces should be perfectly smooth and exact in fit. Any looseness through wear will cause errors in the escapement at the cost of time-keeping. Examine the pallets and crutch to see if they are tight on the arbor. Any looseness in this direction is not uncommon, and in time would cause the clock to stop.

The next procedure is to try the action of the wheel and pallets. Lead the third wheel round with a peg, while the other hand leads the crutch slowly until a tooth drops. Move the crutch in the opposite direction to try the drop on the other pallet. When the drops are excessive, the escapement is too shallow and requires

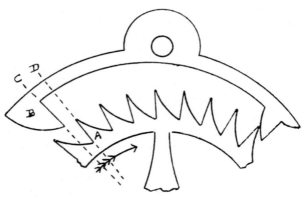

Fig. 100.

a new pallet hole a little nearer the escape wheel, or, if the pallet faces are badly cut, they might be refaced. Too much drop off the outside pallet on to the inside one is a common fault (shown in Fig. 100). This is rectified by closing or bringing them closer together. It is accomplished by softening the arm to prevent cracking. Open the vice wide enough to take the full length of the pallet pads and screw up the vice gently until the pallets have moved slightly. Too much drop is not only a loss of power, but unnecessary wear on the acting faces of the pallets. Under such conditions the pallet faces would be worn into ruts in a very short time.

The tooth A in the sketch has just dropped off the outside pallet B. The distance between the two dotted lines, C and D, represents the distance the tooth A has dropped. It will be seen in this case that the drop is nearly one-third the distance between two teeth. These pallets should therefore be closed to reduce the drop from C and D by at least one-half.

There are many methods of correcting a defective recoil escapement depth. Although the error is usually the cause of wear, original faults often become more prominent which is necessary to rectify to attain a passable working escapement.

Fig. 100 shows too much drop on one pallet. The drop is often equal on both pallets, but unequal on the opposite side of the wheel. The escape wheel in such a case is obviously out of round, or the teeth cut of unequal thickness. To leave a wheel in such a condition is seeking trouble.

The price paid for a clock repair will not always cover the cost of a new wheel, and under such circumstances the old wheel should be repaired to the best advantage. Try the drop of all the teeth on both pallets to form an opinion of the depth at all parts. Worn escape wheel or pallet holes tend to refute any escapement depth. It is advisable, therefore, to note any wide holes and bush them before proceeding to repair the escapement.

Refrain from using chisel, or half-circular hollow punches for closing pivot holes. Closing pivot holes is a useless operation. The new bearing attained is not only very thin, and will wear out in a very short time, but the surface will cut the pivot in a rut and probably stop the clock. The plate is also disfigured, and obviously the value of the clock deteriorated. Always try to emulate the original.

Worn pivots are easily repaired in the lathe. A touch with a smooth pivot file, finished with a buff and burnisher, is all that is usually required to get a smooth-running surface. To fit a new hole, broach the old hole from the inside large enough to admit a new bush. Turn a suitable piece of bush wire in a split chuck until it fits the hole firmly from the inside. Make a scratch to represent the length required and turn it nearly off at the scratch. Drive it in, break it off, and rivet it over. When the new hole fits the pivot rather tight, finish the hole with a round broach to attain a hard, smooth surface.

An escape wheel out of round, or worn at the ends of the teeth, can be topped true in the lathe with a smooth file and finished with a stone.

The backs of the thick teeth should then be filed to bring all the spaces between the teeth equal. A gauge filed to just fit between the two widest teeth will be found the best guide.

An observation from the top of the plates will reveal the relative position of the wheel to the centre of the pallets, also the angular position of the pallet staff an ˙ crutch. When the pallet faces are worn, and the whe is not running in the centre of the pallet faces (shown in sketch by dotted lines) there is generally room to shift the pallets on the collet to get the wheel to run on a new surface. To attain this alteration, knock off the pallets and turn away sufficient shoulder of the collet. When it is necessary to bring the pallets over in the opposite direction, turn up a thin collet with a rivet and fix it to the old pallet staff collet. This is an easy method of effecting a new acting surface.

It is absolutely necessary the pallet staff should be at right angles to the plane of vibration of the pendulum. That is, of course, at right angles to the plates. Any deviation from this line would cause extra friction

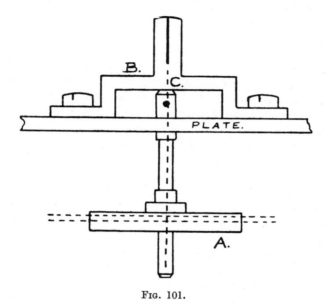

Fig. 101.

at the fork, and, consequently, a sliding motion of the pendulum rod at the fork, which often means " the pendulum wobbles ". It is impossible in the latter case to attain a steady rate of timekeeping.

Fig. 101 shows the pallet arbor and pallets out of angle with the centre of the pallet cock and, obviously, the crutch, the rivet of which is shown in the pallet arbor. This is a common fault, and all attempts at close timekeeping would be useless. The escape wheel under the pallets A is shown by two dotted lines. If the pallets happen to be worn, half the collet could be cut away to bring the wheel on a new acting surface. A new pallet hole in the cock B would be necessary to bring the pallet staff in a line with the suspension of the pendulum, which is indicated by the dotted line C.

We now turn our attention to the examination of the crutch. This is one of the most important parts of a clock, and for some unknown reason seldon receive sufficient attention. The writer has seen more pendulum trouble attributed to faults in the crutch than any other part of the escapement. If the crutch is out of line, or out of angle with the path of the pendulum, the latter will obviously wobble. The impulse from the pallets is conveyed to the pendulum through the crutch. It is quite obvious, therefore, any unnecessary shake or roughness at the point of contact of the crutch would mean a loss of impulse to the pendulum. See that the brass block engages in the centre of the fork with just perceptible shake and the surfaces perfectly smooth.

Having examined and repaired the escapement, the next procedure is to take the clock to pieces. Examine the holes, depths, and freedom of the wheels and make a note of any defects requiring attention.

Worn pinions are often a source of trouble, although the pinions of an 8-day English clock will often run badly worn if the depth is correct. A clock will frequently stop in the going or striking train with worn pinions and a badly pitched depth. The price paid for the repair will not always cover the cost of a new pinion. Under these circumstances the easiest way out of the difficulty is to shift a wheel and pinion and thus attain a new running surface of two pinions.

Fig. 102 shows a side elevation of the striking train from the fly to the pin-wheel. It will be noticed the wheels are running in each pinion with sufficient room

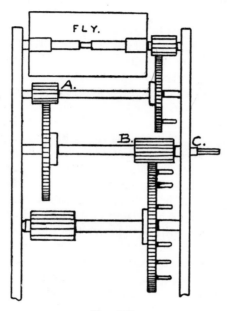

FIG. 102.

to shift for a new acting surface, which is usual in most clocks. When the warning wheel pinion A, or the gathering pallet wheel pinion B is worn, and the cause of a bad depth, move the latter nearer the top or pillar plate, according to the relative parts of the pinions worn and the available freedom of the wheels. The sketch shows the pin-wheel gearing in the end of the pinion nearest the wheel. It would, therefore, be necessary to re-bush the hole nearest the gathering pallet C, leaving it stilted, or projecting above the plate, and cut away the shoulder of the pivot at the other end to make the endshake correct. Of course a little judgment is required to see if the gathering pallet runs well in the rack and is perfectly free of the plate. When there is insufficient room to permit of such alteration the pinwheel can be shifted, and the warning wheel if necessary.

The best form of fitting bush wire is turning in a lathe. Broach the hole in the plate from the inside and fit the bush slightly tapered projecting from the plate about the thickness of the wheel and rivet it over from the outside. Open the hole until the pivot enters tightly. The bush is easily filed to length from the inside to correct the endshake. From half to three-quarters of the thickness of the pin-wheel will be sufficient distance to get a new running surface in the pinion head. A hole should be finished with a round broach to give it a hard, smooth surface. Holes finished in this manner will last double the time. If the pinwheel has much endshake a new hole could be fitted at the pinion end to reduce it and keep the wheel safely in the new running surface of the pinion.

A wheel and pinion should run perfectly free in the pivot holes, with perceptible endshake. Excessive endshake will often cause a wheel to run foul, or a bad depth with a worn pinion. Round broach out any holes showing signs of roughness, and burnish any pivots worn rough. It will pay in the end to spend a little time repairing the acting surfaces to reduce friction, than the useless practice of working the plates to a high polish. Owing to the friction on the warning and fly pinions they are the first to show signs of wear, and to shift the warning wheel is a simple matter as there is plenty of space. Try all the wheels in the plates for freedom before starting the cleaning stage.

The next procedure is the cleaning operation. There are many methods of doing so.

Many repairers prefer the orthodox grease brushing of powdered rotten-stone mixed with oil. Crocus is sometimes substituted for rotten-stone. Some who aspire to a high polish pin their faith to metal polish. The pieces so treated in any grease brushing stage are usually washed in petrol, or they could be wiped with a rag, then brushed with a clean brush and whiting.

The following method is recommended by the writer : Mix 1 lb. of soft soap in a gallon of hot water and add a tablespoonful of 800 ammonia. Place all the parts in the solution over night, and remove in the morning. The parts are brushed lightly, washed in clean water and dried in boxwood dust. A pan to contain the latter should be heated over a flame to dry the parts. Care should be taken that the dust does not get overheated. The usual dry brush process follows. A taper strip of chamois leather, with the large end fixed in a vice, is used to clean the large holes. Thread the loose end through a hole and move the plate in a forward and backward motion until each hole is clean.

The final chalk brushing will be found best accomplished by holding the parts in a clean rag. It is absolutely necessary the holes should be pegged out clean. Neglect in this direction is by no means uncommon. The result is the dirt left in the holes soon begins to mix with the oil, which forms a grinding property to cut the pivots and the clock obviously stops. A hole should be repeatedly pegged out and the peg cut clean until it is removed free from dirt.

Faults in the striking work are often caused by slightly bending a striking work stud with the end of the brush. This accident easily happens, and the operator, unconscious of the fact, invariably proceeds to make other alterations in the striking work, only to find himself in a greater difficulty. The best plan is to unscrew all the studs, placing them one at a time on a piece of cardboard in their relative positions occupied in the plate. This system prevents the studs getting mixed, which would involve an even greater perplexity than bending one if they were left in the plate.

Rusty arbors or flat steel parts can be restored with an emery buff or cloth on a piece of wood. When any of the pinion leaves appear rusty, polish them with fine emery mixed with oil applied on a wedge-shape piece of soft wood.

Before assembling the clock, examine the respective parts to see if there is any inaccuracy likely to cause trouble. Notice if the wheels are tight on the pinions. Test the pallets and crutch. A crutch loose on the pallet arbor would cause a deal of trouble. An escape wheel tooth slightly bent would cause the clock to stop, and a better examination of the teeth can be made before the clock is assembled. Lifting pins occasionally work loose, giving the operator the impression the lifting wheel is in the wrong position. Try the click and spring and notice if the great wheel is perfectly free in its action without being too loose. The latter might lead to many faults.

System is an important feature in putting the clock together. Rest the pillar plate on a clean rag, or a leather placed on the board large enough to overlap the top plate to prevent unnecessary handling it when pressing the plate down. This is also a safeguard against scratching the plate on the board. Screw down the hammer spring and assemble the wheels in their proper places, starting with the centre wheel, the two great wheels, the third wheel, hammer, the pin wheel, the gathering pallet wheel, the warning wheel, the fly and escape wheel. The hammer tail should be just free of a lifting pin, so that the end has just dropped, with the warning pin about one-half of a turn away from the warning slot in the plate. The hammer tail must be of such a length as to drop from the lifting pin to the banking pin, when the acting face is in a line with the

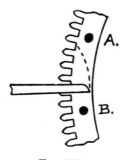

Fig. 103.

centre of the pin wheel, and a space of about the distance between one to two teeth to the next pin, to allow the train to attain motion before lifting the hammer tail.

The next operation is to carefully let down the top plate, guiding the centre and barrel arbors in their holes first. Press the top plate on gently with the leather and guide the pivots in their respective holes, starting from the barrel end. When the plate is down sufficiently the pins can be pushed partly in the lower pillar holes. This will admit greater freedom in getting the small pivots in their holes. Pin down the top plate, and move the striking train round slowly to see if the pin wheel is in its relative position to the warning wheel as described. If it has shifted, remove the two pillar pins, lift the plate slightly and the wheel out of gear with its pinion, then move it round a tooth, replace the pins and test all the wheels for endshake and freedom. A slight movement from the great wheels will verify the latter, and try each wheel separately for endshake.

The striking work is next tested. Fig. 103 shows the position of the hammer tail immediately after the warning. The wheel at the warning has moved the distance from the path described by the end of the tail to the pin A shown by a dotted curve, and at the hour the pin B will be well off the lift.

To attain the ability to cope with any fault in the striking work, it is necessary to trace the cause. Start with the origin of the mechanism and examine its action from one stage to another. Put on temporarily the rack, rack spring, rack hook, the snail, and the gathering pallet on the correct square so that the hammer tail is free of the lifting pins when the gathering pallet is locked against the pin in the rack.

Move the snail round to the highest step and let the rack tail drop. Lead the pallet round slowly and test the intersection with the rack tooth to see if the rack hook falls safely and the pallet locks on the rack pin. If the one and twelve fall and are gathered up correctly, the other numbers are seldom wrong, unless the rack teeth are unequal or worn. Apparent faults in the rack teeth, or rack tail causing the pallet to gather up the wrong number are often mistaken for a fault in the snail. There is practically no wear on the snail, and unless this piece has been operated on by a repairer, we can take it for granted it is faultless.

Faults in the striking work are usually the cause of worn parts. Fig. 104 shows the rack, rack spring, rack hook, the snail and the gathering pallet. The rack has dropped on the lowest step of the snail and the gathering pallet is in the position to start gathering up the twelve teeth. Lead the gathering pallet round slowly from the striking train letting the first finger act as a brake on the fly, and examine the intersection of each tooth until the twelve teeth are gathered and the pallet locks safely on the rack pin.

Examine the rack tail to see if it is perfectly tight on the rack, and notice if the pin drops safely on and at right angle to the edge of the snail. A bent rack stud will often throw this out of gear, or the pin worked loose in the tail.

If the pallet intersects the first tooth more or less than the rest, the fault is probably the pin has dropped too far on the snail and the cause might be a new rack tail fitted the wrong length. This would be noticeable by the point of the rack hook not falling to its position in the teeth.

Many broken rack tails are attributed to carelessness on the part of the repairer. These parts are not only fragile, but have a tendency to work loose with continual falling on the edge of the snail. Riveting at the wrong angle and subsequent bending no doubt accounts for many breakages. Owners are often responsible for damage to the striking work when in the act of carelessly setting the hands back. The rack tail obviously suffers. The erroneous lengths of various tails produced by many clock repairers are characteristic of their horological knowledge, such bungling attempts always reverting to the same disaster—an accumulation of faults and a striking fiasco.

The rule for the length of a rack tail is quite simple. Draw a line on a piece of paper from the centre of motion of the rack to the first tooth shown by the dotted line (Fig. 104 AB). Then draw another line to represent the fall of the rack at the twelve, which means the distance of twelve teeth AC. Now take the full length on the

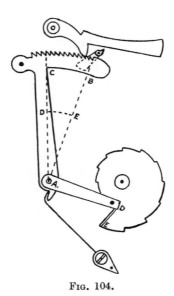

Fig. 104.

snail—the tail has to fall at twelve DE—and mark off DE to coincide with the distance AB and AC are apart. This distance AD will give the length of the rack tail, that is, from the centre of the rack stud hole A to the centre of the tail pin. It will be seen by Fig. 104 that the distance the rack has just dropped is twelve teeth or equal to the angular distance ABC.

The gathering pallet should intersect a rack tooth

sufficiently to lift it a distance of a little more than one tooth, that is, a little more than the distance between one tooth and the next. The rack will then fall back again on the hook. By adopting this method, if the teeth are slightly unequal we can always be certain one will be lifted. Fig 105 explains this. The depth of the gathering pallet will cause it to lift tooth A to the dotted line B, and the tooth C will consequently be lifted to the line D when C will drop back from the line D to the hook.

It is important the pivot behind the gathering pallet should fit the hole without shake. Many faults could be traced to this hole, causing a shallow depth. A short

Fig. 105.

or worn pallet with a shallow intersection is useless, and should be replaced. A new pallet in the rough can be obtained from any material dealer. The filing and fitting required is simple and interesting.

Worn or unequal rack teeth is a common form of trouble in the striking work, which often gives the operator the impression the gathering pallet is at fault. In this case it is essential to notice the depth of the pallet on each tooth. The fault is then obvious, the point of the pallet will catch on the back of one or more of the teeth.

Filing the rack teeth is a job that requires a little experience. The safest plan is to file a piece of brass as a gauge to just fit between the points of two of the rack teeth that are correct, and then file the others to the gauge.

The rack spring should be strong enough to throw the tail safely on the deepest slot of the snail at the twelve. There appears to be a difference of opinion amongst repairers regarding the tension of this spring. Many faults in the rack, or extra friction through a bent stud, are overcome by bending the spring stronger instead of correcting the fault. With an excessive amount of bending the spring obviously breaks. When the rack spring is bent to a greater tenson the gathering pallet has to overcome a greater force at the rack teeth.

The continued falling of the gathering pallet tail on the pin in the rack forms a hollow in the tail, consequently at the warning the rack is locked in the wear mark of the tail and fails to fall. This is another excuse for bending the rack spring stronger. The safest remedy is to leave the spring at its original tension and stone out the wear marks in the tail.

Another cause of " stops on the warning " can be traced to a wear mark on the warning piece through friction of the warning pin rubbing. The wear mark is easily filed and stoned away on the warning piece to given the pin a new acting surface.

Bent striking studs are often the cause of faults in the striking work. Unless the horologist is careful to observe his error, he is apt to bend other pieces, while the original fault will stop the striking and cause a deal of trouble. A bent stud might throw the rack or hook out of line, or the former out with the snail. The screw threads often differ slightly, while the arbors might be the same. In such instances it would be quite an easy matter to overturn a thread by forcing the wrong stud in the hole.

Test the endshake of the respective pieces on their studs when they are finally pinned. A piece is often free on its stud, but tight with the endshake up.

Another cause of stopping in the striking work can be traced to the warning piece bent, or the wheel out of flat, sometimes the error is too much endshake to the wheel. The warning piece foul of any object would obviously cause the lifting pin to bind on the lifting piece and stop the clock. The clock failing to strike is frequently the cause of it stopping. The power of the going part is insufficient to overcome the resistance at the point of contact with the striking, with the usual result the pendulum finally comes to rest.

The going part is depending entirely on the striking mechanism for its satisfactory performance. It does not follow, therefore, that because a clock stops there is a fault in the former.

When a clock stops it frequently happens that the act of removing the dial disturbs the parts that are locked, and, consequently, it starts off with no apparent fault. The best plan in all such cases is to remove the dial and hands, replace the latter and start the clock going. When the pendulum comes to rest a full view of the striking work will be seen and will prove a simple matter to trace the fault. Starting with the motion work, the lifting piece and examine each part back to trace the loss of power.

When the striking work is correct, oil the studs, the acting surfaces, the pivot holes, and put on the motion spring, cannon pinion, lifting piece, and complete the striking work. The hands " fail to carry " is a common fault and due to the motion spring being too weak, or foul of the plate. This spring, although one of the most important parts, often receives insufficient attention.

There is no doubt the original motion spring is often lost in cleaning the clock. Any old piece of brass, regardless of tension, is punched and bent to serve the purpose of driving the hands and letting off the striking part. The result is the hands occasionally get behind, and often prove a puzzle to the repairer. It takes but a few minutes to make a motion spring properly. Select a piece of well-hammered brass ; drill a hole in the centre to fit firmly against the shoulder of the centre pinion. It must be absolutely free of the plate. File the sides flat and bend the ends up to press against the cannon pinion on both sides. Apply a little oil at the points of contact, and pin on the minute hand to see if the tension of the spring is strong enough for the pin in the minute wheel to lift the lifting piece.

Next complete the motion work. Place the minute hand on a square so that it points exactly at the hour when the lifting piece falls off the pin in the minute wheel. This is adjusted by lifting the cannon pinion and moving it round a few teeth in the minute wheel. Oil all the acting surfaces in the striking part. Where there is friction, oil is required. The pallets are next oiled and screwed down. A little care is required getting the back pallet pivot in the hole when the steady pins of the cock are tight ; in such an instance it is by no means a difficult matter to bend the pivot getting the cock on. It is most extraordinary that, while modern English clocks are made with thicker plates, which permit of longer pivots, the manufacturers revert to the old style of short pivots, consequently they wear out in half the time, destroying one great advantage of using thicker plates.

Finally, pin on the dial and screw on the seat board, see that the lines hang correctly, and oil the pulleys.

It is advisable to start the clock going on a rack. Any slight adjustment here is quite simple, which would prove difficult in the case. The pendulum should hang quite rigid on the cock, with just perceptible shake at the crutch. A wobbling pendulum is a hopeless case of regulation. It is mostly the outcome of accidents to the crutch or suspension spring. The suspension spring averages 3 inches long, fixed to a brass block about $1\frac{1}{2}$ inches for the purpose of engaging the crutch. In the event of a suspension spring or crutch being broken, there is no reason why a new one cannot be fitted the correct length, so that the fork engages about the centre of the block. It is always safe to leave the spring on the weak side. More clocks stop with a spring too strong than too weak.

**Clock Train.**—The number of teeth in the wheels and pinions usually employed in a grandfather clock is as follows :

Going part.

> Great wheel 96 diam. $3\frac{3}{16}$ in.
> Centre   ,,   60   ,,   $2\frac{1}{16}$ in., pinion 8.
> Third    ,,   56   ,,   $1\frac{7}{8}$ in., pinion 8.
> Escape  ,,   30   ,,   $1\frac{1}{2}$ in., pinion 7.
> Barrel grooved for 16 turns diam. $1\frac{3}{4}$ in.
> Pallets embrace 8 teeth.

Striking part.

Great wheel 84 diam. $2\frac{7}{8}$ in.
Pin wheel 56 diam. $1\frac{7}{8}$ in., pinion 8.
Gathering pallet wheel 49 diam. $1\frac{9}{16}$ in., pinion 7.
Warning wheel 48 diam. $1\frac{5}{16}$ in., pinion 7.
Fly pinion 7, with 8 pins in the pin wheel.

Cannon and minute wheels 40 teeth each with diam.
$1\frac{1}{4}$ in.    Minute pinion 6.

Hour wheel 72 diam. $2\frac{1}{4}$ in.    Snail diam. $2\frac{1}{16}$.

Length of lifting piece $2\frac{3}{16}$ in.

Length of warning piece $2\frac{3}{8}$ in.

Length of rack 3 ins.

**Fitting a Pair of Recoil Pallets.**—A grandfather clock
is usually fitted with a " recoil " escapement. It is so
named from the action of the pallets which produce a
recoil or backward movement of the escape wheel after
a tooth has dropped.

This style of clock as a rule is allowed to run too long
without attention. The oil obviously evaporates, and
the force of the heavy weights overcomes the extra
friction at the acting surfaces, wearing them into ruts
until the clock finally comes to rest. Such timekeepers
would give infinitely better results driven with weights
2 to 3 lb. lighter and save such senseless remarks,
" My clock has been going well for 30 years and I know
it only requires cleaning."

The early form of recoil employed in long-cased clocks
were fitted with small escapements having escape wheels
of $1\frac{3}{8}$ in. diameter, later they were gradually increased
to $1\frac{5}{8}$ in. diameter and the pallets usually embraced eight
teeth.  Fig. 106 shows the pallets embracing the escape
wheel teeth.

Fitting a new pair of pallets is an interesting piece
of work. A forging or blank for the diameter of the wheel
can be obtained from any material dealer.  When the
old pallets are not at disposal the best plan is to
make an accurate drawing and file the pallets to the
drawing, taking care to leave the pallet pads rather
on the thick side, place them in the plates with

the escape wheel and reduce them finally to attain equal drop.

Draw a circle to represent the actual size of the escape wheel, then a vertical line. The escape wheels usually have 30 teeth, and although they vary in length, the average is a little less than one-fourth of the radius. A second circle to this measurement will give

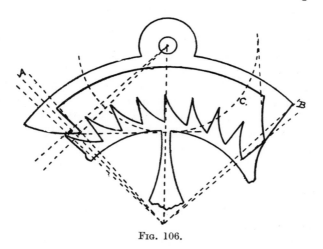

Fig. 106.

the bottoms of the teeth. The space between one tooth and the next, 360 degrees divided by 30, equal 12, and the pallets embrace $7\frac{1}{2}$ spaces, equal 90 degrees. Then 90 divided by 2 equal 45. Set off with a protractor the two radial lines A and B each making an angle of 45 degrees with the vertical line.

Seven spaces is the distance between the points of 8 teeth, and the half space is actually made up from the intersection of the pallets plus drop and the thickness of the tips of the teeth. In practice, the drop averages

$1\frac{1}{2}$ degrees, but in such a drawing it is policy to allow little or no drop—the pallets being finally reduced to attain it. Therefore, $2\frac{1}{2}$ degrees on each side of the line A will serve to mark the acting part of the left hand pallet and $2\frac{1}{2}$ to the right of B marks the point of the right hand pallet.

The backs of the teeth are radial and they may next be drawn starting on the right at B. Where the line A cuts the circle representing the tips of the wheel teeth, draw a tangent through the vertical centre line, this will indicate the position of the pallet staff centre.

From the pallet staff centre describe a circle C half the distance between the escape wheel and pallet staff centres. Tangents to this circle would form the faces of the pallets if they were left flat. The pallet faces are generally curved, the object is to lessen the " pitting ", which the wheel teeth make on the pallets. There should, however, be very little wear on the pallet faces, if the escape wheels are made very light and the escapement pitched with as little drop as possible. A wheel can often be reduced to half its weight by filing the rim and arms as light as possible.

When a tooth has dropped off the right-hand or exit pallet, which is the position of the escapement in the drawing, the amount of impulse is shown by the intersection of the other pallet in the wheel. The impulse measured from the pallet staff centre is usually 4 degrees, shown by the dotted line intersecting the corner of the entering pallet.

File the pallets roughly to the drawing, keeping the pallet faces on the large size. They are first placed on the pallet arbor and screwed in the plates with the wheel. Try a tooth on each pallet face to see the difference in the depth. If a tooth fails to leave the exit pallet,

file a little off the back at B.   Filing the back of the
entering pallet would give more drop on to the exit
pallet.   The drops should be kept as far as possible
equal.

When they are correct for depth, harden the pallet
faces and temper them to a light straw.   Finish the
faces with an emery buff and burnisher.

## CONVERTING 30-HOUR ENGLISH CLOCK

A 30-hour grandfather clock can be made to run about
5 days by throwing the striking work out of action,
because more than three-quarters of the fall of the weight
is used to drive the striking part.   This is the most
simple form of conversion, and the best plan is to remove,
or wedge the lifting piece and add a few links to the chain.

To convert a 30-hour grandfather into an 8-day
striker would involve a great deal of work.   There is at
the present day a great demand for these clocks and
to accomplish the necessary alteration would add at
least £5 to its value.   Any material dealer or metal
warehouse would supply the necessary parts.

An experiment has been made with a series of pulleys
and triple or quadruple lines hung with separate weights.
This not only has the disadvantage of having very heavy
weights necessary for driving, but entails nearly as much
work as fitting new barrels, arbors, and hanging the
weights direct.   The latter is decidedly the most
satisfactory alteration.

The pulley of the going part makes one turn in $6\frac{1}{2}$
hours.   To substitute a barrel with a weight hung direct
is a simple matter.   The main pin wheel, on which is

fixed the chain pulley, makes six turns in twelve hours ;
the trouble is to get sufficient fall for the striking part to
go for a week.

The most satisfactory way to overcome the difficulty
is shown in Fig. 107. The main pin wheel A has thirteen
lifting pins, and there is no room on this arbor to fit
a barrel to give a sufficient number of turns, because
the locking wheel occupies too much room.

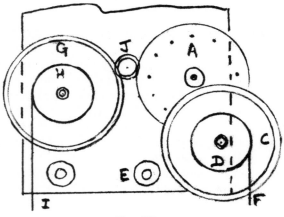

Fig. 107.

The two chain pulleys are discarded, and the main pin
wheel A is mounted on a new pinion arbor. The pinion
B is then driven by a new great wheel C, on the arbor of
which is fitted the new barrel D and winding square.
The barrel is $1\frac{1}{4}$ inches in diameter, grooved to make
twelve turns, and the winding ratchet cut on the flange.

There is plenty of room to get a bearing for the barrel
arbor pivots near the edge of the plates, but the holes
must be drilled as near the edge as possible to free the
hammer spring. The bottom right-hand pillar would

have to be shifted free of the great wheel shown at E, and a slot cut in the seat board to free the great wheel. The weight on the new barrel would hang on the opposite side to the old pulley shown at F.

The click and spring for the ratchet of the striking barrel D is fitted on the new great wheel in the same manner as an 8-day clock.

The new great wheel C and the pinion it drives have a ratio of eight ; therefore a pinion of 12 and a great wheel of 96 would be suitable. The wheel C must be larger in diameter than the pin wheel A so that the barrel arbor shall free the teeth of the pin wheel.

The sketch shows the two new barrels, the pin wheel, with the necessary alteration and the plate removed.

There is no obstacle on the going side to prevent a barrel being fitted from the plate to the great wheel G. The old pulley makes one turn in about $6\frac{1}{2}$ hours. A new barrel H, $1\frac{1}{4}$ inches in diameter and $1\frac{1}{2}$ inches long, is supplied grooved to give 27 or 28 turns. The barrel is fitted tightly on the new arbor, with the winding square filed on the end, and a hole in the dial opposite. The winding ratchet is cut on the flange of the barrel, which is left flush against the old great wheel. The click and spring is screwed to the great wheel in the same manner as an 8-day grandfather. The weight is hung direct from the barrel shown by the line I. The same barrel arbor holes can be used so that the great wheel depth is not altered with the centre pinion J.

A new pillar would be required, but with care the old one could be removed and fixed to free the great wheel C.

A little discretion is required in fitting the new pinion B, which is to form the new arbor for the pin wheel A. A large diameter pinion will be found most suitable, as the force exerted at this part is not only comparatively great, but the hole in the pin wheel will require a large arbor unless the hole is bushed.

The larger in diameter the new wheel C the greater distance the pillar E will have to be moved, which is a disadvantage. The best plan is to turn up a blank for the size of the wheel, and have the pinion sectored from pinion wire, stating the number of teeth in each.

The old pinion on the pin wheel arbor behind the plates which drives the count wheel is usually squared on the arbor. There should be no difficulty in fitting this pinion on the end of the new pinion arbor in the same manner.

Many clocks are made with the pin wheel close to the front plate instead of the back. This would make no difference in conversion. The new pinion head would be fitted close to the wheel to give the new barrel as much room as possible. The conversion only applies to 30-hour clocks with solid plates.

**To Join Rope for a 30-Hour English Clock.**—The ends of the rope can be untwisted for about 4 inches and the ends intertwined. Another method is to place both ends together tightly " cricket bat handle" style for about $1\frac{1}{2}$ in. Bind over the first loose end which is afterwards threaded through with a needle. Then finish the other end in the same manner. Another style overlap the two ends of the rope and bind together. This of course does not make such a neat job.

## 400-DAY  CLOCKS

Four-hundred-day clocks must be perfectly upright
on a solid base and the escapement nicely adjusted,
otherwise they are a source of trouble.  The accumulation of dust is sufficient to render a stand and glass
shade absolutely necessary.

The same rule applies to the pendulum, or balance,
as the balance and spring of a watch.  The vibrations
of the balance of the clock are governed by the strength
of the spring.  The length of the spring plays little
or no part in the performance of the balance, so long
as the latter is perfectly free of any object

It is not necessary the suspension spring should
be made of steel.  A compo spring would give the
same result.  A drum clock balance spring straightened
would answer the purpose.  Select a strong balance
spring, screw on the fork, the suspension, the bottom
block to support the balance, and start the clock for a
trial.  When it is losing more than five minutes a day,
break off a very small piece of spring and screw on the
balance suspension to start a new trial.  Any variation
less can be accomplished with the two adjusting weights
on the balance, which serve the purpose of regulating
by moving the squares at each end of the continuous
thread.  Towards the centre for losing and the opposite
for gaining.

Thinning the suspension spring is the usual procedure
when a clock is found to gain more than is advisable
to alter by the regulator.  This is quite a simple matter,
but requires a little care to reduce the metal at a uniform
rate.  Remove the fork, the suspension at each end,
and place the spring on a piece of soft wood screwed in
the vice.  An old emery buff will be found convenient

for this work, the wood being soft and the edges flat. Three or four brass pins driven into the wood will form a resting place for the edge of the spring and prevent it bending.

File the ends of the pins so that they come flush with the surface of the spring. The latter is then stoned equally the whole length to weaken it. Use plenty of oil in this operation. An emery buff could be employed for speed and finish with an arcansas stone and oil. Pressing the spring with the finger will help to keep it flat, using a circular motion to avoid buckling the spring. A very little reducing will make a great difference in timekeeping. It requires a little experience to judge the right amount the first time. Finally, leave the spring rubbed with oil paper to prevent rust.

The escapement should be pitched as light as possible, a slight lock of about half a degree is sufficient, with just perceptible drop on each pallet. A loss of impulse is the general failure which causes this style of clock to stop, and can be traced to increased friction, too much drop, or shake at the acting surfaces, or a badly adjusted escapement.

Increased friction is usually the cause of a pivot left rough, a hole worn large, wear marks left on the pallet faces, or roughness at the point of contact with the pallet pin and fork. A pivot hole worn large is not always rough, but causes a bad wheel and pinion depth, and absorbs motive power at the cost of the vibration of the balance. The safest plan is to bush any hole worn wide and finish the new hole with a round broach to attain a smooth surface.

The locking or impulse faces of the pallets left rough would mean extra friction and might cause the balance to come to rest. These pallets are usually on the

" Vienna " principle—circular steel pads gripped with
a screw. In such cases there is no difficulty in removing
them to grind out any wear marks with emery, a little
care will be required to keep the angles the same.
Finish the pallet faces with diamantine and a soft
metal polisher.

The spring must be fixed perfectly vertical in the
suspension or the balance is liable to wobble. The best

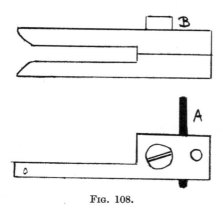

FIG. 108.

plan is to screw the spring in the suspension tight enough
to hold the balance and let the latter pull the spring
straight, then screw the two screws home.

The loss of motive power is often traced to the action
of the pallet pin and fork. The impulse to the balance
is carried through this point, and any loss here would
obviously tell on the vibration of the balance. The
pallet pin and sides of the fork must be perfectly smooth.
Too much shake, or rust on the pin would mean a loss
of impulse. Where there is any doubt burnish the

pin and sides of the notch and close the latter to give
the pin perceptible shake.

The fork must be fixed tightly on the suspension
spring and exactly at right angle to it.   The point
of fixture is about half an inch from the bottom of the
suspension block.   Fig. 108 shows the plan and elevation
of the fork with the spring A running between the
screw B and steady pin.   The vibration of the balance
from the drop of one escape wheel tooth to the next
is about three-quarters of a turn.   The actual vibration,
therefore, must not be less than a turn.   This can easily
be detected by observing the relative position of one
of the weights in the balance at the completion of a
vibration and the position at the end of the next.

The clock must be perfectly in beat or it is liable to
stop.   To set it in beat is the same as bending the
crutch of a clock.   The pallet pin which engages the
fork should move the same angle each side of a vertical
line immediately a tooth has dropped.   When the pallet
pin is perfectly upright, ease the screw at the top of the
suspension and twist the block round a little.

Oil is required at the point of contact with the pallet
pin and fork.

## CARRIAGE  CLOCKS

A carriage clock, being portable, is subject to falls.
The result of the accident is generally a cracked or
broken endstone, jewel-hole, or a bent pivot.

After taking the clock to pieces examine the pivots ;
any showing signs of wear should be polished.

The platform of the escapement usually has a little
side shake before the screws are screwed down, which

enables adjusting until the escape and contrate depth is right. This depth is the greatest fault in the clock. Many are taken to repair comparatively clean, which stop in the contrate depth. Occasionally it happens the escape pinion is worn, and a new surface can be obtained by raising the platform with four collets.

Contrate pivot holes should be quite smooth ; round broach them if they look at all rough. The screw for regulating the endshake should be friction-tight in its hole. If this is loose, close the slot.

It is quite essential that the contrate wheel should be perfectly true in the flat, or it will be impossible to obtain a good depth even if it should happen to go. A bad depth is always unsatisfactory—you may have it through an occasional stop. In the event of the wheel being out of the flat, the safest plan is to remount it. Drive the wheel off the collet ; it often happens that the collet has been soft soldered to the arbor, and comes loose ; in that case turn up a new collet and drive it on the arbor friction tight. Many clockmakers continue to soft solder collets on the arbors, instead of driving them on friction tight ; it is not only ancient and unmechanical, but renders it impossible to shift the collet true along the arbor when desirable in order to get a wheel to run in a new part of the pinion.

The back of the contrate wheel which lay on the collet seat is not parallel and true with the teeth ; therefore, the wheel must be cemented in the lathe, laying the tips of the teeth on a large cement chuck ; peg it true, turn the seat of the collet true, and re-mount the wheel. Before riveting the wheel, try it in the plates with the escape pinion and examine the depth.

Watchmakers without a lathe can accomplish this work in large size screw arbor, and make a cement plate. Remove the screw and nut, turn the shoulder of the ferrule flat ; use a piece of flat brass a little larger in diameter than the wheel ; file one side flat, drill a hole in the centre large enough to admit the screw-arbor. Place the brass on the arbor against the ferrule and drill three or four holes through the two ; chamfer the ends of the holes and rivet them together. Then turn the plate true on its own arbor.

It is a good plan to put the train in the plates before cleaning and try endshakes and depths. If either of the centre wheel holes is wide fit a new one ; a loose centre hole may mean a fault in the motion work, or the hands too close to the dial or to the glass. The motive power should not require less attention ; variation of time for different days can be traced to the mainspring. " Spring foul of cover " or bottom of the barrel are common faults, and can be rectified by filing the eye of the mainspring higher or lower. Use old files for steel, reserving new ones for brass ; a file should have as much attention as a graver ; clean it occasionally on a file cleaner. The application of a little oil makes all the difference in the cut.

Remove the mainspring and try the stop work round each turn, holding the barrel arbor square in the vice. If the finger piece is slightly tight in any of the star-wheel crescents, file the crescent until it is perfectly free. The star-wheel screw is sometimes too high and foul of the plate. Any of these faults, although not causing a stop, would result in bad timekeeping. The quickest method for timing carriage clocks is to note the time at the first blow of each hour.

## QUARTER REPEATING CARRIAGE CLOCKS

A quarter repeating carriage clock is driven only by two trains ; one for the going part and the other for striking and repeating the hours and quarters. In an English quarter clock, the quarters are struck first, and on completion let off the hour part. This principle is reversed in the carriage variety, the hours are struck first, then the rack brings a " quarter piece " into action, which releases both hammers and brings the quarter rack into operation. There is only one gathering pallet and one rack hook, which serves the purpose of holding both racks in position.

The going and striking trains are assembled between the plates in the usual way, and the plates are pinned down. Try the freedom and endshakes of all the wheels and pivots to see if everything is perfectly free. Any fault between the plates might cause the horologist to mistake it for an error in other directions.

Most of the faults in the striking work and repeating mechanism could be traced to badly adjusted springs. They require careful attention, any sign of rust can be removed with an emery buff while the spring is placed on a piece of soft wood in the vice, and the buff used lengthwise. When removing the springs preparatory to cleaning, the best plan is to screw them to a piece of cardboard in the same relative position as they occupy when screwed to the plate. This system will avoid confusion, which often results in forcing screws in the wrong holes and stripping the threads.

The plates and wheels are usually cleaned with crocus, mixed with oil, or metal polish, the latter gives a better finish, or the solution described in " 8-day English Clock ", the parts are washed in petrol,

brushed  with  a  chalk  brush,  and  the  holes  pegged
clean.

The  springs  and  studs  are  screwed  on  the  plate
first.  Those  shown  in  Fig.  109  are  the  shutter  A,  the
quarter  rack  B,  the  quarter  piece  C,  and  the  hour  piece
D.  The  pieces  that  come  nearest  to  the  plate  are  then

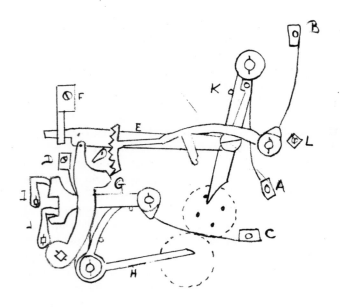

placed  on  their  studs.  The  shutter  E,  with  the  guide
block  F,  the  quarter  piece  G,  and  the  hour  piece  H,
the  hammer  blocks  I  and  J  are  next  pinned  on.  The
cannon  pinion  shown  by  a  dotted  circle  has  four  pins
at  equi-distance  for  lifting  the  shutter  at  each  quarter
of  an  hour  to  release  the  striking.  The  shutter  banks
against  a  screw  in  the  plate  marked  K.  The  spring

must be strong enough to throw the shutter forward to the screw K, and release the rack hook as the pin is discharged every quarter of an hour. Any extra tension from this spring would have to be overcome by the force exerted by the going train at the quarter pins in the cannon pinion, and would mean the vibration of the balance falling off.

The hour piece H is much the same as seen in hour repeating clocks—a right angle arm pinned on a stud. Its object is to prevent the hour rack from falling, except at the hours, when it is moved out of action with the path of the hour rack by a pin in the minute wheel shown by a dotted circle. This piece banks against a pin in the plate, which is sometimes fixed under the lower arm near the minute wheel. The tension of the spring requires to be very weak, just sufficient to keep it against the pin. The quarter piece G has a slot cut at the end to free the lower hammer block and allow the hours to be struck, while the top one is raised by resting on the edge. The spring should be just strong enough to keep the piece against the pin in the plate.

The gathering pallet, rack hook, and quarter rack are next put on, and pinned, as shown in the sketch. The other end of the rack hook above is the locking pallet that locks the striking train. Try the tension of the quarter rack spring A to see if it is strong enough to throw the tail on the snail. The lifting piece has a small spring to keep the shutter resting on the pin in the rack hook. Oil the large screw, the studs, the end of the springs, and any acting surface where there is friction.

At the hour, the hour piece is lifted by a pin in the minute wheel, and the rack hook thrown out by the step in the shutter coming in contact with a pin in the

top of the hook.  The hour rack is then free to fall on
the hour snail, and as the striking train starts to run,
and the gathering pallet commences to gather up
a tooth, the hammer blocks are lifted, which then allows
the quarter piece to fall on its banking pin.  The top
hammer block then falls on the edge of the quarter
piece, only allowing the bottom block free to strike the
hours as shown in the sketch.

When the last blow of the hours is struck, a pin in
the end of the hour rack comes in contact with the
bottom of the quarter piece and lifts it far enough for
the top hammer block to fall in the slot of the quarter
piece and allow both hammers to strike the quarters,
the bottom block being then below the edge of the
quarter piece.

It takes the distance between two hour rack teeth
to lift the quarter piece sufficiently for the hammer
blocks to fall free of the edge of the quarter piece.
This accounts for a dummy blow to be struck on the
first tooth after the hour is struck, as both the hammer
blocks at this stage fall on the edge of the quarter piece.
At the next rotation of the gathering pallet the pin in
the hour rack has lifted the quarter piece high enough
to allow the quarters to be struck.

The hour rack stud is shown at L in Fig. 109.
Place the rack on its stud and test the two racks
together to see if the quarter rack is gathered
up after the hour.

Both racks fall together on their respective snails,
and although the gathering pallet will appear to gather
up the teeth in both at the hour, the rack hook is not
sufficiently forward to hold the quarter rack teeth
(which slips back) until the hour rack teeth are
gathered up.

Fig. 110 shows the lower part of the hour rack with the pin lifting the quarter piece. At the first rotation of the gathering pallet, the pin has lifted the hour piece shown in Fig. 111, so that both hammer blocks fall on the edge. This causes the dummy blow, or the hammers lifted away from the gongs. With the next rotation of the gathering pallet, the pin has lifted the quarter piece in the position shown in Fig. 112, when the first quarter is struck.

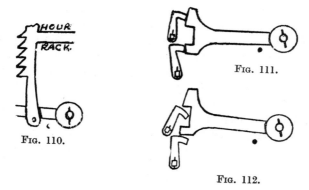

FIG. 110.

FIG. 111.

FIG. 112.

The rack hook at this stage is sufficiently forward to hold the quarter rack teeth as the gathering pallet intersects them, until the quarters are struck when the locking arm at the other end of the rack hook arbor locks the striking train. The gathering pallet in this class of clock consists of a double finger, or pallet, one to gather the hour rack teeth, and one for the quarter rack, with a long arm to lift the shutter and so free the rack hook.

The quarter snail is next placed in position, and all the quarters tested with both racks pinned on. Oil the two pins for lifting the star wheel, the point of contact of all the springs, the studs, and all surfaces where any friction occurs. Complete the motion work with the star wheel and hour snail. Fix the pins, test the freedom of all the pieces, and try the striking work round. If it is right at the lowest and highest steps of the hour snail, that is the 12 and 1, it is usually correct at the others. The repeating and "strike and silent" pieces are put on last. Test the motion work and examine the hour wheel pipe to see if the hole is perfectly clean and runs free on the cannon pinion.

It is quite possible to convert a French striking carriage clock into a repeater. It would often avoid the loss of a sale to convert one in the workshop. It entails a good deal more work than appears at first sight, because a striking clock is made with "warning" which would obviously have to be abolished.

The first step is to remove the hands and dial. Cut out a paper pattern of a repeating piece, as applied in a carriage clock, and hold it over the striking work in position to see what alteration is required. The bottom of the curve arm should come level with the rack hook and hour piece, so that, when the pin is fitted, these pieces are lifted to allow the clock to repeat the last hour. Cut the pattern until it is correct. Mark the plate for the stud hole, which would come nearly under the corner of the escapement platform. Drill the hole, tap it, and make a stud.

Select a piece of well-hammered sheet brass and file the repeating arm to the pattern, drill a small hole to fit the stud for preparatory fitting. This hole is later broached and fitted on a shoulder of a piece of bush wire to form the pipe for the stud.

The top end can be bent over, or a right angle piece

screwed on to come flush with the push piece in the case. On the left of the stud hole or pipe is a steel arbor which forms the banking through a hole in the plate. These two holes next require to be drilled in a line. A long thin spring is then planted on the plate to press against the arbor and keep the repeating piece flush against the push piece.

The pin in the end of the piece is the last to be made. Make a dot just free of the hour piece, drill it, and fit the pin. Open the banking hole in the plate sufficiently to allow the repeating piece enough movement for the pin to throw the rack hook and hour piece out of action.

The warning piece is next permanently removed, the motion work and hour piece taken off. It is then necessary to make a sketch, or cut a paper pattern of the shutter. An illustration, which would do for a copy, is shown in Fig. 109. The pieces with the two springs are marked A and E, with the guide block F. The shutter is made in two pieces of hammered brass, fixed with a large shouldered screw. The plate is marked for a stud hole, drilled, a stud turned, and the shutter shouldered to a brass pipe to fit the stud.

It will be found necessary to rivet a piece. of flat brass on the end of the rack hook to take a steel pin for engaging the shutter. The length necessary can be determined by fixing on the rack, hook, and shutter. The banking screw K is fitted when the other parts are correct.

The gathering pallet will need a little addition in the shape of a long arm to lift the shutter. This can be accomplished with a piece of thin brass near the plate in a line with the shutter fixed firmly with the pallet.

Graduated snails might be accurate when the rack

tail only falls once in an hour, but for a repeater the numbers are certain to be wrong in places.  The safest plan to step cut the snail is to let the tail rest on it at the beginning and end of each hour, notice the difference in the intersection of the gathering pallet, and file each step separately.

## FRENCH STRIKERS

A French clock which strikes the hours and half-hours known as a " French Striker ", is considered easy to clean and repair.  And beyond repairing a few worn pivots, new holes, and grinding the wear marks from the pallet faces, there is little to learn.  The cleaning is simple.  (See Repairing 8-Day Clock.)

To assemble the clock hold the pillar plate in a cloth, place the centre wheel in first, then the two barrels which are marked with one dot for the gong, and two for the striking.  Next the hammer arbor, the locking detent arbor, and the pin wheel.  Adjust the former so that the tail is tight against the banking pin, and move the pin wheel for a pin to come free of the tail, in the position when it has just dropped off.  It is at this position the pin in the gathering pallet wheel falls on the lock piece.  The latter is next placed with the pin locked as stated.  The warning wheel is next inserted with the pin about one-third of a turn from the slot in the plate, which represents the warning piece.  The fly and eight-day wheel complete the train. Let the top plate on gently and guide the pivots in their holes with the tweezers starting with the large ones. At this stage a pin placed in the pillar hole near the barrels will prevent it rising while the smaller  pivots are guided in. In the older style with count wheel, the detent should drop in the centre of a notch at the completion of the number to be struck. If it fails try the count wheel on a different square. When this is not successful, lift the top plate and move the wheel round a tooth.

To start a clock with a wobbling pendulum is time wasted, and there are many causes of this.

The block of the Brocot suspension must be rigid ; loose steady pins, or a badly-fitted screw, is often the cause of trouble.

The most common form of " wobbling " is the suspension spring being kinked or loose in the block. Such a spring may have the marks burnished out. Place it on a piece of wood in the vice and rub it with a half-round burnisher. If the spring is badly bent fit a new one. The bottom of the slot in the Brocot block, which forms the chops, should be burnished over, so that the suspension spring has no shake. Remove it from the block before attempting to burnish over the brass ; this is a general cure for " wobbling ".

The suspension spring is often made of two thin pieces ; the object, is to allow the pendulum to hang plumb and lessen any liability to wobble. This is right enough, but they frequently get buckled, and when one receives more attention from burnishing it assumes a greater length than the other, and a " wobble " is the result. In this case replace it.

Suspension springs too strong cause a bad arc of vibration and frequently stop.

The crutch is often loose on the arbor or too wide in the notch. Crutch out of angle is another cause of wobble. Clocks have often been seen going in the rack with the end of the slot in the crutch pressing hard on

the pendulum rod.  Shake in the notch means loss
of impulse.  When it is necessary to close a notch, file
the sides parallel, burnish out any file marks, and leave
the crutch as originally.

The bob should be free from shake on the rod.  A loose
bob will cause an erratic path of the pendulum.  If the
bob has side shake, remove the rod and burnish down
the edges of the hole which receives the rod.

When a clock gains with the bob at the bottom of the
rod there is usually a fault in the escapement.  When
corrected it is necessary to screw up the nut.  When
a clock gains, and there is no apparent fault in the
escapement, with the bob at the bottom, it has often
been remarked, " Put a heavier bob."

Adding to or subtracting weight from the pendulum
bob makes no material difference to the time of vibration
unless it is above or below the centre of oscillation.

Regulate a clock as far as possible by the bob, with
the brass slide half-way down the suspension spring ;
this leaves room for any final adjustment from the
Breguet block after the clock is taken home.
Occasionally, the bob touches the bottom of the case,
with the clock gaining.  Assuming that everything
else is correct, file away a piece from the bottom of
the bob and screw the nut down.  This will bring the
centre of oscillation nearer the bottom of the rod.


## PIN   PALLET   ESCAPEMENT

The pin pallet escapement is, or should be, a  dead
beat ;  the form employed in the French visible is
frequently far from perfect in construction, consequently
destroying the principle under which it was originally

intended. Pins the wrong size, or out of angle, are the most common faults.

The cause of all the trouble in this escapement can be summarized in the pallet pins—resulting in a loss of impulse. It would be folly to state these faults are all original. The repairer often plays a prominent part, and for lack of knowledge fits a new pin the wrong size, or the wrong angle. Under such conditions the vibration of the pendulum must suffer, and consequently timekeeping would be rendered useless.

The pallet pins are usually agate, or cornelian, semi-circular, and should be a trifle less in diameter than the distance between two teeth. To attain the correct amount of impulse the escape wheel teeth should drop dead on the largest diameter of a pallet pin. Assuming a pin is the correct size, the drop would be slight, about one degree.

Too much drop is not only a loss of motive power, but a loss of impulse and unnecessary wear on the pins. The amount of drop should be as small as possible, just sufficient to give the pallet pins clearance from the backs of the escape wheel teeth.

Large size " visibles " with long pendulums usually have thirty teeth to the escape wheel, with pallets embracing eleven teeth. Wheels with thirty-four and thirty-eight are made with smaller escapements. Clocks with the latter number frequently give trouble because there is not sufficient freedom at the backs of the wheel teeth to get the latter to drop dead on the largest part of the pin. There is obviously in such a case a recoil.

Fig. 113 shows a common fault—the escapement too shallow, with a recoil, too much drop, and insufficient

impulse    A tooth has just left the exit pallet B and
dropped on to the entering pin A.  The distance from
the two dotted lines, that is from the point of the tooth
to the corner of the pin B, is the amount the tooth has
dropped.    Warm the shellac and move the exit pin
B round a little, so that the flat is half-way between its
present position and the point of the tooth.  The pin
A will then have moved a larger intersection of the
wheel when the tooth B drops, and therefore fall on the

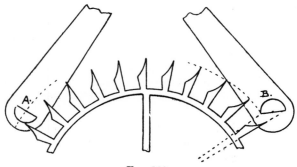

Fig. 113.

largest part of the pin A, shown by a dotted curve
through the centre.    The exit pin would also take a
larger intersection of the wheel teeth before the tooth
dropped from the pin A, because it would have a greater
distance to travel before reaching the corner at the
flatted part.  The impulse would also be increased
on both pins equal to the distance from the point of
the tooth to the dotted curve at A.

A pallet pin out of upright might cause unequal
drops and a loss of impulse.  In such instances soften
the shellac and push the pin upright.

Steel pallet pins often require replacing through wear. This operation is comparatively easy, as they are invariably the correct size. Hold the flatted end over a hollow punch held in the vice, and drive out from the back with a flat-ended punch the same size as the pin. Select a piece of rod steel the same diameter as the old pin, or turn a piece to size, and buff out the graver marks. Turn a ring to mark the shoulder of the flat and file half the diameter of the pin away, resting the edge of the file against the ring. Buff out the file marks, then harden and temper to a light straw. The pin is then polished with diamantine and burnished, held in position to the correct angle, and driven home with a flat punch resting on the corner of the pin.

The French visible is usually on the " self-setting " type. The writer has often wondered why so many have been made a fixture by the repairer. Large, unsightly pieces of soft solder project where the crutch is supposed to swing on the pallet arbor, and so set itself in beat. Because a piece of mechanism was made correctly is no reason why it should be destroyed because it has contracted a fault. It is quite a simple matter to tighten it, and this is easily accomplished. The boss of the crutch is usually split and screwed on the pallet arbor. Unscrew it and slightly close the slot in the vice until it screws on just tight enough to carry. Count the number of turns when removing the crutch from the arbor, so that it can be screwed on in the same place.

Assuming the escapement is correct, the trouble arising from stopping is generally traced to the depth of the fourth wheel and escape pinion. The arbor of this wheel is cut short and run in two cocks. The pivot holes often get worn, and obviously cause a bad depth with the escape pinion. Instead of fitting new holes, many horologists have a weakness for broaching the steady pin holes, and pressing the cock over with the object of improving the depth. This accounts for so many cocks with loose steady pin holes which do not screw down twice alike. A new pair of pivot holes, and re-steady pin, the cock upright will frequently put this matter right.

There is a tendency in this escapement to draw the oil away from the pallet pins. A little oil applied to the pins will often cure the fault of stopping.


## DEAD  BEAT  ESCAPEMENT

To make a dead beat or Graham escapement is a fine and interesting piece of work. Many regulators fitted with this class of escapement under favourable conditions have a given rate of a second a week.

The escape wheel is usually $1\frac{3}{4}$ inches in diameter. To obtain cutters in pre-war days was by no means an easy matter, but to attempt it now would be time wasted. To make your own cutters without any experience at wheel cutting is a demoralizing operation. The easiest plan, therefore, would be to send to a wheel cutter for a $1\frac{3}{4}$ inch dead beat escape wheel, and to make an accurate drawing and file the pallets to the drawing, leaving the pads on the thick side. (Dimensions for the drawing see Regulator Clock.) They are then placed in the frame with the escape wheel and finally reduced to attain equal drops.

When the pallets are not jewelled, the faces should be hardened in oil. The escape wheel is screwed to a brass collet with three screws, and the latter fixed to the escape pinion arbor in the same manner as the pallets.

The tendency of wear on the pallets of a " dead beat " escapement cuts a groove on the dead or locking faces and across the impulse faces traversed by the escape wheel teeth. It is quite obvious therefore with a light locking of half a degree, a pair of pallets correctly pitched for depth would " miss locking " when badly worn.

It is necessary the teeth should drop on the dead or locking corner, and not on the impulse face. The usual procedure by the repairer in such cases is to file and buff out the wear marks and close up the pallets. It is making the best of a bad job, for the pallets are never the same angle, and cannot therefore be expected to give the same results in close timekeeping. Having properly constructed a pair of " dead beat " pallets, the wisest plan is to jewel them, and save unnecessary wear, which means altering their angles.

Pallets jewelled in sapphire are the best, but this work should only be attempted by a jeweller experienced in the work.

Many clockmakers have jewelled their own pallets with agate, which is a hard stone and will last for many years. To accomplish this work, soften the pallet faces and slit them where the escape wheel teeth come in contact. The measurement from the locking corner should be just over an eighth of an inch. The width of the slit is about one and a quarter times the thickness of the escape wheel. The slits may be cut with a file, or a milling tool, in the lathe. When the latter course is adopted, the best plan is to make a circular milling cutter especially for the purpose to fit a split chuck. The pallets should be held perfectly upright and

firm on the rest while the milling tool cuts the slit.
Stones let into these slits will then take the whole of the
friction of the escape wheel teeth.

To fit agate stones to the slits is by no means difficult :
it is a slow operation, but interesting. They are first
ground flat on both sides, then ground to the shape of
the pallets, leaving them projecting slightly beyond
the locking and impulse faces and fitted to the slots.
The stones can be ground in the lathe on an iron lap or
disc charged with emery powder and water. A hood

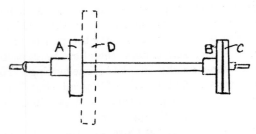

FIG. 114.

should be provided during the grinding stages to catch
the water thrown from the rotating wheel. The agates
are then fixed to the pallets with shellac, and the acting
faces ground flush with the steel to attain a correct
depth, trying them in the plates with the escape wheel
occasionally to be on the safe side. Finally polish
them with putty powder on a boxwood mill or chuck
in the lathe. Most jewellers have a collection of odd
stones, and you would find agate of suitable size
amongst the treasures of your friend.

Two thick brass collets are driven tight on the pallet
arbor, one to form a seat for the pallets the other for

the crutch. The old form of fixing these collets was soft solder, but with experience we have become wiser. The collet for holding the pallets is driven on far enough to come opposite the escape wheel, so that when the pallets are fitted they are perfectly in line with the escape wheel teeth running in line central of the pallet stones. Fig. 114 shows the pallet staff—A the pallet collet, B the crutch collet, C the crutch, and D the thickness of the pallets.

The two collets are next turned true on the pallet arbor and the pallets fitted tightly and fixed with three small screws, the threads being tapped in the collet. The pallets are then easily removed for jewelling.

The crutch collet seat is turned back and the crutch fitted tightly so that it is well free of the back cock. Three small screws are fitted to hold it in the same manner as the pallets. This collet can be finished thinner than the pallet, with the diameter of the two the same.

The thickness of the crutch is about the same as the escape wheel, with a large thin boss to fit against the shoulder of the collet and form a symmetrical appearance with the pallet boss. The crutch is of steel, light but rigid, flat or rounding back and front according to preference.

It is advisable to finish the escape pinion and pallet staff before jewelling the pallets. The pivots should be made small in diameter, but there is nothing gained in leaving them short. A long pivot will have a much longer life than a short one. We must bear in mind the old maxim : Friction is proportional to pressure. It is independent of extent of surface.

The escape wheel is usually made with five or six arms. To " cross out " or file up the rim and arms equal is a nice piece of work. Make them thin. Lightness is one of the main features in an escape wheel if the timekeeper is to give a fine rate.

## GRAVITY ESCAPEMENT

Opinions have been expressed by authorities on the comparative merits of the dead beat and gravity escapements for regulator clocks. Many well-known makers have shown some fine results with their favourite escapement, and speaking from practical experience and without prejudice the writer has handled several clocks of this type fitted with the " Graham " having an exceedingly close rate that would be hard to beat.

There is no question of doubt as to which escapement is best adapted to a turret clock. The late Lord Grimthorpe designed the gravity for the Westminster clock. The writer has had the privilege of inspecting it, and if we accept this escapement as a standard of what the inventor intended, it is, indeed, not surprising at the many uncomplimentary remarks made on imitations of Lord Grimthorpe's gravity escapement.

Many turrets have been made with escapements altogether too heavy and out of proportion. More stability in the motive power to drive the hands against the resistance of all weather and less in escapement would give " gravity turrets " a better chance of recording time in keeping with their reputation. The resistance of the wind against the hands, the inconsistency in the force at the escape wheel due to imperfections of mechanical constructions, or the thickening of oil in no way affects the impulse of the pendulum, which remains a constant unit, the force of gravity bringing the pallet arm on the pendulum rod.

Some years ago a North of England firm showed me the gravity escape wheel of a clock entrusted to them. It was not only found necessary to fit a new wheel one-fourth the weight, but the gravity arms were too heavy and altogether out of proportion to attain the desired result.

It is essential a gravity should be nicely constructed and adjusted to a regulator to give a closer rate than a " Graham ". Attempts to make many gravity escapements contradictory to their theoretical rules have proved a bungling fiasco.

When a pallet has fallen as far as a beat pin permits it is lifted by the motive power through the lifting pins a little before the pendulum rod returns. The difference between this amount and the actual lift constitutes the work or impulse by falling, or force of gravity on the impulse arm which keeps the pendulum in a uniform arc of vibration. The swing of the pendulum, therefore, is in no way effected by the motive power, and its impulse is received when the train is at rest, simply by the weight of the gravity arm. The friction in unlocking would vary with the force exerted through the train, but the effect of this variation can be regarded as an unimportant factor.

The sketch in Fig. 115 is made on the principle of Lord Grimthorpe's four-legged design for regulators. Seen from behind the train is inverted to save height in the frame and clockcase. The escape wheel, which is 3 in. in diameter, has four long arms acting as teeth ; the fronts are struck radial. At the centre of the wheel eight steel pins are fixed equi-distant projecting about one-eighth of an inch. The four front pins lift the left-hand pallet, and the four back lift the right. To avoid wear on the pallets and risk of tripping the regulation

of velocity is accomplished by a fly mounted on the
escape wheel arbor. The seconds wheel arbor A is
shortened and run in a cock in the frame to free the

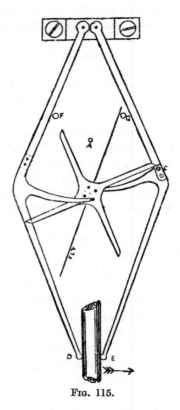

Fig. 115.

fly, which is a 2 in. radius. The escape wheel is very
light cut from thin steel plate and screwed on the arbor
to a shoulder with a left-handed thread, so that the
action tends to tighten it, or " squared " on.

It is expedient to study lightness in the gravity arms ; many failures in this escapement are due from this respect. They are made of thin steel plates ; the shape is immaterial so long as the stops or locking blocks B and C are fixed at right angles. The right-handed pallet is behind the wheel engaging the four back lifting pins and the other the pins in front. The gravity arms are pivoted as near as possible in a line with the bending point of the suspension spring. The blocks and acting faces of the pallets are hardened to reduce wear ; the former, in many instances are jewelled. Care is required in marking the lifting pins so that the lift occurs equally across the line of centres.

A gravity escapement requires a heavier weight than a " Graham ", assuming other depending properties are equal. It must be strong enough to lift the pallets sharply away. Assuming a seconds pendulum is employed, the escape wheel makes one rotation in 8 seconds—$7\frac{1}{2}$ turns to one of the seconds arbor.

The length of the tails of the pallets carrying the beat pins D and E is more a matter of fancy. The pins are more important ; they are usually brass or ivory, left perfectly smooth. No oil is required, or the action of the escapement will surely suffer. The banking pins are shown as F and G.

## PENDULUMS

**Length of Pendulum from the Train.**—The pendulum is one of the most important parts of a clock. Its regularity in timekeeping is solely governed by its performance. Except for receiving a sufficient impulse to maintain its vibration, the pendulum should be perfectly free in its movement and uninfluenced by the train.

Galileo, the famous astronomer, discovered isochronism in the time of vibration of a pendulum when describing long and short arcs. His son is credited to be the first to use a pendulum as a timekeeper. A working model of Galileo's pendulum clock is to be seen in South Kensington Museum. It is a very rough contrivance, consisting of a train of wheels and a prehistoric sort of escapement to keep the pendulum in motion.

To calculate the length of pendulum from the train, first determine the number of vibrations per minute, which is worked by counting the number of teeth in the wheels multiplied together and divide by the number of leaves in the pinions multiplied together. Take, as example, centre wheel 84, third 70, escape 30, with pinions of 7. Then we have $\dfrac{84 \times 70 \times 30 \times 2}{7 \times 7} = 7,200$ vibrations of pendulum per hour. $\dfrac{7,200}{60} = 120$ vibrations of pendulum per minute. The method now adopted to find the length of pendulum, which gives 120 vibrations per minute, is to multiply the length of a pendulum which vibrates seconds by the square of 60, the number of seconds in a minute, and divide by the square of the number required. The length of a pendulum beating seconds, that is, a one-seconds pendulum, is 39·14 in. Therefore $\dfrac{39 \cdot 14 \times 60^2}{120^2} =$ the length of pendulum required. The square of 60 is $60 \times 60 = 3,600$. Now, if we multiply 39·14 by 3,600, which equals 140,904, and divide by the square of 120, the answer will be the length of pendulum required. The square of 120 is

$120 \times 120 = 14,400$, and 140,904 divided by 14,400 $=$ 9·78 in., or a little over nine and seven-tenths of an inch. The answers to these calculations represent the length of pendulum to the centre of oscillation, or the centre of gravity. For practical work it will be found sufficiently accurate to call it the centre of the bob and make the pendulum the length stated from the point of suspension to the centre of the bob, plus half the length of the bob and the usual length at the bottom for the timing nut.

To determine the length of any pendulum, it is always necessary to multiply the length of a seconds pendulum by the square of 60 and divide by the square of the vibrations required. Assuming the length required is to give 70 vibrations per minute, we should have

$$\frac{39 \cdot 14 \times 60 \times 60}{70 \times 70}$$

In many shops pendulums receive insufficient attention. Being detached, they are regarded as necessary evils.

When making a new pendulum the selection of material for the rod should be governed by the price allowed for the work. An iron rod serves the purpose of a " grandfather " where cheapness is the main consideration, but with changes of temperature the variations of such a pendulum are obvious. A wood rod with a lead bob is a cheap form of compensation, and assuming other depending properties are correct, some close rates are attained with this combination for either recoil or dead beat escapements.

**Wood Rod and Lead Bob.**—A lead bob 12 inches long by 2·25 inches in diameter will be found to nearly equalize the temperature error of a 45 in. wooden pendulum rod. The hole should be just large enough to pass freely over the wood rod. The bottom of the bob rests on a washer above the rating nut.

Casting the bob is by no means difficult. A cylindrical card or wood box of the given dimensions will be found convenient for the mould. Brown paper rolled tightly round a cylinder many times would answer the purpose with wood or cardboard fixed at the top and bottom. Strike the centre of the top and bottom with a pair of compasses, and describe and cut two circles large enough to just admit the rod. Place the box which is to form the mould in a larger box or on a piece of wood. Next insert a temporary rod through the two holes in the cylinder, and build round it with plaster, whitening or sand. A little care must be taken to see it is rigid enough to support the molten metal. An accident in this direction might prove serious. Two holes are required in the lid, a large one for pouring the metal, and a small air-hole opposite.

It is remarkable the wood rod and lead bob combination is not more generally adopted in grandfather clocks. The rate attained is decidedly closer than with an iron rod. The cost of manufacture is small compared with a mercurial or zinc and steel compensation, which makes it popular in a better-class clock. Ebony is often used for the rod, especially in pendulums of the shorter variety. This wood is equal to any and safe for pinning and fitting the brass caps without fear of splitting. It should be perfectly straight in the grain and well seasoned. Many pendulum makers have had their strips of wood in stock for fifty or sixty years and country clockmakers who have successfully made their own delight in relating how they procured well-seasoned wood.

Deal is usually selected for the purpose, although

mahogany and lance are occasionally used. If the wood is not well matured, atmospheric changes will affect the timekeeping and the result obtained will be useless. Cabinet-makers have often been known to oblige. Mahogany is perhaps the most likely.

A friend of mine bought an Oriental spear at a second-hand dealer's. This kind of store is certainly a likely place to do business.

For a seconds pendulum the rod should be ·5 in. in diameter, 45 in. long from the top of the free part of the suspension spring to the bottom of the bob. Scrape and smooth the rod with glasspaper. Many clock-makers paint their rods. Paraffin well rubbed in and finished with oil or a coat of fine varnish will be found equal to anything to repel atmospheric influence.

A thin piece of brass tube is soldered to a brass block to form the clip of the suspension spring. The clip is then slotted and filed to shape. A piece of brass tube is fitted tightly over the rod where it is engaged by the crutch, fixed with two pins, drilled and slotted to fit the crutch pin (Fig. 116). The top, or suspension, tube is then fitted to the rod and pinned (Fig. 116). The screw for the rating nut is soldered to a piece of brass tube the same diameter as the rod, fitted and pinned on, as shown in Fig. 117.

The rigidity of the pendulum is one of the most important features in close timekeeping. Many clocks fail in this respect ; the end of the cock which has to bear the weight of the pendulum could have three times the amount of metal to advantage. The most perfectly constructed pendulum would fail to give a close rate hung on a weak bracket. All best class regulators have the cock to support the pendulum screwed to the back of the case, and in most instances

this cock is fixed to a cast-iron bracket, which supports
the movement.  The suspension should be adjusted so
that the bend of the spring is opposite the centre of the
pallet staff, that is the staff pivot.  The crutch will then
have as little friction on the pendulum as possible.

Many faults in timekeeping are attributed to the
crutch, which, generally speaking, receives insufficient

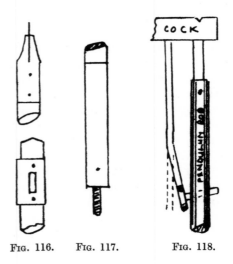

FIG. 116.     FIG. 117.         FIG. 118.

attention.  The apprentice is inclined to regard the
crutch as a hook of minor importance to connect the
pendulum with the escapement.  It is essential the crutch
should be perfectly adjusted in every detail or errors
in timekeeping will perplex the young horologist, and
his investigations in this respect are invariably in the
wrong direction.

It is necessary that the plane of vibration of the
pendulum should be exactly at right angles to the arbor

of the pallet staff, or there will be extra friction and a sliding movement of the pendulum rod at the fork. A loss of impulse at the crutch resulting in a loss of vibration of the pendulum can be traced to the former loose on the pallet arbor. Too much shake at the fork. The fork rough at point of contact with the pendulum. The latter should be polished or burnished to advantage. The smoother the surfaces of contact the lesser the amount of friction. The fork too tight, crutch out of angle with the pendulum rod. Either of the last two faults would probably cause a clock to stop ; they are by no means uncommon. Fig. 118 shows an instance of the end of the crutch foul of the top of the pendulum rod slot. The crutch often gets bent in removal from a customer's house or in the workshop. One or two bends is all that is necessary to bring the crutch parallel with the rod and the end at right angles to it. Dotted lines will explain this. The slot in the rod is shown by four long dots.

The greatest evil is perhaps to be found in clocks with shorter pendulums. The cause is usually traced to a badly fitted suspension. Seconds pendulums often wobble through the end of the crutch or fork being out of angle with the pendulum rod looking from the suspension. A slight bend is all that is required to rectify this. A suspension spring bent or kinked is quite common. An accident is usually the cause. A few minutes' work with a burnisher will set a spring right. Lenticular bobs often fit badly on the rod. A wobble is what we might expect in this case. Apply a little oil to all acting surfaces where there is friction, including the crutch.

**Zinc and Steel.**—The zinc and steel combination is one of the best forms of compensation pendulum.

Besides the Westminster, many well-known clocks are fitted with it. Although this class of pendulum is generally known as " zinc and steel ", iron is often employed instead of steel, being easier to obtain in tubes, and the coefficient of expansion is almost the same. Some very fine results are obtained with tube pendulums.

The principle of this pendulum is the supporting of a metal tube from the bottom of the rod, with another tube of a different metal hanging from the top of the inner tube and supporting the bob. The coefficient of expansion for different metals varies, therefore by arranging tubes of various metals of different lengths according to their rate of expansion for temperature resting on each other, the outer tube should support the bob without any variation in length for any different range of temperature.

Lead or zinc expands and contracts, roughly, twice the amount of iron or steel. A bob, being great in bulk, answers comparatively slowly to changes of temperature, and it is now considered preferable to support the bob at the centre, so as to be neutral as far as temperature is concerned.

This pendulum gives infinitely closer results in time-keeping than a wood rod with a lead bob. For a one seconds pendulum with the bob supported at the centre, the rod should be steel about ·3 in. diameter and 46 inches long from the top of the free part of the suspension spring to the bottom of the rod, with a cap on top to receive the suspension spring. It is usual to pin the cap to prevent it slipping. On the bottom of the rod for about 3 inches is a screw thread of fine pitch to receive the rating nut. A thick collar or washer is next fitted to the rod to pass freely over the rod and rest on the rating nut. Its object is to form a resting place for the zinc tube. In order to prevent the collar from rotating

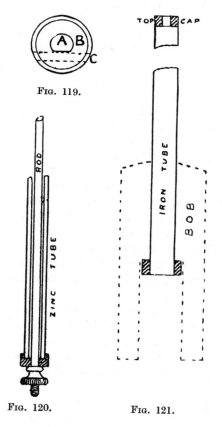

Fig. 119.

Fig. 120.  Fig. 121.

when the rating nut is moved, it is advisable to file a slight flat on the bottom of the rod, and drill a hole in the collar and fit a pin so that the latter comes flush with the flat on the rod and allows it to slide freely up and down without turning, as shown in Fig. 119. A is the pendulum rod, B the collar, with a hollow turned out to fit the zinc tube, and C the pin.

A zinc tube large enough to pass freely over the rod about 2 in. thick is next cut to length 28 inches long, and rests on the collar shown in Fig. 120. An iron tube is now fitted outside the zinc tube to slip freely over it, having at the top a cap recessed so as to rest on the top of the zinc tube, and a hole drilled in the centre of the cap to slip freely over the rod. The iron tube is 24 inches long, and an outside cap fitted at the bottom to form a seat for the bob. Solid drawn ¾ inch gas tube would be convenient for the outer tube and correct in the bore, and easily turned with screw threads cut on both ends to fit the two caps. Fig. 121 shows the iron tube with the top cap screwed from the inside to rest on the zinc tube and the bottom cap screwed from the outside to form a seat for the bob. Many clockmakers cut a series of slots in the iron tube to allow the air to get freely to the zinc tube and thus permit freedom in feeling the effect of the change of temperature.

The lead bob is 9 inches long by 3·5 in. in diameter, and supported at the centre. The top half of the hole passes freely over the iron tube, with the lower half enlarged to free the collar. By this plan a seat is provided for the centre of the bob to rest on the cap or the iron tube.

For a lighter pendulum a rod ·25 in. in diameter would be strong enough to bear a bob 8 inches long and 2·5 inches in diameter, weighing about 15 lb. With a rise in temperature the rod lengthens downwards and the zinc tube upwards nearly twice the amount, and the iron tube downwards. Therefore the combined lengthening of the rod and iron tube should equalize the lengthening of the zinc tube, and thus keep the bob or centre of gravity the same for any variation of temperature.

The temperature error, although, perhaps, the largest, is only one of many which a pendulum is subjected to in recording its time of vibration. The barometric error is due to the variation in the density of the air recorded by the rise and fall of the barometer. With an increase in the pressure of the air which means a rise in the barometer, the pendulum diminishes its arc of vibration, and a decrease in the pressure of the air would mean an increase in the arc of vibration. Lord Grimthorpe stated that with a large arc of vibration to the pendulum the " circular " error just compensates for the barometric error, but this would only apply to gravity escapement clocks. In a dead beat the thickening of oil would cause an escapement error.

The circular error is due to the path described by the pendulum being a part of a circle and not a cycloid. The error is more pronounced when a pendulum performs a large arc.

The suspension spring plays an important part of any pendulum. Any neglect in this direction will prove attempts at close regulation to be a fiasco. The spring should be riveted tightly, and central at both ends, hang at right angles to the chops, and perfectly free from kinks. The pendulum spring is about 5 in. wide, not less than $1\frac{1}{4}$ in. long in the free part, by ·008 in. thick. A spring a little on the strong or short side will cause the arc of the pendulum to be nearly circular instead of cycloidal.

**Mercurial.**—The mercurial pendulum invented by George Graham about 1730 is one of the most popular of the compensated class for regulator clocks. Although the mercurial pendulum is not so convenient from a portable point of view, it gives a regulator a very fine appearance. A second a month steady rate is quite

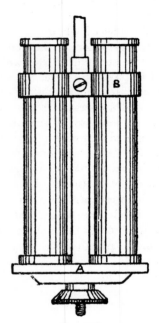

Fig. 122.

within the reach of the performance of clocks fitted with a Graham pendulum.

The mercury being a fluid must be in a jar of either glass or iron. The former is usually selected for the visible artistic appearance of the mercury. Any other metal than iron would be unsuitable, as the mercury would destroy and amalgamate the metal. Many authorities condemn a glass jar for closeness in time-keeping. They contend that the mercury does not answer so quickly to a change of temperature as the iron jar. That may be so. There is a difficulty in obtaining really true jars of equable thickness, but under certain conditions it is very doubtful if there is much difference between the rate attained in metal and glass jars. The writer has in his possession a regulator with a Graham pendulum and a glass jar, with a steady rate of eight seconds in six months. Many makers have constructed pendulums with the mercury divided between two jars. There is no doubt the mercury answers quicker to changes of temperature in this method, and it is none the less artistic in appearance. Fig. 122 shows the frame for holding the jars arranged on a platform A at the end of the rod. A brass clip B supports the top of the jars. The bottom of the rod is square to receive the frame. Two cups are fitted to the platform to take the bottoms of the jars.

The form of Graham's mercurial pendulum consisted of a steel rod with a stirrup containing the glass jar of mercury. Graham employed a sliding weight upon the rod as a means of regulation. Although this form has practically been abolished, the weight principle is generally adopted instead of using the rating nut for final and close regulation. Several small weights of different sizes are placed on the cover of the jar, and are removed or replaced after trial, as the case may be, to bring the clock nearer to time. For example, the regulator loses five seconds a week, and a small weight is placed on the flat cover of the jar without stopping the clock, and at the end of the next week we find the clock has gained three seconds. We should therefore

remove the weight with a pair of tweezers and replace
one a little more than half the weight.

There are several advantages claimed for an iron jar.
The mercury can be heated to drive off any air bubbles

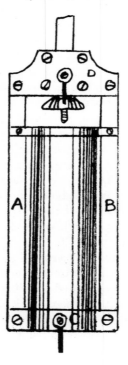

or moisture that appear between the mercury and the
jar.  The extra height required for the weight of the
jar.  The dimensions of an iron jar to be driven by
the same weight as a glass would be 9 inches in height
turned out to $\frac{1}{4}$ in. thick, and enamelled inside to

stop up all pores. It is better to adjust the height of mercury necessary for compensation by trial.

To make a mercurial pendulum is an interesting piece of work. Fig. 123 shows the stirrup and jar of the pendulum of the regulator in my possession many years with a very close rate.

The rod is seven-sixteenths inch wide by three-sixteenths inch. The stirrup is of flat steel, the whole height 10 inches by 3¼ inches, finished flat and left with fine emery. The sides A and B are screwed to the brass base C and the top pieces D with four screws. The top consists of three plates each three-sixteenths inch thick. The centre plate has a piece cut away at the middle to form a slot to free the pendulum rod. The plates are fastened together with four screws. The sides A and B are seven-sixteenths of an inch by 9¼ inches. The brass base is turned cup shape to fit the jar, which is 2 inches in diameter, stands 7¾ inches, and contains 7 inches of mercury. The brass cap is turned out to fit the top of the jar and fixed to the side pieces with two small screws. The lacquered brass work gives a nice appearance to the contrast of the bright steel and mercury. The rating nut is engraved and silvered, the washer brass. The base has a steel index fitted for the degree plate. The top index is left flush with the rating nut.

## MAKING A REGULATOR CLOCK

There is no better practice for an ambitious horologist than to make his own regulator.

It must be clearly understood that the illustrations of the regulator although drawn to scale, in many instances have to be reduced for convenience. It will therefore be more reliable for those who intend to start on the work to make full size drawings from the dimensions given.

The plates are 8¾ in. by 7½ in. and from ⅛ in. to $\frac{3}{16}$ in. thick, the latter thickness being the best. Fig. 124, which is half-scale, shows the plates, centre wheel, hour, and great wheels, barrel with line, and pillar holes drilled. It is unnecessary to procure any elaborate instruments to make a full-size drawing of this, with a side elevation.   A pair of compasses, a foot rule, two set squares, one 45 degrees, the other 60, or two of 45, a sheet of paper and pencil will be sufficient.

A side elevation which, of course, is a view of the wheels looking between the plates from the side, showing the freedoms.   This drawing can always be projected from the front elevation (Fig. 124), without a board and tee square.   The 60 set square is placed with the edge flush with any straight line, held tightly while the 45 square is pressed against it.   The sliding action of the latter will enable you to draw lines at right angles, or parallel as desired.

The clock plates are hammered flat and filed up true. The old-fashioned method of shaving the plates is right enough for clockmakers with experience in this work, but as the shaver is a long heavy tool with a handle at each end, the operator without practice would do more harm than good.   The best plan is to get the metal warehouse who supply the plates to flatten and planish them, which is done for a small sum.

The plates are first pinned together with two small holes drilled near the edges at opposite corners for the purpose of filing the edges true, and drilling the pillar, centre, escape wheel, and hour wheel holes exactly

opposite. Scratch a line down the centre of the plate,
and another across the centre at right angles to it,
where these lines meet will give us the centre wheel
holes (see Fig. 124). It is advisable in an 11 or 12 inch
dial to get the hour and seconds circle as large as possible,

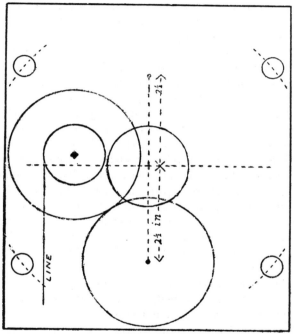

Fig. 124.

and with the train we are about to use, $2\frac{1}{2}$ inches, marked
from the centre hole on the centre line will give us
the escape wheel and hour wheel holes. No motion
work is required, the hour hand being fitted to the
arbor of a wheel driven by the great wheel, as shown

in Fig. 124. The barrel is an inch and a half in diameter. The sketch shows that care must be taken in marking the four pillar holes to get them uniform, equal distance from the centre hole, and the bottom left hand pillar free of the line

Another method is to drill the pillar holes close together and run the line over a travelling pulley, or leading off barrel to free the line of the bottom, left-hand pillar. The argument in its favour is that the double line is brought nearer to the side of the case, and consequently the weight is not so close to the pendulum bob when it reaches its level. The bob and weight undoubtedly have an attraction for each other, and if there is any noticeable swing from the weight the effect is certain to tell on the performance of the pendulum. The difference in the position of the weight with a leading off barrel is so slight compared with the extra work of the barrel, the writer considers the claimed advantage is not worth consideration. Quite as much, or more, distance between the two objects can be gained by hanging the pendulum on a cock from the iron bracket as close to the back of the case as possible. Many horologists prefer to case the weight in, so that it falls in a separate chute.

The pillar holes, which are three-eighths inch in diameter, are next drilled, and the plates can then be separated by knocking out rivets.

The next operation is to turn the pillars. It is important they should be rigid. It is therefore not advisable to use castings. They should be cut from a length of three-quarter inch round brass rod, or " Muntz " metal. All the pillars can be turned from one length of rod brass or other suitable tough metal. When a screw-cutting lathe is available threads can be

cut at each end and the plates fixed with nuts.    Fig.
125 shows a full size finished bottom pillar.

Filing a hexagon nut is fine practice.    Select a square
piece of flat sheet steel, scratch a line across it and mark
off 120 degrees.    File away the space which forms the
angle, and the steel will act as a gauge to test the sides
of each nut to get them all accurate.    Brass nut castings

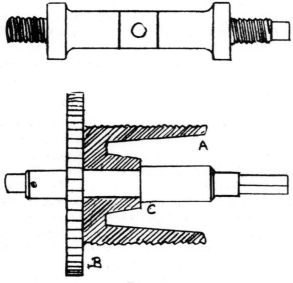

Fig. 126.

can be obtained in a row of about half a dozen from any
metal warehouse.

The pillars are half an inch in diameter, with large
collars to form seats for the plates, the distance between
the plates is $2\frac{1}{4}$ inches, and $\frac{3}{4}$ inch between the shoulder
of the collar and dial.    Total length, $3\frac{1}{2}$ inches.    The
bottom pillars are square in the middle, with a hole

drilled and tapped in each for receiving the two screws when fixing the movement to the iron bracket which serves as a seat board.

The pillars could be drilled and the plates pinned on in the old style if desired.

The barrel (Fig. 126) is an inch and a half in diameter, and makes one turn in twelve hours, making sixteen rotations in eight days. The weight, which is 4 lb., is hung from a double line, so that a fall of 4 feet will be sufficient to drive the clock eight days. The barrel should be planted on the left of the frame, the advantage thus gained is in keeping the weight when run down as far from the pendulum bob as possible.

Some time ago clockmakers made their barrels with a piece of brass tube, and a cover fitted at each end. This method is quite unnecessary for obvious reasons. A barrel cover for a weight clock is not required, the line being fixed through a hole at the front A (Fig. 126), and winds with the line running from the front to back. The barrel is therefore made in one casting, shown in section, with a long bearing for the arbor, and the winding ratchet cut on the flange B. Engineers' tool steel, which is equal to hardened and tempered steel, will be found best for the barrel arbor.

A pattern for the barrel casting can be made from a piece of $1\frac{1}{2}$ inch tube, or a cylindrical chocolate box fixed to a circular wood or cardboard flange and thickened with plaster of paris.

The barrel is heated, the arbor driven or shrunk on flush with the shoulder C, and the barrel turned true on its own arbor ready for grooving and cutting the ratchet teeth. The inside can be turned and finished with black enamel to give it a good appearance. A small hole drilled in the opposite end to the square is for pinning the maintaining ratchet and great wheel. This should be drilled after the wheels are fitted to the arbor.

The actual diameter equals the pitch plus twice the addendum of the tooth. Blanks to the following dimensions can be obtained from any metal warehouse and turned to the correct size. Great and hour wheels, $3\frac{1}{2}$ inches, centre wheel $2\frac{1}{2}$ inches, third wheel $2\frac{1}{4}$, and escape wheel $1\frac{7}{8}$ inches. The great wheel when finished is about $\frac{5}{32}$ inch thick, the hour wheel about half, and the others in their relative proportions. The maintaining ratchet, being thin, could be crossed out from a brass disc.

Having turned the wheels to size, send them together with the barrel to the wheel cutter with the usual instructions regarding number of teeth for each wheel. Great and hour wheels 144, centre 96, third 90, and scape 30.

The pinions have all 12 leaves, and these are sectored from the wheels by the clock material dealer if pinion wire is used, or by the wheel cutter if they are to be cut. Of course the latter are the best.

The centre wheel is riveted to the pinion in the usual way, as there is no room for a collet. The other wheels, pallets, and detent are screwed with three screws at equi-distant to brass collets fixed on the arbor. The centre wheel will be found the most convenient to commence with. The lower pivot should be turned close to the great wheel to allow freedom between the centre and great wheel. The pinion arbor and pivots can be next finished to run in the frame. The lower pivot is about 12 douziemes and the top 21.

The escape and third pinions are turned next. The

back pivot of the former is 5 douziemes and the seconds pivot 9. The pivot of the latter pinion is about 10.

There is nothing gained in soft soldering the collets on the arbors. Driving them on is more mechanical. The collet should be turned true on its own arbor and the wheel fitted.

The escape and third wheels are next fitted. The collets are turned true on their own arbors. The wheel is fitted tightly against a shoulder of the brass collet, with a ring turned on the shoulder at the back and three dots at equal distance to mark the position of the screw holes. The dots are then drilled through the collet and wheel. Tap the holes in the former, and broach the latter to just clear the threads.

Three screws are then fitted to the collet holes to fix the wheel. They are hardened and tempered to a dark blue. The escape, third, and hour wheels, detent pallets, and crutch are screwed to collets in this manner with two screws for the crutch.

The pivot holes should be drilled with the plates pinned together. The escape wheel holes are marked $2\frac{1}{2}$ inches from the centre holes on the vertical line shown in the sketch. We now come to the third wheel holes. A clock depth tool is a great asset at this stage, but the outlay is not necessary unless required for further use. The writer made a full size accurate drawing of the pitch circles of the wheels and pinions. In the case of pitch circles, they just touch each other, and represent the rolling circles of the wheels and pinions.

Place the drawing on the plate and mark the centres through the paper on to the plate. If the depth is a little too deep or shallow, pin the plates together, draw file the holes and re-bush them. With careful procedure the wheel will run perfectly upright. Another method is to mark off a pair of compasses on a strip of brass the distance of centres from your drawing, taking care the distance is rather short than long Next drill and broach the holes in the strip of brass to receive the arbors tightly and upright. Stretch the brass a little by hammering it until the depth is correct. The holes in the piece of brass will then act as the template for drilling the holes in the clock plates.

The train consists of the following numbers. Great and hour wheels 144, centre 96, third 90, and escape 30. The pinions have all 12 leaves.

There are probably more horologists who have no convenience for turning the heavy parts, barrel, pillars, etc., to whom the acquaintance of an engineering friend would prove useful. The writer was lucky enough to have a screw-cutting lathe placed at his disposal.

The hour wheel is fitted and screwed to a collet, which is driven on its own arbor. The back pivot is about the same size as the back centre, and the top pivot which carries the hour hand a trifle larger. The wheel, which is simply a follower, should be the same diameter as the great wheel and about half the thickness. It is crossed out with six arms. The pivot holes are drilled on the centre line of the plate $2\frac{1}{2}$ inches below the centre wheel holes shown in the sketch.

The barrel arbor can be planted from the instruction given, and the depth to coincide with great wheel, centre pinion, and hour wheel from the full-size drawing placed on the clock plate, in the same manner as the third wheel depth. Hold the barrel upright over the pivot hole before it is large enough to enter, with the centre wheel resting in the lower plate. You will then see if it requires draw filing to attain the correct depth. Pin the plates

together and make the top hole concentric with the
bottom.

There are many forms of maintaining work employed
for clocks. The sketch (Fig. 127) shows a simple style
which is often used for regulators. There are two
springs planted at opposite sides of the maintaining
ratchet and each acting on an arm of the great wheel.
The great wheel A and maintaining ratchets B each
have six arms. Two opposite spaces between the arms

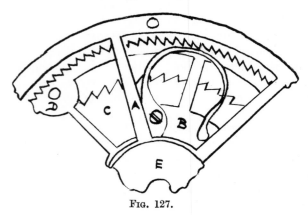

Fig. 127.

of the ratchet are cut smaller to allow the maintaining
springs to be screwed to the wheel. In the sketch one
of the springs is seen in action, the end presses against
the arm of the great wheel. It is made of sheet steel,
hardened and tempered. The winding ratchet C is cut
on the barrel flange. One of the maintaining ratchet
arms terminates at a semicircular boss, for planting
the winding click, the end of the screw is marked D.
The rim of the maintaining ratchet is left a little wider
at a point about one-third of the circumference from

the click screw to fix the screws of the click spring. The great wheel and maintaining ratchet are kept in position by a large collet E which is pinned on the arbor.

The maintaining springs should be of sufficient strength to drive the clock while it is being wound. To test the springs, screw them on the wheel before

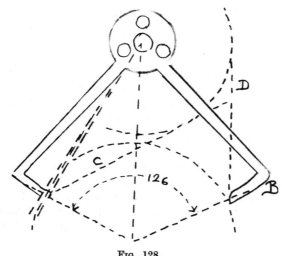

Fig. 128.

hardening and tempering, and hang a 2 lb. weight with a single line on the barrel. They should be left rather on the strong side, and finally thinned if required. A steel banking pin is screwed in the rim of the maintaining ratchet at a point about $2\frac{1}{2}$ ratchet teeth from the great wheel arm. The pin will then bank against the arm and prevent unnecessary tension on the maintaining springs.

The detent is $2\frac{1}{2}$ inches long from the arbor hole to the point. The arbor is pivoted and run in the plates in the usual way. There is little or no wear on the point of the detent, a piece of soft sheet steel will therefore be found convenient for this purpose, and screwed to a brass collet driven on the arbor in the same manner as the wheels. It will be found quicker to use the same size tap and screws for all the collet holes. The pivot holes are drilled about 2 inches above the barrel holes, so that its weight keeps the point resting on the maintaining ratchet teeth.

Fig. 128 shows the actual size of the escape wheel and pallets. The best plan is to make an accurate drawing and file the pallets to the drawing, taking care to leave the pallet pads rather on the thick side, place them in the plates with the escape wheel and reduce them finally to attain equal drop.

Draw a circle $1\frac{3}{4}$ inches in diameter, to represent the actual size of the escape wheel, then a vertical line shown dotted. There are 30 teeth in the escape wheel, therefore 360 degrees divided by $30 = 12$, the distance between two teeth. The pallets embrace 11 teeth, which equals 10 spaces. $10 \times 12 = 120$, and plus half a space $= 126$.

Now if we set off 63 degrees each side of the dotted vertical line from the centre of the escape wheel, we get the centre of each pad, shown by the dotted lines A and B, which equals 126 degrees between the centre of each pad. From the points where the two dotted lines A and B cross the circumference of the escape wheel, we take as distance and mark it off from the centre of either pallet pad to the vertical line, and this will give the pallet staff centre. Therefore from either locking corner to the pallet staff centre is equal to the distance between the two locking corners.

Next draw a tangent to the left side of the escape wheel from the pallet staff centre and set off $\frac{1}{2}$ and $1\frac{1}{2}$ degrees for locking and impulse respectively, shown by three dotted lines. From the centre of the wheel mark off two radial lines hardly 3 degrees on each side of the radial lines A and B which marked the centre of the pallets. The curves to form the pads are then struck from the pallet staff centre, just touching the radial lines last drawn.

Two degrees of escaping arc (that is $\frac{1}{2}$ for locking and $1\frac{1}{2}$ impulse) is sufficient for any dead beat escapement, any increase will be at the cost of its rate in timekeeping. Occasionally the writer comes across a pair of " Graham " pallets which have had the ruts filed away by a repairer in such a manner that the impulse planes have been altered to about $2\frac{1}{2}$ degrees, thus destroying the principle of the escapement under which it was originally intended.

From the point on the curve just struck on the left of the sketch to form the locking face, which crosses the centre of the three dotted lines, we draw a line through the point where the outer curve crosses the lower (or impulse) line. This will give the impulse face. Now if we continue this line shown at C, and strike a circle from the pallet staff centre just to touch the line, the other impulse face drawn from the pad on the right just clear of the circle of the wheel to touch the circle from the pallet staff, will be the same $1\frac{1}{2}$ degrees shown at D.

The arms of the pallets should be drawn to the centre slightly taper for strength. The boss is sufficiently large to conveniently drill three screw holes with counter sinks for the heads. The escape wheel has been omitted from the sketch to make it appear as simple as possible.

The thickness of the pallets is about 28 douziemes, or a little more than twice the thickness of the escape wheel, with the faces left almost flat. When they are correct for depth, send them to the jeweller for garnet or sapphire. The cost of the latter pre-war days was about 24s. The writer had a pair jewelled in sapphire, and after running for thirty years shows no signs of wear. The clock is cleaned every two years. (See Dead Beat Escapement.)

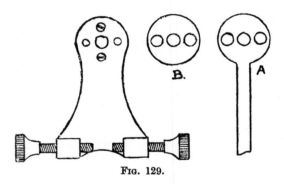

FIG. 129.

The pallets are fitted and screwed to a collet driven on the pallet arbor. A brass bridge or bar about three-sixteenths inch thick is screwed and steady pinned to the back plate to take the back pallet arbor pivot. A pattern made for a brass casting will be found best for this work. The length of the pallet arbor between the shoulders is $2\frac{7}{8}$ inches.

Near the bridge end of the pallet arbor the brass crutch adjustment is fitted and screwed to a collet. The holes are counter-sunk, so that the screw-heads are flush with the top of the brass. Two holes are next drilled and tapped in the adjustment and collet at right angles to the screw-heads for fixing the crutch (Fig. 129), which shows the crutch adjustment screwed to the collet. The boss of the steel crutch A is held in its place on the adjustment by a brass collet B, in which the screw-heads are sunk, the holes in the crutch are left larger to allow it to move on its centre when the adjustment screws are altered.

The blocks of the adjustment are drilled and tapped to receive the adjustment screws. The heads are brass, with milled edges, shown in Fig. 129. The crutch is 8 in., and terminates at a boss, which is drilled for the pivot or fork. Two banking pins are planted on the back plate, about half-way between the centre and hour wheel holes, and about 1 inch apart, for the crutch to bank and prevent the pallet stones knocking the rim of the escape wheel.

The old style of bending a crutch as a means of setting a clock in beat is a wrong principle. Pendulum clocks should be made with a crutch adjustment, or " self-setters ". There are many repairers who fail to understand that the " self-setter " should be just tight enough to give impulse to the pendulum. Of course, we hear complaints that " It won't set itself in beat ", or " It's too loose to carry ". In the first case open the slot a trifle or unscrew the crutch a turn. The latter instance is very prevalent. Close the slot a trifle and screw on the crutch.

It is important, in all clocks where close timekeeping is required, the support for the pendulum should be rigid and on the same bracket as the movement. Many 8-day English clocks fail for want of rigidity ; the brass cock which supports the pendulum is often too weak, or the movement is dependent on its own weight to keep it fixed to the seat board. Any odd pieces of wire, bent

hook shape, will suffice to grip the pillars, the threads
for the nut is quite a secondary consideration.  Such
a clock either stops, or gets out of beat, and is a source
of trouble to the repairer.

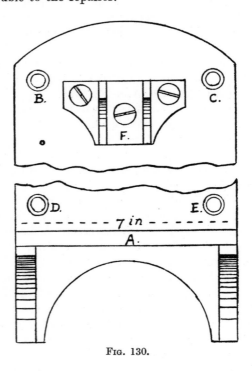

Fig. 130.

Fig. 130 shows the top and bottom of a 7 inch iron
bracket for supporting the movement and pendulum.
The movement rests on the ledge A, which is $\frac{1}{2}$ inch
thick, $5\frac{1}{2}$ inches deep, and fixed with two brass-headed
screws, with milled edges, which screw into the centre
of the two lower pillars.  The bracket is 15 inches long

by 7 inches, and screwed to the back of the case with six screws ; the two top and bottom counter-sunk holes are marked B, C, D, and E. A brass bracket, F, for hanging the pendulum, is screwed to the iron bracket with three large screws.

The length of the brass bracket F is about 3 inches. It projects $1\frac{1}{2}$ inches and about $\frac{1}{4}$ inch thick all over. The iron bracket is, or should be, the stock size, and can be obtained from any metal warehouse, or a casting to pattern.

The minute hand is squared on the pipe of a dummy and pinned with a collet to the centre arbor. A motion spring rests against the shoulder of the arbor, with the end pressing on the dummy. The hour and seconds hands are fitted friction-tight in the usual way.

The ends of the four pillars are drilled and tapped to take the screws for holding the dial ; the holes in the dial are counter-sunk, with the screw-heads left flush.

The movement is finally assembled to examine the depths and endshakes ; when everything appears correct, strip the plates, the wheels, and barrel. Stone the file marks out of the plates and wheels, finishing the surface with charcoal and water, using a circular motion to attain a better appearance. The plates, wheels, and other brass parts are now lacquered. Clean each part in petrol before this operation, heat the parts and apply lacquer with a fine hair brush, taking care to move the brush in one direction. On no account touch any part with the fingers before applying lacquer.

" Invar " pendulums are now usually fitted to long case clocks. The metal invented by Dr. C. E. Guillaume, is a nickel-steel alloy with a very small co-efficient of expansion. That is, it has a very slight expansion or contraction on being subjected to changes of temperature. This pendulum is obviously cheaper and more portable than a " Graham ". The metal is supplied by material dealers in rods about 3 ft. 10 in. especially for this purpose. The bobs are about 9 lb. for a regulator and 14 for a heavier clock. Type metal containing a percentage of tin is more porous and therefore generally used.· They can be cast on the same principle, see " Wood Rod and Lead Bob ". When ordering, state nickel-steel rod for a seconds pendulum.

Any clock case maker would oblige with an estimate for a mahogany case 6 feet 3 inches by 8 inches deep, with a 1½ inch back, semicircular top, and glass door.

### QUARTER CHIMES

**Making Pin Drum for Quarter Chimes.**—An English chiming clock is driven by an independent train, sometimes known as a " three part clock ". The minute wheel is furnished with four lifting pins for letting off the chime at each quarter. A pin in the end of the quarter rack falls against the hour rack hook at the hours (its greatest distance), allowing it to warn. As the last tooth of the quarter rack is gathered up the pin in the rack comes in contact with the hour warning piece and lets off the hour striking train.

The Whittington and St. Michael chimes are now most generally used for clocks with eight tubes or bells. Of course the Westminster or any other can be included on the same pin barrel.

Fig. 131 shows the notes of both chimes, which each consist of five separate peals repeated in one hour, making ten peals for the four quarters. All that is necessary, therefore, is to mark out the five peals on the pin barrel, which makes two turns for the four quarters.

The best plan is to cut a piece of drawing paper to exactly fit round the pin barrel, then place it flat on a drawing-board and make a drawing the same size of the relative positions of the pins.

Assuming the smallest bell will be called 1, the numbers

FIG. 131.

in the five peals of the Whittington chimes, as shown by the notes illustrated, are as follows :—

| 1st peal | 1 | 2 | 3 | 4 | 5 | 6 | 7 | 8 |
|---|---|---|---|---|---|---|---|---|
| 2nd ,, | 1 | 2 | 3 | 7 | 6 | 5 | 4 | 8 |
| 3rd ,, | 1 | 3 | 5 | 7 | 2 | 4 | 6 | 8 |
| 4th ,, | 7 | 5 | 3 | 1 | 2 | 4 | 6 | 8 |
| 5th ,, | 2 | 1 | 6 | 3 | 5 | 7 | 4 | 8 |

The barrel can be divided into five equal portions in the lathe, each representing the space for one peal. Assuming a sketch is made, it is divided in a like manner. The next step is to leave a slight space between each peal. Then divide the space for each peal into seven, which will give eight lines, and mark the whole drawing, which includes the five peals, with eight vertical lines of equal distance apart. Accuracy is a great feature in marking the lines or the chiming will be irregular.

The circles for the pin holes must be marked with the first representing the barrel at one end if a change of chimes is desired.

The next procedure is to mark the pin holes, and a little care is required in this direction to keep the dots exactly on the lines indicated for the different notes. The sketch in Fig. 132 shows the dots for the five peals of the Whittington chimes marked in numbers as shown above from 1 to the highest note F to the lowest note F.

Fig. 132 represents a piece of paper cut to fit round the circumference of the barrel. The spaces to denote each chime are equal, and each space is divided into seven, giving eight lines, which should be accurately marked. The vertical lines which encircle the barrel are shown dotted, and on these as shown the pins are marked, and if kept on the small side will give plenty of room for a double change of chimes. The drawing can be fixed on the barrel for the purpose of marking the pin holes.

One revolution of the gathering pallet wheel must equal one-fifth of a revolution of the pin barrel, that is equal to one peal. When a change of chimes is desired, it is advisable to cut the seven circles on the barrel in the lathe to get all the pins equal to lift each hammer tail. The lines shown in the sketch of Fig. 132 should also be

# WHITTINGTON.

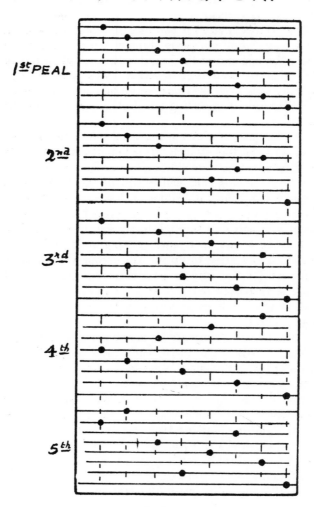

marked on the barrel so that each pin lifts a hammer tail at equal times.

The change device for two or three chimes is worked by a long sliding pin going through the pin barrel and a snail on one end of the barrel with a coiled spring on the other to keep it in position. The length of the hammer tails from the centre of motion is about $\frac{7}{8}$ inch, and the pins not exceeding $\frac{1}{8}$ inch standing out from the barrel.

The hammer blades are made of thin iron or sheet steel not exceeding $\frac{1}{16}$ inch. It is important they should all fit nicely, free from side shake on the pin on which they turn running from end to end of the brass block. There is a difficulty in drilling such a long, small hole ; a very good plan is to saw cut the brass block from the under side half-way through in the centre from end to end, using a fine hack saw. A long strip of brass is next filed and fitted to fill the slot except a small space sufficient for the wire to pass through. The strip of brass is then soldered and filed off flush. The centre wire or pin is left to project at both ends to effect an easy removal.

The hammer springs are all in one piece, on the comb principle, with eight teeth, each bent to engage the hammer rod. The comb is screwed to the brass frame with three or four small screws.

The hammer heads are of brass and will be found more satisfactory if screwed on to the hammer stalks.

The following chiming train can be used.

> Great wheel 100 teeth.
> Second wheel 80 teeth, pinion 8 leaves.
> Chiming wheel 40 teeth.
> Gathering pallet wheel 64 teeth, pinion 8 leaves.
> Warning wheel 56 teeth, pinion 8 leaves.
> Fly pinion 8 leaves.

**Rod Gongs.**—Quarter chiming clocks of a cheap grade are now quite general with English makers. Rod gongs are employed in sets of four, five, and eight. In most instances the rods are fixed in a metal sounding tube which obviously improves the tone. Complete sets of five are supplied for the Westminster chime (one being for the hour), fixed in a sounding tube which is about $2\frac{1}{2}$ inches long. Separate rods can be obtained with either plain ends to push in friction tight

FIG. 133.

or tapped ends. The main difficulty is to get them in tune. Final tuning can be done by filing the hollow, a little near the block. Fig 133 shows the sounding tube solid with the flange and screwed to the tube which is left thick at the top to take a screw. A clearance hole is cut at the bottom of the tube to free the rod.

Chiming clocks of a better quality are usually fitted with 9 metal tubes, 8 being hung in a row close to the back of the case. The rod for support is fixed to a bracket screwed at each side of the case.

It is by no means difficult to convert the method of

hanging to the modern principle. The rod is, or can be replaced by a flat strip about 1 inch by $\frac{1}{4}$. Two saw cuts are made at the top of the strip opposite the end edges of each tube. A hole is drilled at the end of each saw cut. The loop of the cord passes in front of the strip over the top to lie in the two saw cuts at the back level with the two holes. By this means any single tube can be removed.

## PORTABLE CLOCKS

Portable clocks have come to stay, not because they are better timekeepers than those controlled by pendulums, although their performances are expected to compare favourably, and this is where the trouble commences. There is a marked difference in the variation in the daily rate of a spring driven balance clock. These faults can be traced to faults in the train (see inconsistent timekeeping) or a mainspring giving an unequable pull. Removing the mainspring would reveal its condition. A "lumpy" spring should be replaced. Motor clocks can be treated in the same manner. To correct faults in the escapement (see Wristlet Watches).

## REPAIRING TURRET CLOCKS

Turret clock-work is a branch in itself. There are many instances where country clockmakers are entrusted with these timekeepers, and the price paid for repairs will not cover the expenses of engaging turret men from a factory.

The cleaning and repairing of a turret clock is a dirty job at any time, and the difficulties arising from such an undertaking are many. " Overalls " will be found most economical for this work.

The use of heavy tools is another proposition. An engineer might prove a useful friend on these occasions. Many church towers are dark, very dirty, and so small that to attempt the work in so limited a space is not worth consideration. It is, however, advisable to clean and repair the clock in the turret when opportunities permit.

Operations should commence with a general examination of the clock, and notes made of any parts defective. It will pay any watchmaker who has the winding contract of a public clock to spend a little extra time about one visit a week for regulation, and keep it within a few seconds a week. It is a splendid advertisement. The method is simple : keep a rate of the clock and a few little weights of different sizes, which are added or removed from the top of the pendulum bob according to the performance of the clock. The public are not slow in finding who attends to the clock, and sums up the ability of the horologist by its performance.

An apprentice might be found a valuable assistant in the tower. This class of work is not only difficult single-handed, but will prove very instructive to the pupil. While the motive power is being let down, examine the lines for any weak place ; to take the responsibility of a broken strand is running a risk. New iron or steel lines can be obtained from turret clock-makers. When fitting a new line care must be exercised not to get it kinked. The method is the same as applied to a " grandfather ". Lines that are exposed to a damp atmosphere are rubbed with tallow as a protection against rust. The pendulum is easily removed, and the connecting rods from the bevel wheel to the motion work.

All that is necessary to disconnect the latter is to drive
out the pin (Fig. 134).   Remove the leading off wire from
the hammer tail to the hammer, and the going and
striking parts are taken to pieces.

In the older style or bird-cage, the wheels are run in
a square frame, consisting of several cross pieces : each
bar running vertically is fixed separately with a nut.
To take this pattern to pieces, it is necessary to remove

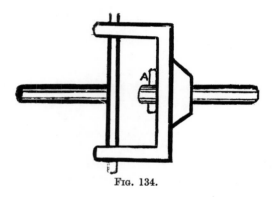

FIG. 134.

each cross bar carrying the bushes for the pivots, when
their respective wheels drop out.   Many modern clocks
have the bushes fixed with small screws to the frame
instead of riveting them into the bars.   This is a great
improvement, and enables each wheel to be taken out
separately.   The majority of clocks have no stop work,
and as the weights are not usually visible when being
wound, many clockmakers chalk about six inches
of line which has just appeared when the weight is high
enough to prevent overwinding.

New bushes for any wide holes are turned in the workshop when a clockmaker's lathe is at disposal, or an

engineer would undertake the work. A worn leading off wire from the hammer tail is a common occurrence, this can be put right with a new bend or new wire. The hammer is unsafe to leave too close to the bell, a double blow would be the result, and possibly a cracked bell. This fault is often the cause of a worn hammer spring, the latter is sometimes adjustable. Fig 135 shows a notch worn in the spring B, with the hammer nearly touching the bell. When there is no chance of adjusting

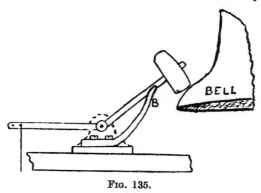

FIG. 135.

the spring, a local smith will be found useful for any of the heavy work. Paraffin is used to clean the wheels, etc. Painted iron work showing signs of rust should be repainted. Turret clock oil is the best lubricant, obtainable at turret clockmakers'.

In quarter clocks the hour part is usually let off by the quarters. The quarter cam wheel for lifting the quarter hammer tails and makes one turn in an hour, should be placed so that it warns the hour on the last quarter. When trying the striking round, press down the hammer tails so that the lift is slight enough to feel, count the number and keep the hammer from striking the bells.

## CUCKOO CLOCKS

These clocks are roughly made and after the style of a Dutch clock. The arbors are iron and most of the frames strips of wood with brass holes bushed for the pivot holes. The cuckoo is mounted upon an arbor which is thrown forward and opens the door as the clock begins to strike.

Fig. 136 shows the back elevation of the striking and lifting arbors, the locking piece, and wheel and the cuckoo arbor. At the warning the lifting piece A, which is a wire bent over and fixed to the lifting arbor B, is moved by the motion work.

Fixed at the other end of the arbor B is another wire C which engages and lifts the locking piece D. This is really a brass piece fixed to the locking arbor. It allows the pin to fall off the step on the nose of the brass piece and warns on the end of the wire C. This occurs when the locking piece D is lifted free of the locking wheel E. At the other end of the locking arbor F is fixed a wire G which lifts a pin in the bird arbor H and throws the bird forward. There are five arbors running across the frame of the striking part, the pivot ends are shown in the sketch F, B, I, J, and K. The arbors are pivoted at one end, the pivots being fitted in a metal plate, with a pin through a hole in each to form the endshake. The back ends of the arbors are run in a thin brass plate L, screwed to the wood frame.

Fitted on the end of the pin wheel arbor is usually a pinion of 10 which drives a wheel of 90 on which is fixed the count wheel, shown by a dotted circle. A pin is fixed in the locking piece D to engage the wire on the lifting piece C. The locking piece for the count wheel is a wire M fitted through a hole in the locking piece, bent over and riveted with the end flattened which

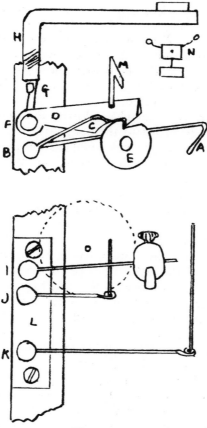

Fig. 136.

projects through the frame to drop in the slots on the edge of the count wheel.

The hammer arbor and wire for striking the gong which precedes the cuckoo is on top, shown I. The short cuckoo wire is placed next at the arbor J and is connected by a loop wire to the bellows on the striking side. The long wire is fastened in the same manner shown at K and leads to operate the bellows on the right. A projecting wire on the top of this comes in contact with the bird's tail and at each opening of the bellows throws the bird forward simultaneously bowing and opens the wings and beak.

The bird is of carved wood, with the wings separate pieces, each hinged to the body with two small wire eyes, and a straight wire running through and pinned down at each end. The body of the bird is cut right through at the centre to allow it to swing on a square wooden block. A pin is passed through the body and block to form the centre of motion. The base of the bird is shown at N with the legs and square block, the pivot hole, and two short eyelet wires at the back for operating the wings and one longer, one in the front to form a contact with the beak. The action of the bird depends on the working of the wires. Examine the wings and beak to see if they are perfectly free at the loop holes, and the bird swings freely on the block. The wire to connect the door is sometimes left too long. Assuming these are correct the wire on the left-hand bellows at each opening should bring the bird into action.

At the hour the hammer strikes first, then the short wire lifts the bellows on the striking side to call " cuc ", then the long wire on the other side to sound " koo ". Examine the thin bent wire M that drops into the slots of the count wheel and regulates the number of blows struck. It should fall clear of the sides and well into the slots, so that the other part of the same arm D locks the striking train properly. When the wheels are running fast it is difficult to examine the action ; this can be accomplished by placing a finger on the fly and letting it run very slowly. When the hour hand is behind the number to be struck, and too tight to shift on the wheel, raise the warning lever and strike it round until the hands correspond.

Trouble is often caused by a bad sound which can be traced to a leakage in the bellows, or pipe. The former can be repaired by a piece of chamois or a strip of kid. A piece of an old glove will be found convenient for this work. To replace the leather, fold the kid over from the end, to overlap the frame so that the crease projects in at the highest part. The leather should be pressed on ironed to form a permanent crease, then glued to the frame.

A pipe is sometimes broken on removal. To make a new one is by no means difficult. Cigar box wood will be found quite suitable and the correct thickness. The pipes are one inch square. Cut four strips one inch and thin down two to join up the square. Cutting the lip is the next step : make a line across the wide piece half an inch from the top end and another parallel $\frac{1}{4}$ inch from it. A sharp chisel is then required to cut out the space between the two lines, leaving the thickness of the side pieces on each side uncut. Next form the lip with a chisel ; make a sloping cut nearly $\frac{3}{4}$ inch from the opening and bring the edge fine to a slight flat. The blocks are then cut to fit the ends. The opening between the block and the cap for the wind is a little less than a sixpence. Glue the pieces together and clamp tightly, or bind with cord until dry.

### CALENDAR WORK

To fit the simple calendar mechanism to an English clock is by no means difficult, assuming there is sufficient room. It is necessary to know the exact space between the dial and plate, and the position of the winding squares, in order to make a sketch of the new wheels and their relative position.

If the distance is less than an inch, the space would be insufficient, but longer dial feet could be supplied to accommodate it. If the motion work has a bridge, the calendar wheels could be fitted to another plate, or on the back of the dial.

The motion work, as a rule, is fitted with a bridge, and in this case the best plan is to make a new plate to fit over the motion work and come flush with the top of the bridge, the plate of course would be cut away to free. A full size drawing should then be made and the wheels planted in suitable positions to free the winding squares and other motion parts.

Fig. 137 shows the mechanism of simple calendar work. Fixed to the hour wheel A is a wheel B with about 20 or 24 teeth and drives two wheels C and D, each having twice the number of teeth, and each making one turn in twenty-four hours.

It is quite immaterial if these wheels turn on shouldered screws or studs screwed in the plate and pinned. Of course the latter is best if room permits.

The wheel C carries a pin which just engages a tooth of a star wheel of 7 teeth, which gives the days of the week. This wheel rides on a stud, the pipe of which carries a hand to indicate the days of the week. The wheel is kept in position by a spring detent. It is only necessary for the pin to engage a tooth to lift over the corner of the detent, when the latter will force the tooth forward to complete the space.

The wheel D has a pin fixed so as to engage one tooth of the day-of-the-month wheel of 31 teeth E. This wheel is jumped forward the last half a space in the same manner by a spring detent. The pipe of this wheel carries the day of the month hand and runs on a stud in the plate.

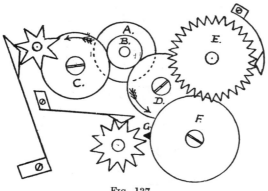

FIG. 137.

The star wheel E of 31 drives another wheel F with the same number of teeth and the same diameter. This wheel can be cut with either ordinary or V-shaped teeth. One tooth is left a little longer shown at G to intersect a tooth of the month of the year wheel for each rotation, which is 31 days. The month of the year wheel has therefore 12 teeth and is held in position by a spring detent. The wheel F turns on a shouldered screw, and can be cut in the ordinary way with equal teeth, the longer tooth being fitted afterwards.

The day of the week, day of the month, and month of the year wheels can be made quite thin, but must fit their respective studs without shake, and the detents which hold them in their places are planted in any convenient position and the screw holes drilled so that they are free of any object. The point of the V or acting surface should rest at equidistance between two teeth,

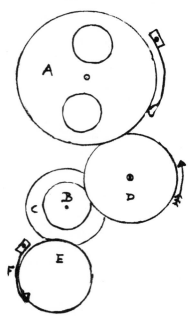

Fig. 138.

and the spring should be very weak, with sufficient tension to draw the point home.

There are two or three different methods of moving the moon disc and day of the month wheel in a Grandfather clock. They are all worked on the same principle, from the hour wheel, or a 24-hour wheel driven from it.

Some clocks are made with a pin or finger-piece fixed to the hour wheel and engages a tooth in the date wheel every twelve hours. In this device the day of the month wheel would require 62 V-shape teeth. This, of course, is the most simple arrangement. The most general method and which is certainly the best, is to fit a small wheel tightly on the hour wheel to drive another with twice the number of teeth to give one turn in 24 hours. Any number of teeth would do so long as the ratio of the two wheels is two to one.

A moon disc having two moons painted on opposite sides for showing the age of the moon is roughly $29\frac{1}{2}$ days. The disc would therefore make one turn in $29\frac{1}{2}$ multiplied by 2, which equals 59 days. It will therefore have 59 or 118 teeth. If the latter number, two teeth will be moved forward for every turn of the 24-hour wheel.

The moon disc A, shown in Fig. 138, is kept in position by a weak V-shaped jumper and spring screwed on the back of the dial plate. There are probably screw and steady pin-holes for this purpose. Fixed to the hour wheel B is a small wheel C, which drives a wheel D, with twice the number of teeth, making one turn in 24 hours. The wheel D is fixed to a pipe and turns on a stud screwed in the plate. When the wheel D is missing, the stud, or screw hole, forms a guide to determine the position of a new wheel, which should be twice the diameter of the driver.

It is extraordinary the number of grandfather calendars that have had parts removed by unscrupulous persons sooner than put them in order.

A pin is fixed in the wheel D shown to engage a tooth or two of the moon disc as the case may be. When a tooth is lifted over the point of the detent it jumps the wheel forward the distance of half a tooth, so that

both sides of the detent are pressing against the points
of two teeth to keep the wheel in position.

A pin in the hour wheel C moves a tooth of the
calendar wheel E forward in a similar manner.
Occasionally the teeth of the calendar wheel are not
close enough for a pin in the hour wheel to engage.
In such instances it is intended for a finger-piece,
which projects above the surface of the wheel with
the end extending beyond the teeth.    The calendar

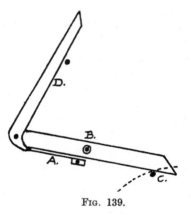

FIG. 139.

wheel makes one turn in 31 days, and has, therefore,
62 teeth, one being moved every 12 hours.  The wheel
is kept in position by a jumper and spring F in one
piece screwed to the dial plate in the same manner.
The days of the month are painted on the front of the
wheel to show through the slot in the dial.

A sliding arm is sometimes employed.  A pin in the
snail or hour wheel lifts a sliding arm fixed to the back
of the dial with two screws riding in slots, or a lever
pivoted to a stud with a loose pivoted arm at the other

end, Fig. 139. The point of the arm presses forward a tooth of the moon disc and the lever and loose end kept in position by a weak spring A. The lever turns on a stud at B, which is fixed to the back of the dial, C, the pin in the hour wheel which lifts the lever.

The lever in Fig. 139 is usually found in clocks of a superior make. The loose piece D is pivoted to the lever and kept in position by the pin E and the weak spring. As the centre of motion is at the stud B, the pin in the hour wheel coming in contact with the point of the lever lifts it, which draws the loose piece down, until the point of the lever falls off the pin C. The loose piece then jumps forward and pushes the teeth in the date wheel forward. This device often fails to act for the want of attention. Oil required at the pivot of the loose piece, the spring failing to act, or the stud tight at the hole.

The moon disc A, Fig. 138, often fails because the jumper is either bent the wrong shape, or perished with age, and when made of brass they are usually bent from a solid piece. To replace one is quite a simple matter. The moon disc is pinned to a long stud, which should be cleaned and oiled in order to run perfectly free. The calendar mechanism of these clocks is allowed to run without cleaning or oiling, as though these parts did not belong to the clock.

## PERPETUAL CALENDAR

A perpetual calendar is driven from the hour wheel in much the same way as a simple except in the former provision has to be made for the different lengths of the months with a device for the extra day in Leap Year.

A simple calendar has usually three wheels, each

turning once in twenty-four hours. They are all driven from the hour wheel. A pin in each wheel engages a tooth of a star wheel to carry the day of the week, the month, or month of the year hand. For the short months push pieces are provided in the band of the case to advance the star wheel and make any necessary

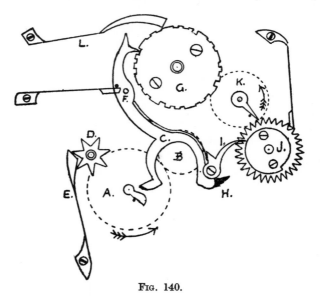

Fig. 140.

alteration. The hands are fixed on the sockets of their respective star wheels.

Fig. 140 shows the general construction of a perpetual calendar. The wheel A, driven by the hour wheel B, makes one turn in twenty-four hours and carries a movable cam which by contact with a pin moves the armed lever C.

A pin in the wheel A moves the day of the week,

star wheel D one tooth. It is kept in position by a jumper E. The wheel A is furnished with a pin to intersect a tooth of the star wheel showing the phases of the moon, which has 59 teeth. This is not shown in sketch, it is worked the same as a simple calendar.

The lever C, which has its centre of motion at F, is kept at rest on the four-year wheel G by a weak spring pressing against a pin. The cam on the wheel A makes a daily contact with the lever and in passing ; the arm H moves a tooth in the day of the month wheel of 31 teeth, while the point of the arm I glides over the edge of the snail J, which is screwed to the day of the month wheel.

The detent or arm I is fixed to the lever C with a shouldered screw and the point kept resting on the snail by a weak spring.

The wheel K has 31 teeth and engages with the day of the month wheel and therefore makes one complete turn in 31 days. It passes at each turn by means of a movable finger one tooth of the star wheel which is fixed to G by two screws. This star wheel, which represents four years, has 48 teeth, and is kept in position by the jumper L.

The circumference of the four-year disc G corresponds to the months of 31 days, the shallow notches to those of 30 days, and the four quarter notches to the month of February. The notch shown in Fig. 140 in which the point of the lever is resting represents Leap Year. It is therefore hardly so deep as the other three for February.

Each day immediately after moving the day of the month the lever C, pressed by its spring, returns its top end to rest on the circumference of the count disc G, or in one of the notches according to the position of the disc.

The part of the mechanism which renders the calendar perpetual consists of the point of the arm I pressed by its spring resting on the snail J. Before the last day of the month it acts on to the small part of the snail, and then its action is substituted for that of the arm H. The point of the piece I presses against the notch of the snail, and advances the star wheel the number of teeth necessary for the hand to indicate the 1st of the following month. It will be seen by Fig 140 that the distance the point of the piece I pushes is regulated by the position of the lever on the disc G or in one of its notches.

The illustration shows the mechanism set for Leap Year. At the end of the month the lever I would push the snail a distance equal to the advancement of three teeth.

The cam on the wheel A is movable to permit of putting the hands back without fear of damaging other parts. When the wheel A is turned back, the cam is locked by the lever C, and as it is sloped at the back the pin carried by the wheel is able to pass easily because the elasticity of the piece allows it to give.

To assume the calendar place the snail J to come into action at the end of the month with the arm I ready to push, and the finger piece on K at point of intersection with G. Move the wheel A until the cam comes into action, and immediately after move the lever the required number to give the day of the month wheel the correct number of teeth to coincide with the calendar. The four-year wheel being fixed to give the correct month, and the hands being put on at twelve o'clock immediately the lever C has been moved, which would represent 12 o'clock midnight.

## FITTING A GATHERING PALLET

The gathering pallet is one of the most important parts of the striking work. Most of the faults in the latter can be traced to the action of the pallet, the rack, and tail.

A Grandfather clock gathering pallet in the rough can be obtained from any material dealer.

The first operation is to open the hole with a square file until it fits tightly on the square.

It is necessary at this stage to put on the rack and hook and take a general survey of the superfluous metal to be removed in relation to its action with the

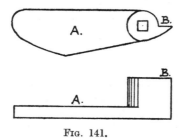

Fig. 141.

rack teeth. Although the rough pallet has actually an abundance of metal, the acting surfaces will require careful fitting, as it is quite simple to file away too much.

Fig. 141 shows plan and elevation of the average pallet when finished. The tail A as a rule works behind the rack and locks on to a pin when the last tooth is gathered. It all depends on the amount of room at disposal and the position of the pin will decide whether back or front.

To fit a gathering pallet is very good practise in filing. File the two sides of the tail, keeping them

parallel with the safe edge against the back of the pallet
to attain a square shoulder.   Long smooth-cut file
will be found best for this work.

The life of a file greatly depends on the treatment.
New ones should be kept for brass, and when worn for
this purpose, used on steel.   They should be cleaned
when the operation is finished.   An old stiff clock brush
makes a very serviceable cleaner.   When a file appears
worn and fails to cut apply oil.   This makes a vast
difference in the progress of the work.

The back of the pallet is next filed round, as shown
in Fig. 141, and the face B filed to a radial line, keeping
it rather long.   At this stage it is placed on the square
and tested with the rack teeth.   The point of the pallet
is left just long enough to intersect and lift a tooth
a little more than the distance between two teeth, so
that it lifts a tooth safely over the point of the rack
hook and allows it to drop back on the hook and lock.

The tail is next filed long enough to lock on the
pin when the last tooth in the rack is gathered ; and
the end of the pallet filed flush with the pin hole.

The gathering pallet is next tested for its action.
Place in position on their respective studs the rack,
the rack hook, and screw on the rack spring.   Lead the
pallet round slowly from the striking train to examine
the intersection of each tooth, until twelve are gathered
and the pallet locks safely on the rack pin.   Notice
if each tooth is gathered a little more than the distance
between two teeth.   If a pallet is left long enough to
be just free of the preceding tooth, the intersection
of the pallet will be correct.   When the teeth gathered
are correct with the racktail falling on the highest and
lowest steps of the snail (that is one and twelve), the
others are usually correct.

When the pallet intersects the first tooth more or less than the rest, the fault is probably the pin has dropped too far on the snail and the cause might be a new rack tail fitted the wrong length.

The pivot hole behind the gathering pallet worn large is often the cause of faults in the striking work. It is quite obvious a wide hole would cause a shallow depth with the gathering pallet and rack teeth. Faults due to a shallow depth of the rack teeth, or the rack tail causing the pallet to gather up the wrong number are often mistaken for faults in the snail. It is a safe policy to rebush a worn gathering pallet hole.

Rack tails have a tendency to work loose with continual falling on the edge of the snail. Riveting at the wrong angle and subsequent bending no doubt accounts for many breakages.

The rack spring should be strong enough to throw the tail safely on the deepest step of the snail. There appears to be a difference of opinion amongst repairers regarding the tension of this spring. Many faults in the rack are overcome by bending the spring stronger instead of correcting the fault. When the spring is bent to a greater tension the gathering pallet has to overcome a greater force at the rack teeth.

A sketch of the method to determine the correct length of a new rack tail, and an enlarged sketch of the intersection of the gathering pallet with the rack teeth, with description, is given on page 241.

## CLOCKS

Portable clocks in wooden cases are replacing the pendulum for domestic use, not because they are better timekeepers, although their performance is expected to compare favourably, and this is where the trouble commences. There is a marked difference in the variation in the daily rate of a spring-driven balance clock. These domestic or house timekeepers show variations from day to day due to faults in the motive power or the lever escapement, and occasionally in the train.

The escapements being on the Swiss pattern, with visible stones, the latter are easily shifted for adjustment. The locking and "run" should be slight, and the pivots free from roughness. The escapements as a rule give little or no trouble. The weakness is in the motive power.

It requires a mainspring with nearly an equable pull to drive a lever clock for eight days recording consistent time. A spring jerky in its motion should be changed. One foul in any part of the barrel can be rectified by turning the latter or filing the hooks up or down as the case may be.

Another folding clock of good style has the motion work driven from the third wheel. Fitted to the third wheel arbor above the top plate is an extra pinion of 20 driving a small centre wheel of 80. This latter wheel turns once in an hour and its arbor is run in the hollow centre pinion. Its object is to drive the motion work. The cannon pinion is snapped on the centre arbor in the usual way. The pinion and arbor being large, there is plenty of thickness to raise a bur and form a sound motion tension. A hole in the top plate is cut away to free the large pinion head of 20 and allow the top plate to be lifted off. The third pinion arbor is run in a cock screwed to the top plate. The large centre wheel has 112 teeth and drives a third pinion of 7. The wheel therefore makes one turn in four hours. The great wheel has 90 teeth and drives a centre pinion of 10, and the barrel makes one turn in 36 hours.

The return piece made together with the spring is altogether different in construction. A locking corner is provided with just sufficient angle to draw the piece home. It is well proportioned and too substantial to cause any trouble.

Portable 30-hour clocks of a cheap class known as " Folders ", or " Goliath ", give considerable trouble. They might be furnished with an artistic leather folding case, or encased in suitably finished metal to attract the eye. Most of the lever escapements are on the pin pallet principle. The hands are driven from a wheel fixed or rubbed on to the barrel cover, and this is where the continuous worry begins. The idea is right enough if correctly fitted. There is an excuse for leaving the parts rough for cheapness, but, combined with badly fitted mechanism, often requires a great deal of time to make the piece reliable.

The cannon pinion, driven from a wheel on the barrel cover, turns on a stud screwed in the plate. The stud is usually very rough and the hole in the cannon large and taper, giving too much shake at the pinion head. Side shake in the depth that would stop in the train wheels might cause no inconvenience in the motion work because there is no resistance against the hour wheel. These side shakes are in evidence in the two wheels, with the result they wobble round.

There is usually plenty of room between the dial and inside of the glass, and for some unknown reason the top of the brass cannon terminates about one-fourth of the distance from the dial, leaving the other three-quarters wasted space. It is quite obvious in such instances, to get the hands to run true and free of each other is a problem.

It is quite clear the hour hand, when pressed home

free of the dial, would project above the top of the hour
wheel pipe and the shake would have to depend on
the minute hand, which would have insufficient contact
with the cannon pipe to be safe. The hour hand would
ultimately push the minute off, with the usual request :
" Fix minute hand."

To make a permanent fixture for the minute hand,
broach the hole in the cannon and fit a new pipe, or
piece of bush wire, to come nearer the glass and give
a longer seat for the minute hand.

Another method is to collet the minute hand. When
the shoulder on the pinion to form the seat of the minute
hand is below the top of the hour wheel, and there is
not sufficient metal to lower the hour wheel pipe, the
safest plan is to collet the boss of the minute hand
and turn the boss small enough to free the inside of
the hour pipe to fit flush against the shoulder. A brass
collet would be effective for the new boss, and the
hour wheel end shake adjusted from the minute hand.

Before fitting a new pipe to the cannon it is advisable
to examine the hands and motion work. There is often
a combination of faults. The hour hand must have a little
side shake at every point. The end shake of the hand
is proportioned to the end shake of the hour wheel or
adjusted by the minute hand. A common fault is the
rocking of the hour hand, which inevitably causes it
to foul the minute hand. This irregular movement can
usually be traced to a badly-fitted hand, a split pipe,
or a bent cannon pinion stud, the pipe of the hour
hand too taper, or the hole of the hour wheel too large
with too much shake.

Any attempt to tighten a hand with the hour wheel
socket the wrong shape is courting trouble. The hour
hand would become loose when pressed home if the wheel

pipe is too large on the end. Too large at the root, or too taper forward with a bent cannon pinion stud, is a common combination of faults. When the hour hand is pressed home it only grips the wheel in one place, while the boss of the hand occasionally rubs against the minute socket and quickly works loose. In this instance mount the wheel on an arbor, turn the socket slightly taper and fit a new hand.

## MOTOR CLOCKS

Motor clocks are fitted flush with the switchboard, and in most instances fixed at the back with a bolt and screw. There are several methods of fixing, but with examination there will be no difficulty in removing the clock.

Better class motor clocks have a fine improvement in the winding work. The winding button is on the bezel with a hole to carry the shaft to the movement. The winding mechanism is on the " pull out " principle. The shaft being at right angle to the plates, direct gearing is attained.

Fig. 142 shows the winding and set hands mechanism. A winding pinion A is cut solid with the shaft gearing with the winding wheel. The shaft B is carried the distance between the plates and run in the back with the usual pivot. A strong spring C screwed to the plate is bent over at right angle and engages the lower incline of a V-shaped groove holding the shaft in position. To set hands the button is pulled until the spring is forced over the high part of the groove when the pinion A is changed gear with the set hands wheel D.

The winding wheel is the same diameter as the

barrel, therefore making the winding from the pinion easy. It is fitted with a modern click which banks against the third tooth beyond the point. The set hands wheel D gears with the minute wheel in the usual way.

The following train is generally used. Great wheel 80 teeth, diam. 1¼ in. Eight-day wheel 72, pinion 12. Centre wheel 96, pinion 12. Third wheel 100, pinion 10. Fourth wheel 50, pinion 10. Escape pinion 8. The winding mechanism of these clocks give little trouble. The movements are interchangeable and parts can be obtained from the maker.

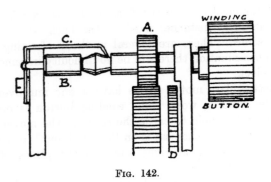

FIG. 142.

Another clock of good style winds by rotating the bezel which runs on balls, and the bezel pulls out for altering the hands. The winding work is an ingenious arrangement consisting of a sink cut in the brass plate with ratchet teeth on the edge. In the centre of the sink a fingerpiece turns square on the barrel arbor, which engages a slot on a brass cam or disc. Its outer edges are furnished with teeth which grip the sink as the mainspring pulls.

## VESTA BOX OR FOB WATCHES

A silver watch, vesta box shape, in a case obscuring the dial with a jump ring for attaching a chain is now quite popular. The watch is carried in the pocket or bag, and on being removed is opened by the operator with one hand. It is not exposed to damage. The least amount of trouble is necessary to see the time, and its safe custody is ensured by the chain.

There are two styles, one opens in the centre showing the square dial, and the other by means of a push piece raising the top half by a coiled spring at a uniform rate.

In the latter instance the tension of the coiled spring presses the cover up, while a train of wheels with a fly comes into action. The teeth of the large wheel project beyond the plate and gear with vertical teeth cut in a steel rod fixed to the cover. By this means the cover is raised with the running of the train until it reaches its farthest point. The action of closing the cover compresses the coiled spring, while the tension of the steel rod trips over the teeth of the large wheel in the fly train. The latter is run on the end of the plates of the going train.

In both examples, the inner cases are removed by pressing in the steel plate at the back close to the edge of the case to release the catch (which is formed in the steel plate), when the case will pull off in two sections. A little observation is required to note which side of the case is cut away to receive the catch. They appear similar, but close inspection will show a difference.

In the pull-out pattern, which shows the square dial in the centre, two-teethed runners are furnished, each having a pivot at right angle. These runners are

apt to work loose when taking out the movement,
and unless placed in their proper position the covers
will close, but the edges fail to meet.

Each cover has a flange or projection on the bottom
of the inside with a hole to take the stop piece or pivot.
To assemble the case the pivot on the end of the runner
shown in Fig. 143 (A) fits in the hole at the bottom of
the inside of case.   The pivot on the opposite runner

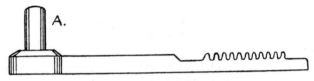

Fig. 143.

is placed in a reversed position with the other end in
the groove, so that one runner travels on the top groove
of case and the other in the bottom. They will then both
gear with the wheel behind the button with the opening
and shutting of the case.

When the inner case is removed from the outer,
the back of the movement is hidden from view by the
steel plate which is riveted to a soft nicked plate. The
latter is snapped on the inner case. A knife inserted
at the corner, which is cut away for the purpose, will
disclose the movement.   The winding shaft and dial
is then removed in the usual manner. A sink cut in the
case to free the pinion on the winding shaft allows
contact with the teeth of the runners. The latter require
a little oil. The cases are beautifully made with a perfect
fit in every detail. The movements are of high standard
in design and finish and should give no trouble.

## WALTHAM WATCH BARREL

There are two patterns of Waltham " screw barrel ". They are very similar, both on the same principle. One is probably an improvement on the other.

The form of applying the motive power in the barrel has been greatly improved in the Waltham watch. The latest improvement is in the barrel arbor which reduces, more friction. The mainspring for many years has consisted of a very weak gauge giving a comparatively small variation in force between the top and bottom

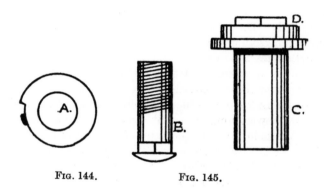

Fig. 144.     Fig. 145.

turns, and with the application of a resting barrel the coils are unwound from the other end, giving almost an equable pull with a minimum of coil friction.

There is a large percentage of friction taking place in the average barrel. Friction is proportional to pressure, and where it is excessive a large amount of the power is used before it reaches the escapement. A bad vibration to the escapement, therefore, in these instances does not signify the latter is at fault. It is by no means uncommon to find the barrel holes and barrel arbor pivots badly worn. In such cases the best plan is to polish the pivots and fit new holes to attain a better vibration to the balance.

The Waltham new barrel is made immune of this trouble by fitting a pair of jewel-holes in the boss. It is really a very fine piece of work with only a small space between the two holes.

The centre wheel holes are the most important in the train ; the friction is great, and on the running of the centre wheel depends the action and depth of the motion work, the running and freedom of the hands. Except in high class watches these holes are seldom jewelled. The expense of jewelling could be turned in this direction to advantage instead of the third and fourth holes. There are no depending properties on these, and when worn can always be rebushed. It would mean another step in the right direction.

Reducing friction is the main object to obtain a weak motive power giving an equable pull in the mainspring. The Waltham Watch Company have realized this fact, and now run their centre pinions and barrel arbors in jewel-holes. There is always danger in cracking a centre jewel-hole on removing a centre arbor from a hollow pinion if the head is larger than the pivot. This difficulty can be overcome by reducing the head to the actual diameter of the pivot so that the plate or bar can be removed first and the cannon pinion taken off with brass-nosed pliers. The general form of fixing a cannon pinion spring tight on a solid centre pinion arbor is far from perfect. The shell of the pinion is too thin to hold a bur sufficiently tight to hold in the groove. When removed from the pinion the bur becomes too easy to carry the hands. The " Waltham " Company overcome this difficulty by slotting the shell to form a spring.

Fig. 144 shows the boss and hook of the arbor to which is fixed the great wheel. These holes are jewelled at A. It is the same as the previous pattern except the boss is fitted with two jewel-holes. Fig. 145 shows the barrel arbor, which is made in two pieces. The new arbor is really a tube tapped on the inside. The lower part B consists of a square and shoulder to form a resting place for the barrel, which has a square hole, and the part B is furnished with a thread to screw into the tube.

The barrel only moves when the watch is wound by the square hole which fits the square on the lower part B.

To assemble the barrel and arbor, push the boss, Fig. 144, into the barrel and move it round so that the hook catches the hole in the eye of the mainspring. The arbor C is oiled and placed in the hole from the great wheel end. Reverse the arbor and grip it with the nippers on the square at D. The lower part B is placed in last from the barrel end and screwed up. Let the barrel down so that it rests on the square of B. By holding the nippers and barrel edge the arbor is screwed up tightly.

To dissemble the barrel, hold the top square D with the nippers and unscrew the barrel by gripping the edge. It is a right-handed screw, so that the pull of the mainspring tends to tighten it.

The other form is precisely the same, except the screw thread is on the outside of the pipe.

With this improvement the barrel is kept rigid without fear of working out of the square hole, the mainspring is unwound from the other end, reducing coil friction, and the arbor turns on a pair of jewel-holes set in the barrel body, which is a fixture with the great wheel.

## ENGLISH DOUBLE ROLLER BALANCE STAFF

To turn an English double roller balance staff to match the original is really a very fine piece of work. As such a part is all polished, it is preferable to spend a little extra time to emulate the copy rather than study the side of the financial transaction.

Many of the old school do all their turnings and pivoting in the turns, and claim that it is the only form to attain the best class work. The lathe is certainly quicker, but it is more convenient to rough it out in this tool.

The best plan is to place the old staff with the balance in the frame, and if the heights are correct, measure them on a metric gauge. A little allowance can be made if the balance is too high or low.

The rivet is first turned away and the old staff removed from the balance. This is best accomplished in the lathe.

Select a suitable tempered steel block and turn the superfluous metal in the lathe, the remainder of the work can then be accomplished in the turns. Screw on the lower arbor of the steel block a small screw ferrule, about three times the diameter of the flange. Use a weak horse-hair bow, and screw the staff in the centres of the turns, using an eccentric back centre which will come opposite a circle of small centres on the right-hand runner.

Turn the flange or largest part first, gauging the larger diameter from the old one. The flange of a free sprung must be exactly the same diameter and thickness as the old one to obtain the same weight of metal, or it would be necessary to disturb the timing screws, which is not advisable in this class of watch.

The graver marks are removed with a soft steel polisher and oilstone dust mixed with oil. After removing all traces of the mixture, the flange is polished with diamantine or red-stuff and steel or bell-metal. The selection is quite a matter of fancy. A reverse motion is quicker for polishing, a bow therefore has the advantage of a lathe in this respect. Use a quick up and down and reversed motion with the bow until the diamantine becomes almost dry, and draw file the polisher between successive applications of the polishing material.

The screw ferrule is next fixed on the bottom arbor and the staff turned to fit the balance with the shoulder to form the end of the flange. See Fig. 146. The flange A seat of balance B. It is important the balance should fit tightly, allowing a little drive to the shoulder. While the balance is in this position the rivet is turned with a long pointed graver and a very weak horse-hair bow. A very little rivet is required, it should come above the balance about two-thousandths of an inch.

The top arbor is next turned to fit the spring collet, Fig. 146 C, leaving the edge of the rivet as shoulder.

Reverse the screw ferrule, turn the lower arbor until the larger roller fits about half way to the flange and turn the arbor off to represent the end of the lower pivot, which can be measured in a gauge from the old staff, or the distance from the lower endstone to the seat of the balance.

At this stage the lower arbor is polished to let the large roller, Fig. 147 D, up to the flange. A little care is here required to keep the staff at a uniform taper to allow the small roller, E, to fit the staff flush with the large one, Fig. 147.

Just free of the small roller the back slope is turned, ground with oil-stone dust, and polished. The lower pivot is then turned to nearly fit the jewel-hole.

The whole height of the staff is taken by turning the top arbor to length measured from the distance

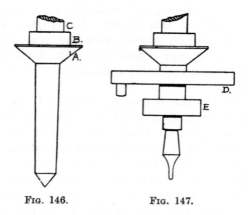

FIG. 146.          FIG. 147.

between the two endstones. A very useful home-made tool for taking these heights is described with illustrations on page 46.

The top arbor is polished in the usual way and the top backslope turned and polished, being finished with diamantine, and the top pivot turned to just fit the jewel-hole

The pivots are turned to shape with a half-circular pointed graver, using a weak hair bow. There are two methods generally adopted for finishing them, burnishing by means of a jacot tool and polishing in the turns.

With the latter principle, soft taper metal polishers are used, filed to the shape of the cone and pivot, while the latter is supported on a runner bed similar to that of a " jacot ". A little more experience is required with polishing pivots in the turns.

## MINUTE CHRONOGRAPH

A chronograph, strictly speaking, is a timekeeper that leaves a record of its performance. It is understood to mean a watch with a centre seconds hand driven from the fourth wheel, which may be started, stopped, and caused to fly back to zero by pressing the pendant.

A cheap form of watch often mistaken for a chronograph is somewhat similar in its recording, called a " stop watch ". The centre seconds hand is brought back to zero by means of a heart piece and a third press from the pendant; the difference being the going train is stopped by a weak spring pressing on the balance, actuated by pressing the pendant. This is obviously not so reliable where accuracy is the main object.

It would be practically impossible to describe the many varieties of design in the chronograph, but the principles under which they are governed are the same. An 18,000 train is necessary and the chronograph hand beats fifths of a second.

Horologists who are used to complicated work usually have ideas of their own, but all work to a system.

Fig. 148 shows a general form of chronograph arranged on the top of the movement. Only necessary pieces of the mechanism are shown to make its action simple to follow.

The illustration shows the watch at zero, that is

with the lever pressing on the heart piece and the
centre seconds hand at 60.    There are three wheels
in the chronograph train, A, B, and C, all of the same
size and cut with very fine teeth ; the former is fixed
friction tight on the fourth wheel arbor, making one
complete turn in a minute, and drives the wheel B,
carried in an arm with a stud as centre of motion.

There are three separate levers, D, E, and F.    One
end of each is pressed against a star wheel by a weak

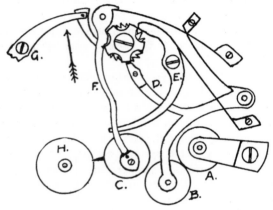

FIG. 148.

spring    This wheel turns on a shouldered screw and
fixed to a ratchet wheel which is held in position by
a click and spring in one piece.    The star wheel only
moves one ratchet tooth at a time. Most modern watches
are made with a star wheel of five outer edges, or five
crescents, and the number of teeth in the ratchet must
be three to one ;    therefore the ratchet must have
fifteen teeth.

The action of the chronograph is worked by pressing
the pendant ;    this engages a long circular lever on the

outer edge of the plate, which turns on a shouldered screw G. It is kept in position by a spring, the force exerted at the pendant overcomes the spring, and the other end of the lever turns in the opposite direction shown by an arrow. Pivoted at the end is a click with its point kept close with the ratchet teeth by a weak spring. The contact at the pendant should enable the click to travel the distance of a tooth and a half to be certain a tooth is moved each time.

There are three separate actions at the star wheel; the first starts the chronograph, that is the end of the lever D, falls into a crescent, and the wheel B at the other end is moved up to gear with the wheel C, while the lever F is lifted free of the heart piece. The second press at the button brings the tail of the lever E on the edge of the centre chronograph wheel C. The third action moves another tooth round and causes the wheel B to be thrown out of gear with C and the lever F to fall on the heart piece and move it to its lowest point near the centre.

Most chronographs record for thirty minutes, shown on a separate circle of the dial; a finger-piece is fitted to the wheel C which moves a tooth of the wheel H for each revolution. The wheel H is fitted with a heart piece and another lever to bring it to zero. In some instances this wheel is driven from the train, making one turn in thirty minutes.

When cleaning the parts, it is advisable to keep the screws together with their respective springs; the former are different lengths, and a screw finding its way into the wrong hole will often foul another object and cause a deal of trouble. The fine cut chronograph wheels should be cleaned in petrol, brushed lengthways and covered free from damage. It is a mistake to keep

these wheels all in gear while the watch is running as
an ordinary timekeeper.  If allowed to run the whole
time the fine teeth get worn, become useless for the
purpose they were intended, and they are expensive
to replace.

To assemble, screw on the star wheel first with its
click or jumper, next the other pieces which lie close
to the plate, and examine the freedom at the stud holes.
The lower pivot of the centre chronograph wheel (which
runs in the hollow centre pinion) requires a very little
oil, which should be applied at the shoulder ; the other
pivots can be oiled with safety in the ordinary way.
The face of the jumper for the minute recording wheel
requires a little oil, the friction at this place is small,
but it is unwise to leave it dry.  Apply oil at all parts of
contact where friction occurs.   A little adjustment
is sometimes required with the lever D ; the depth is
regulated by an eccentric screw head.   The circular
lever with a shouldered screw G must be perfectly free
to move one tooth at each action ;  this can often be
adjusted when the movement is in the case.

**Set-Hands Mechanism.**—The lock piece, or bolt to
hold the winding shaft, would be improved by making
the sides of the pivot undercut so that it tends to grip
the slot when power is applied in the act of pulling
the shaft.

This is one of the greatest failings in the modern
watch.   There is no reason why the centre of motion
for the lock piece should not be a pivot instead of
a screw.  Because it has always been a screw and given
endless trouble is no reason why it should continue.
The continual pulling out and in of the shaft in the act
of setting hands has a tendency to loosen the screw,
either a right or left-handed thread, and that is exactly

what happens : many repairers in despair have riveted the end of the screw. This method certainly ends this form of trouble until the watch has to be taken to pieces, when the operator is faced with a greater puzzle.

The intersection of the lock piece with the slot in the shaft or stem is comparatively small and will not permit any side shake of the latter ; the shoulders of the slot are often left rounding, and when the button is pulled

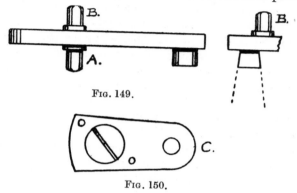

FIG. 149.

FIG. 150.

it is quite obvious instead of the lock piece advancing with it, the pivot is forced up the incline and out of the slot. In such cases turn the shoulders slightly undercut.

The lock piece or bolt, Fig. 149, can remain the same shape. Fitted to it in place of the screw hole is a short arbor having two large pivots ; the lower A turns in a hole in the plate, which would take the place of the arbor hole. The top pivot B is run in a small thick cock C. Fig. 150. The pivot of the bolt or lock piece is undercut, shown by dotted lines, so that when the shaft is pulled it has a firm grip in the slot (which should be undercut).

## QUARTER CHIMES

The Westminster chime clock with a three-part train has undoubtedly come to stay. Rod gongs are fitted in most instances which give a remarkably fine tone. Bracket clocks to accommodate a shallow mantelshelf have the gongs arranged under the movement.

The earliest chime clocks were struck on bells with the pin barrel between the plates, and the bells surmounting the movement. With this plan eight or ten could be fixed on one rod attached to the plate. Later the coiled form of gong was introduced ; this required a longer pin barrel carried in a cock to the back plate. These groups fixed behind the movement obviously required a deeper case.

Carriage quarter chime clocks strike the hours first and then the quarters. There are many who regard this as being the most convenient method ; they argue the listener is more concerned on the hours than the quarters, and by the other method it is necessary to hear the whole chime in order to determine the hour.

English chime trains have the going part in the centre, and the hour striking on the left. The minute wheel has four pins for engaging the quarter lifting piece every quarter, and the quarter snail with four steps turns once in an hour. Fig. 151 shows the action of the full chime with the quarter and hour racks. The gathering pallets, rack tails, and snails are not shown, to make it as simple as possible.

The quarter rack hook A is lifted every quarter of an hour, and the quarter rack B falls to chime one, two, three, or four quarters, according to the position of the snail on which the tail falls. At the hour, when the quarter rack is allowed to fall its greatest distance,

it comes in contact with the arm of the hour rack hook C
and allows the hour rack to fall. This action of the
quarter rack automatically releases the tail of the hour
warning piece and allows it to warn by means of the
pin D.

As the last tooth of the quarter rack is gathered up
the pin D lifts the hour warning piece E and lets off
the hour striking. The warning pallet which is shown at

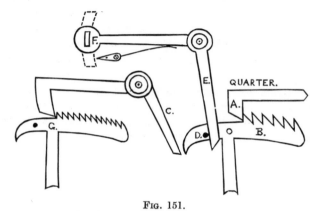

Fig. 151.

F with the plate cut away in a slot is shown dotted and
the arm which turns on a stud is kept in position by a
weak spring. The hour rack is marked G.

The rack springs require careful adjustment. It is
quite clear they must be strong enough to throw the
tails firmly on the snails at the deepest step, without
causing too much resistance to the gathering pallet
in the act of gathering up the teeth. Failure to strike
the hour sometimes occurs through too weak a quarter
rack spring; they are liable to get bent in cleaning.
Another fault is the liability of the clock striking the

hour at the third quarter through the tail of the hour rack hook C being bent; any slight adjustment can be made at the centre of motion—the rivet at the stud hole.

The continual falling of the rack tail on the deepest step of the snail has a tendency to loosen the former and cause the wrong number to be struck, or the pin worked loose in the tail. This is most prevalent in the hour part. It is quite a simple matter to tighten the tail, or the pin, and it is adjusted to its correct position by testing the intersection of the gathering pallet with the rack teeth.

Lead the gathering pallet round slowly from the striking train, and examine the intersection of each tooth until the twelve teeth have been gathered and the pallet locks safely on the rack pin. If the pallet intersects the first tooth more or less than the rest, the fault is probably the pin has dropped too far on the snail and the cause might be a new rack tail fitted the wrong length.

## THIRTY-HOUR LONG-CASE CLOCK

An English thirty-hour long-case clock is driven with one weight and an endless chain on Huygens endless cord principle. When assembling the clock there is a right and wrong way of hanging the weight.

The winding pulley is on the main striking wheel and fixed to a circular spring click which locks on the arms of the main wheel. The illustration in Fig. 152 shows the method of hanging the weight: G is the going pulley, and S the striking. The weight is pulling on the left side of each pulley. The chain on

the right-hand side of S is pulled down in the act
of winding shown by an arrow. The loose loop of the
chain is kept taut by a small weight, and often a small
lead ring.

This style of clock giving trouble in winding usually
requires new spikes and a chain. The links of the latter

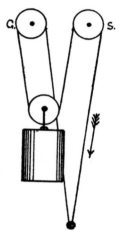

Fig. 152.

get badly worn in contact with the pins. Or a chain
has sometimes been fitted the wrong pitch, causing it
to kick and jump over the spikes.

The thirty-hour English clock, which is quite a country
maker's production, and furnished with an hour hand
only, was quite popular until near the end of the
eighteenth century. Although new chains can often
be obtained from a material dealer it was quite customary
with country makers to produce their own.

To fit new spikes it is necessary to drill out the old. The pulley on the going part is fixed to the great wheel with three rivets. A little care is required to punch out these rivets from the small end, to remove the pulley from the great wheel, as the drilling process would obviously be difficult without removing it. When they are nearly out the rivets can be nipped off.

We next come to the drilling stage and this operation is most important, for it is quite obvious should a drill run out into the brass a new pulley might be necessary. It is essential that each stump should be centred for drilling straight, and drilling is best accomplished in the lathe, using the back centre. Use a sharp drill with plenty of oil and drill to the centre hole. The drilling process is a slow job, and when no lathe is at disposal it can be accomplished with a gut bow, but in this instance there should be plenty of clearance behind the blade, because it is not such an easy matter to keep it straight, and a broken drill in such a place is disheartening and not easy to extract.

The old stumps are next removed by using a broach or tap to unscrew them. When the threads are damaged it will be found best to re-tap the holes, unless it is decided to drive in the new spikes tightly. This latter procedure is quite effective assuming the fit is correct.

Tempered steel let down to a light blue should be used for the new spikes; they can be turned or filed as desired. If the ends are tapped to fit the holes a little care is required as they are liable to snap off in the hole. The outer ends are left pointed so that the chain passes freely over the spikes. There is plenty of bearing to hold the spikes friction tight, and when this plan is adopted the surface of the steel should be finished with a stone or emery buff, very slightly tapered to give it a firm hold.

Country makers manufacture their own chains from the principle shown in Fig. 153. An old file to give a suitable pitch is selected as gauge and a soft dummy made to pattern, Fig. 153 A. The wire B is bound round rightly from end to end, then saw-cut lengthways. The links are then opened, joined, and

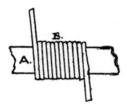

Fig. 153.

closed up. The method is really the same as a jeweller adopts to make his jump rings. The length of chain should be sufficient to drive the clock for thirty hours, or it can be measured from the old one. When the old one is not at disposal it can be measured with a piece of string forming a double loop to bottom of case, with the long loop.

The locking of the click on the arms of the wheel is often unsafe. The continual rubbing causes wear-marks on the arms; these will be found to graduate more on the corner and thus lessen the amount of lock to ensure safety. When there is no chance of reversing the wheel the click can be re-undercut and pieces dove-tailed or riveted to the arms of the wheel to form a new locking surface.

### GIRL IN THE SWING CLOCK

The visible girl in the swing forms the pendulum in this style of French clock, and the swing moves the reverse way—that is from back to front, and the pendulum moves at right angles to the plane of the train wheels. They often give a deal of trouble through loss of impulse and, obviously, the " swing " comes to rest.

The escapement, although different in construction, is really very simple and easily adjusted. The pendulum is of the spring suspension variety and hung on a small bracket with the pallet arbor running at right angles to the pendulum rod, parallel with the back plate.

Twin escape wheels are furnished on the pinion arbor, about $\frac{1}{4}$ in. apart, with a pallet arbor at right angles pivoted on two studs or cocks in the plate.

A crutch is fitted near the end of the pallet arbor in the usual way and engages the pendulum rod. There should be a little or no shake at this point of contact (see Fig. 154). The twin wheels A are fitted on the same arbor, the pallets are shown at B. The teeth of one wheel drop on the pallet at C and the other wheel at D. The pallet B is shown separately. The escape wheel teeth are not shown, but the actual diameter of the wheels to the tips of the teeth are a little larger than the circles shown in A.

The loss of impulse is mostly attributed to the action of the wheel and pallets. Any wear marks should be stoned from the pallet faces, and the impulse faces left at exactly the same angle, because the pendulum only swings sufficiently for the pallets to unlock a wheel at C and at D to C.

Assuming the two wheels to be mounted with the

teeth equally apart, viewed from the top pivot, the
" drops " should be equal.

The writer once had a similar clock that had given
trouble, and found one wheel had become loose and
riveted in the wrong position, giving too much drop
on one pallet in order to free the shake of the tooth at
the next. Turning away the rivet was a simple matter
to move the wheel slightly, the drops were than equal
and the escapement deepened.

The escapement can be deepened by altering the
adjustment of the pallet arbor at E or fitting a new pivot
hole at the cock F.

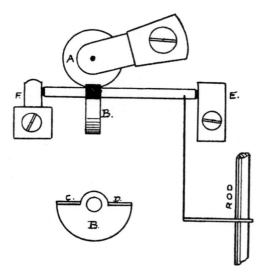

Fig. 154.

## ALARM WATCHES

There are several forms of alarm watch, the most reliable is fitted with two push pieces, one for the alarm set, and the other for the going part. Fitted to the winding stem is a wheel that gears with one riding in a slot and winds both winding wheels alternately, driving the alarm winding wheel with the back action.

The alarm train consists of three wheels and the pallets run in a plate under the dial. This has the advantage of being assembled separately.

The going train of the watch is assembled first in the usual way, and the pivot holes oiled, on the back plate ;  the alarm train follows.

The alarm is let off by the hour wheel, which presses on a long spring screwed to the plate. The free end of the alarm spring has a nose piece which engages the hammer tail ;  the latter is free to move and come into action as the alarm spring is released. When the hour wheel is raised the spring which is pressing against it follows ;  this action takes place when the stud in the hour wheel falls in the slot of the alarm wheel.

The most common fault in this style of watch is the failure of the alarm to àct, or to go off before its time. The latter is usually because the point of contact is too light, or the nose of the spring bent to the wrong angle. There should be a decided square locking face on the spring to engage the hammer tail. The end of the spring is easily bent down to attain a deeper contact.

The alarm will fail to act if the motion tension is too weak, or the hour wheel rough, causing it to bind on the cannon pinion. Its sliding action must be quite free and for this reason it is advisable to polish the cannon if at all rough. Such marks often appear when the pinion has been removed with steel pliers. The face of the stud requires to be smooth to travel easily out of the notch after the action of the alarm. It will pay to reduce friction to its minimum at these acting surfaces and apply oil at the stud and notch.

The alarm wheel is held in position by a plate screwed over the set hands wheels. These screws are not always the same length, and should be kept in their relative position during cleaning; an old watch barrel with a number of holes drilled will be found useful for this purpose. A screw with a long thread screwed into a thin part of the plate would have a disastrous effect; a broken wheel or bar is often the result of attempted speed. The minute, set hands, and intermediate wheels should be placed into position and oiled; the freedom tested when the plate is screwed on.

The gong can usually be screwed on after the movement is in the case and the hammer adjusted. Wind the alarm and give it a trial before placing the movement in the case. The alarm hand is put on to the time shown as the alarm goes off. The alarm pallets and wheel are oiled in the usual way and all places of contact where friction occurs.

## GEARING—CORRECTING BAD DEPTHS

A bad depth is another instance of inconsistent time-keeping. A watch that stops through a bad depth is best located by tracing the loss of power from the escape wheel. A worn hole, or one bushed out of upright is often the cause of the fault. A wheel out of round, or too deep, should be topped. The best plan is to try the

escape pinion and fourth wheel separately in the frame.
Hold the escape wheel with a peg, lead the fourth wheel
round slowly, and try the shake ; a shallow depth will
probably make a buzzing noise. Then try the fourth
pinion and third wheel in the same way.

The fourth wheel and escape pinion depth gives more
trouble through the pinion being too small than too

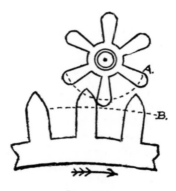

Fig. 155.

large. When the wheel is a little out of round, topping
it true would improve the depth by bringing it shallower.

Fig. 155 shows an escape pinion of 6 too small for the
wheel. If the depth was pitched, assuming the pinion
was the correct size, we should get the teeth " catching "
on the pinion leaf. The depth has been corrected by
topping the teeth of the wheel to bring the depth shallow.
The pitch circles A and B would meet, when the
escape pinion was the correct size. There is more
engaging friction, which is quite unavoidable with low-
numbered pinions, but they have the advantage of
more shake, and therefore carry more dust without

stopping. An escape pinion too large for the fourth wheel, although not so common, is another form of trouble ; it will often stop in the depth, and in this instance the wheel requires pitching deeper (see correcting bad depths).

## POISING A SCREW BALANCE

A balance out of poise would account for bad time-keeping. It might run perfectly true in the round and flat, and yet be out of poise. All modern balances are poised by means of the screws, and these of different sizes and washers are often fitted to a balance with the object of regulation, without testing it on a tool. It is not usual to alter a Breguet spring at the stud ; and to open the index pins is by no means a more successful operation ; all possibility of close time-keeping in the long and short arcs would be lost.

It is often necessary to poise a screw balance by adding weight ; this is easily accomplished with an assortment of balance collets ; the general method consists of removing weight at the heaviest part. Many watch-makers use the callipers for this test, but a poising tool will be found quicker and safer for beginners.

To poise a balance with a Breguet spring, and the regulator over to the slow, it is usual to add weight, using balance washers, or heavier screws. A little discretion is required in changing the screws as a very little makes a great difference, and it is better for a beginner to confine his operation to washers.

Fig. 156 shows a balance out of poise. The heaviest part comes to rest at the bottom A. It could be poised by adding washers under the screw heads from B to

C D. Sometimes one at C would be found sufficient or changing B and D for thinner ones. Or by reducing weight at screws from E F. It is always advisable to start with a very little off at the lowest or heaviest part A and then try it on the poising tool.

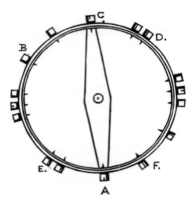

Fig. 156.

## OILING A WATCH

There are certain parts where it is difficult to retain the oil to the acting surfaces, and this is where the trouble begins. Capillary attraction comes into play and the oil is drawn away.

The lower centre wheel hole is the most notable, and this is the reason this pivot is often found badly worn. After repairing it will be found safer to apply a little oil at the shoulders before assembling the wheels; it ensures the oil running all over the acting surface.

The lower centre wheel hole is usually very short,

and the cannon pinion too close to the plate, the latter obviously pushed down to the shoulder. When it is rubbing the plate and the endshake is not great, the plate should be turned away to a sink until the shoulder stands above (see Fig. 157) or fit a new centre wheel hole to reduce the endshake ; and if there is no shake to the hour wheel with the dial fixed, turn back the bottom of the pinion, or sink the seat of the hour wheel.

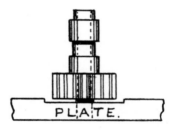

Fig. 157.

The absence of an oil sink partly accounts for the oil being drawn away from this hole. This is one of the weakest points of the modern watch. A raised hole with the head of the cannon pinion sunk to bring the pinion head free of the plate would be a great improvement, or better still, run this pivot in a jewel hole, instead of jewelling the top third and fourth. There is comparatively little wear on these holes, unless the third pinion is close to the top pivot.

### ASSEMBLING A FRENCH STRIKING CLOCK

Hold the pillar plate in a leather, or cloth, and having placed the centre wheel in first, followed by the two barrels. The pin wheel follows with the hammer arbor, then the warning wheels with the locking detent. It will be found an improvement to place a little oil on the shoulders of the large pivots ; oil applied later will then be certain to find its way to the shoulders. The two eight-day wheels follow.

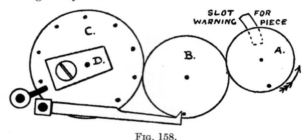

Fig. 158.

Fig. 158 shows the pin wheel, gathering pallet, and warning wheels with the locking decent in their relative positions on assembling the clock. Half a turn of the warning wheel A will be found sufficient with the pin in wheel B locked on the detent. The fly is inserted last. When these two wheels are correct with the plates pinned down, the cock D may be unscrewed and the wheel C lifted out and moved round in the position shown.

Let the top plate on gently and guide the pivots in their holes with the tweezers starting with the large ones. At this stage a pin placed in the pillar hole near the barrels will prevent it rising while the smaller pivots are guided in.

# INDEX

373                                    B b

# HOROLOGY

**Carriage Clocks, Their History and Development** by Charles Allix, illus. by P. Bonnert. A mammoth volume covering the history, traditions, manufacture, development and multi-national nature of travelling clocks including hitherto undiscovered information on cases and descriptions of all known types. *11½ins. x 8½ins. 484 pages. 500 b. & w. illus. 16 in col. ISBN 0 902028 25 1.*

**The Camerer Cuss Book of Antique Watches** by T.P. Camerer Cuss. A completely revised new edition of this well-known standard work of reference. A newly added 250 page section provides an important illustrated chronology of the development of the watch. The new photographs show most watches over size so that details of decoration and mechanism are more readily appreciated. *11ins. x 8½ins. 332 pages. 364 b. & w. illus. 8 in col. ISBN 0 902028 33 2.*

**Thomas Cole and Victorian Clockmaking** by J.B. Hawkins. The names on most high grade Victorian clocks are those of the retailer. The quality and ingenuity of the work produced by Thomas Cole was of such a high order that his work was in demand by most of the leading retailers. This book also contains extracts from exhibition catalogues and the reports of Jurors on the two major international exhibitions in Britain. *11ins. x 8½ins. 256 pages. 90 b. & w. illus. 3 in col. ISBN 0-9598503-0-9.*

**Watch and Clock Maker's Handbook, Dictionary and Guide** by F.J. Britten. This work has been out of print for a considerable time. It is a reprint of the 11th edition, first published in 1907. It is in the form of a dictionary and much valuable information that was left out of later editions is to be found in this volume. *8½ins. x 5½ins. 490 pages. Several hundred engravings. ISBN 0 902028 46 4.*

**English Domestic Clocks** by Cescinsky & Webster. The classic introduction has never been bettered by modern writers. *12ins. x 9ins. 240 pages. Over 400 b. & w. illus. ISBN 0 902028 37 5.*

*Further lists available from:*
Antique Collectors' Club, 5 Church Street, Woodbridge, Suffolk.